# Elegant Glassware of the Depression Era

## 6th Edition

## By Gene Florence

**COLLECTOR BOOKS**

*A Division of Schroeder Publishing Co., Inc.*

## Searching For A Publisher?

We are always looking for knowledgeable people considered to be experts within their fields. If you feel that there is a real need for a book on your collectible subject and have a large, comprehensive collection, contact us.

COLLECTOR BOOKS
P.O. Box 3009
Paducah, Kentucky 42002-3009

*On The Cover:*
Upper left – American vase (opaque blue).
Upper right – Old Sandwich decanter (Sahara).
Middle – Stanhope candle box (crystal).
Lower left – Ipswich water goblet (Sahara).
Lower right – Twist oil bottle (Moongleam).

# DEDICATION

This book is dedicated to Gladys Florence, "Grannie Bear," my Mom. She oversaw my shop for seventeen years... after running a day care center for twenty-eight! She packed glass, kept pricing records, traveled local markets, and did anything else that needed doing to make my writing easier. She lent valuable assistance to this book. I am truly sorry that this dedication is being done posthumously.

# FOREWORD

"Elegant" glassware, as defined in this book, refers to the handmade and acid etched glassware that was sold in the department stores and jewelry stores during the Depression era through the 1950's as opposed to the dime store and give-away glass that has become known as Depression Glass. The word "Elegant" has become standard terminology among today's dealers for describing handmade glassware.

The rapid growth of collecting "Elegant" glassware has been phenomenal and many dealers who wouldn't dare buy that crystal stuff a few years ago are acquiring as much "Elegant" as basic Depression Glass. Depression Glass shows used to be stocked with only 15% to 20% "Elegant" glass, but now there is more than 50% at many shows.

The enormous reception of the first five books has precipitated this sixth. New patterns, more catalogue reprints and an additional sixteen pages await you.

I hope you enjoy this book, and I hope you will feel the years of striving to give you the best books possible on "Elegant" glassware were well spent.

# PRICING

**ALL PRICES IN THIS BOOK ARE RETAIL PRICES FOR MINT CONDITION GLASSWARE.** This book is only intended as **A GUIDE TO PRICES**. There remain regional price differences that cannot be reasonably dealt with herein.

You may expect dealers to pay approximately thirty to sixty percent less than the prices listed. My personal knowledge of prices comes from my experience of selling glass in my Grannie Bear Antique Shop in Lexington, and from my traveling to and selling at shows in various parts of the United States. Due to the death of my Mother last July and the ensuing closing of my Lexington shop, I will be working even harder at markets and shows to remain in contact with the ever changing prices. I readily admit soliciting price information from persons known to be experts in these various fields to provide you with the latest, most accurate pricing information possible. However, final pricing judgments are mine; so, for any bloopers (or praises), the buck always stops here.

# MEASUREMENTS AND TERMS

All measurements and terms in this book are from factory catalogues or actual measurements from the piece. It has been my experience that actual measurements vary slightly from those listed in catalogues; so don't get unduly concerned over slight variations. For example, Fostoria always measured plates to the nearest inch, but I have found that most Fostoria plates are never exact inches in measurement.

# ACKNOWLEDGMENTS

Photography sessions for this book were spread over a two year period with two sessions lasting six days each. A special tribute is due Dick and Pat Spencer for their lending of glass and work at the photography sessions and their information and pricing help on Heisey in this book. Dick's new glass animal book required much of his valuable time and I appreciate the effort made to also help me! Pat is due even more credit for the flower arrangement in the Plantation photograph!

There are so many people behind the scenes in the production of this book that it's hard to believe! Some lent glass, some, their time; others lent their talents and expertise. Many of these people are friends even after tedious hours of packing, unpacking, arranging, sorting, and repacking glass! Some traveled hundreds of miles to bring their valuable glass to share with **you**, the public. Others spent hours discussing and recording their prices, often after already long show hours. Without these extraordinary people, this book would not exist. Those special people include: Earl and Beverly Hines, Dan Tucker and Lorrie Kitchen, Charles Larson, Paul and Margaret Arras, Gary and Sue Clark, John and Judy Bine, Bill and Lottie Porter, Quinten Keech, Charlie and Ruth Collins, Yvonne Heil, Kenn Whitmyer, Ralph and Fran Leslie, John and Raymond Day, Dale Mitchell, Debbie and Randy Coe, John and Linda Neary, Jane White, Sherry Kraus, Gail Ashburn, Lisa Stroup, Beth Summers, and numerous unnamed readers from throughout the U.S. and Canada who shared pictures and information about their heretofore unlisted pieces. Richard Walker and Charley Lynch did all the new photography for this book. If you think I am not a taskmaster, ask Richard who said, "I walk up the (photographer's) ladder and come down **S-L-O-W-L-Y**, and **that** is my rest!"

Family is the single most important aid in my work. Were it not for my mom, "Grannie Bear," who listed and packed the glass after Dad cleaned it for our first photography session, some of it might never have been seen in my books. Her invaluable help will be sorely missed! Charles helped cart boxes from storage and built shelves in the new house while Sybil spent several days helping Cathy sort glass into various patterns and boxes. Chad and Marc have both helped loading and unloading van loads of glass for each photography session, not to mention seeing to the home fires when I am traveling.

Cathy, with her editing pencil, continues to toil to make some sense out of the volumes of material that I write. I deal with concepts; she tries to arrange subjects and verbs. My writing in Florida and her traveling back and forth to Kentucky is a bigger chore than we anticipated. UPS Next Day Air loves me for sending my unedited pages for her corrections. She's had twenty-three years of this glass and book business experience (research, editing, proofing, travels, packing and unpacking, both me and the glassware). We reach thirty years of marriage in December; so most of our married life has been wrapped up in deadlines for books! We both trained to teach. I hope we have been successful at teaching in ways we never thought of in our youth!

Thanks also to Sherry Kraus of Collector Books for transcribing all my Microsoft Words into Quark and my scribbled prices into reality! Her cheerful giggle on the other end of the phone can brighten up a dull day at the keyboard!

You, my readers, are the motivation to continue. As long as you keep sending me pertinent information and listings that may have suffered omission or some inaccuracy, I'll continue to pass the information to the public. Your encouragement keeps me going!

# CONTENTS

# CONTENTS BY COMPANY

# AMERICAN, Line #2056, Fostoria Glass Company, 1915 – 1986

Colors: crystal; some amber, blue, green, yellow, pink tinting to purple in late 1920's; white, red in 1980's, and currently being made in red and crystal for Lancaster Colony by Dalzell Viking

Lancaster Colony now produces the American pattern under Fostoria's label since the closing of the **original** Fostoria factory in 1986. Lancaster Colony has also continued to market its "Whitehall" glassware line which is similar to American, but made by Indiana Glass at Dunkirk, Indiana. At present you will find an abundance of "Whitehall" in colors of pink, an avocado green, and a smoky blue. Check the glassware section of your local discount store for new colors and items being made. Whitehall's pink colored ware is often confused by novice collectors with Jeannette's Cube pattern from the Depression era!

All my mail pertaining to the American pattern concerns the producer of various pieces. None of the American or "look-alike" American pieces are marked in any way. Red is currently being marketed at the Fostoria "outlet" stores in an abundance of pieces. This excellent quality glassware is being made at Dalzell Viking. Any piece that is marked with an asterisk (*) in the listings below has **recently** been or is **scheduled** to be reissued by them. American was never made in red until the 1980's, and then it was made by Viking Glass for Fostoria. Dalzell Viking has now taken over the manufacturing of red for Lancaster Colony. You can see the **original** green and blue colors in the pictures on the next few pages. The red vase is from the original 1980's issue. The green sugar shown in the top photo on page 7 is often confused with Jeannette's Cube. You must train yourself to notice details of glass. For instance, the edge of the Cube sugar is smooth!

Colored pieces of older American are in demand, but know from whom you are buying if you are a novice. If the price seems too good to be true, then it probably is!

Reissued cookie jars have been a big problem for collectors! Be sure to read **this** about the cookie jars before buying one! **Most** of the new issues I have seen have wavy lines in the pattern itself and crooked knobs on the top. Old cookie jars do not. A telling point that works **80%** of the time is to try to turn the lid around while it rests inside the cookie jar. The new lids seem to hang-up and stop somewhere along the inside making the whole cookie jar turn. The old jars will allow you to turn the lid completely around without catching on the sides! This one reissued item has been a tremendous setback to longtime collectors of American. However, it is not unusual for a company's monetary concerns to be placed above those of collectors. Both styles of ice cream saucers are shown in the top photo on page 7. After everyone found out what these were, the price dropped. This has occurred due to supply suddenly outdistancing the demand of collectors searching for them.

| | *Crystal | | *Crystal |
|---|---|---|---|
| Appetizer, tray, 10½", w/6 inserts | 240.00 | Bowl, 5", nappy, w/cover | 27.50 |
| Appetizer, insert, 3¼" | 27.50 | Bowl, 5", rose | 25.00 |
| Ash tray, 2⅞", sq. | 7.50 | Bowl, 5½", lemon, w/cover | 42.50 |
| Ash tray, 3⅞", oval | 9.00 | Bowl, 5½", preserve, 2 hdld., w/cover. | 80.00 |
| Ash tray, 5", sq. | 40.00 | Bowl, 6", bonbon, 3 ftd. | 15.00 |
| Ash tray, 5½", oval | 18.00 | * Bowl, 6", nappy | 15.00 |
| Basket, w/reed handle, 7" x 9" | 90.00 | Bowl, 6", olive, oblong | 12.00 |
| Basket, 10", new in 1988 | 30.00 | Bowl, 6½", wedding, | |
| Bell | 325.00 | w/cover, sq., ped.ft., 8" h. | 87.50 |
| Bottle, bitters, w/tube, 5¾", 4½ oz. | 65.00 | Bowl, 6½", wedding, sq., ped. ft., 5¼" h. | 50.00 |
| Bottle, condiment or catsup w/stopper.. | 115.00 | Bowl, 7", bonbon, 3 ftd. | 12.50 |
| Bottle, cologne, w/stopper, 6 oz., 5¾" | 70.00 | Bowl, 7", cupped, 4½" h. | 50.00 |
| Bottle, cologne, w/stopper, 7¼", 8 oz. | 80.00 | * Bowl, 7", nappy | 25.00 |
| Bottle, cordial, w/stopper, 7¼", 9 oz. | 90.00 | Bowl, 8", bonbon, 3 ftd. | 17.50 |
| Bottle, water, 44 oz., 9¼" | 550.00 | Bowl, 8", deep | 55.00 |
| Bowl, banana split, 9" x 3½" | 300.00 | Bowl, 8", ftd. | 57.50 |
| Bowl, finger, 4½" diam., smooth edge . | 35.00 | Bowl, 8", ftd., 2 hdld., "trophy" cup ... | 100.00 |
| Bowl, 3½", rose | 20.00 | * Bowl, 8", nappy | 22.00 |
| Bowl, 3¾", almond, oval | 18.00 | * Bowl, 8", pickle, oblong | 13.00 |
| Bowl, 4¼", jelly, 4¼" h. | 15.00 | Bowl, 8½", 2 hdld. | 45.00 |
| * Bowl, 4½", 1 hdld. | 10.00 | * Bowl, 8½", boat | 15.00 |
| Bowl, 4½", 1 hdld., sq. | 11.00 | Bowl, 9", boat, 2 pt. | 10.50 |
| Bowl, 4½", jelly, w/cover, 6¾" h. | 22.00 | * Bowl, 9", oval veg. | 25.00 |
| * Bowl, 4½", nappy | 12.00 | Bowl, 9½", centerpiece | 42.50 |
| Bowl, 4½", oval | 15.00 | Bowl, 9½", 3 pt., 6" w. | 37.50 |
| Bowl, 4¾", fruit, flared | 15.00 | Bowl, 10", celery, oblong | 20.00 |
| Bowl, 5", cream soup, 2 hdld. | 45.00 | * Bowl, 10", deep | 35.00 |
| Bowl, 5", 1 hdld., tri-corner | 12.00 | Bowl, 10", float | 45.00 |
| * Bowl, 5", nappy | 10.00 | Bowl, 10", oval, float | 32.50 |

* See note on new American on page 11.

# AMERICAN, Line #2056, Fostoria Glass Company, 1915 – 1986 (continued)

|  | *Crystal |
|---|---|
| Bowl, 10", oval, veg., 2 pt. | 35.00 |
| Bowl, 10½", fruit, 3 ftd. | 35.00 |
| Bowl, 11", centerpiece | 40.00 |
| Bowl, 11", centerpiece, tri-corner | 42.50 |
| Bowl, 11", relish/celery, 3 pt. | 30.00 |
| Bowl, 11½", float | 55.00 |
| Bowl, 11½", fruit, rolled edge, 2¾" h. | 42.50 |
| Bowl, 11½", oval, float | 45.00 |
| Bowl, 11½", rolled edge | 45.00 |
| Bowl, 11¾", oval, deep | 40.00 |
| Bowl, 12", boat | 17.50 |
| Bowl, 12", fruit/sm. punch, ped. ft., (Tom & Jerry) | 165.00 |
| Bowl, 12", lily pond | 65.00 |
| Bowl, 12", relish "boat," 2 pt. | 20.00 |
| Bowl, 13", fruit, shallow | 65.00 |
| Bowl, 14", punch, w/high ft. base (2 gal.) | 225.00 |
| Bowl, 14", punch, w/low ft. base | 200.00 |
| Bowl, 15", centerpiece, "hat" shape | 155.00 |
| Bowl, 16", flat, fruit, ped. ft. | 165.00 |
| Bowl, 18", punch, w/low ft. base (3¾ gal.) | 315.00 |
| Box, pomade, 2" square | 350.00 |
| * Box, w/cover, puff, 3⅛" x 2¾" | 200.00 |
| Box, w/cover, 4½" x 4½" | 200.00 |
| Box, w/cover, handkerchief, 5⅝" x 4⅝" | 250.00 |
| Box, w/cover, hairpin, 3½" x 1¾" | 300.00 |
| Box, w/cover, jewel, 5¼" x 2¼" | 300.00 |
| Box, w/cover, jewel, 2 drawer, 4¼" x 3¼". | 1,750.00 |
| * Box, w/cover, glove, 9½" x 3½" | 275.00 |
| * Butter, w/cover, rnd. plate, 7¼" | 115.00 |
| * Butter, w/cover, ¼ lb. | 25.00 |
| Cake stand, (see salver) | |
| Candelabrum, 6½", 2-lite, bell base w/bobeche & prisms | 110.00 |
| Candle lamp, 8½", w/chimney, candle part, 3½" | 125.00 |
| Candlestick, twin, 4⅛" h., 8½" spread. | 55.00 |
| Candlestick, 2", chamber with fingerhold | 40.00 |
| Candlestick, 3", rnd. ft. | 15.00 |
| Candlestick, 4⅜", 2-lite, rnd. ft. | 35.00 |
| Candlestick, 6", octagon ft. | 25.00 |
| Candlestick, 6½", 2-lite, bell base | 90.00 |
| Candlestick, 6¼", round ft. | 200.00 |
| * Candlestick, 7", sq. column | 95.00 |
| Candlestick, 7¼", "Eiffel" tower | 125.00 |
| Candy box, w/cover, 3 pt., triangular | 75.00 |
| Candy, w/cover, ped. ft. | 35.00 |
| Cheese (5¾" compote) & cracker (11½" plate) | 50.00 |
| Cigarette box, w/cover, 4¾" | 37.50 |
| Coaster, 3¾" | 8.00 |
| Comport, 4½", jelly | 15.00 |
| * Comport, 5", jelly, flared | 15.00 |
| * Comport, 6¾", jelly, w/cover | 35.00 |
| Comport, 8½", 4" high | 40.00 |

|  | *Crystal |
|---|---|
| Comport, 9½", 5¼" high | 50.00 |
| Comport, w/cover, 5" | 25.00 |
| * Cookie jar, w/cover, 8⅞" h. | 275.00 |
| Creamer, tea, 3 oz., 2⅜" (#2056½) | 9.00 |
| Creamer, individual, 4¾ oz. | 9.00 |
| Creamer, 9½ oz. | 12.50 |
| Crushed fruit, w/cover & spoon, 10" | 1,250.00 |
| Cup, flat | 7.50 |
| Cup, ftd., 7 oz. | 8.00 |
| Cup, punch, flared rim | 11.00 |
| Cup, punch, straight edge | 10.00 |
| Decanter, w/stopper, 24 oz., 9¼" h. | 100.00 |
| Dresser set: powder boxes w/covers & tray | 400.00 |
| Flower pot, w/perforated cover, 9½" diam.; 5½" h. | 1,250.00 |
| Goblet, #2056, 2½ oz., wine, hex ft., 4⅜" h. | 12.00 |
| Goblet, #2056, 4½ oz., oyster cocktail, 3½" h. | 17.50 |
| Goblet, #2056, 4½ oz., sherbet, flared, 4⅜" h. | 9.00 |
| Goblet, #2056, 4½ oz., fruit, hex ft., 4¾" h. | 9.00 |
| Goblet, #2056, 5 oz., low ft., sherbet, flared, 3¼" h. | 9.00 |
| Goblet, #2056, 6 oz., low ft., sundae, 3⅛" h. | 9.00 |
| Goblet, #2056, 7 oz., claret, 4⅞" h. | 40.00 |
| * Goblet, #2056, 9 oz., low ft., 4⅜" h. | 11.00 |
| Goblet, #2056, 10 oz., hex ft., water, 6⅞" h. | 13.00 |
| Goblet, #2056, 12 oz., low ft., tea, 5¾" h. | 14.00 |
| Goblet, #2056½, 4½ oz., sherbet, 4½" h. | 10.00 |
| Goblet, #2056½, 5 oz., low sherbet, 3½" h. | 10.00 |
| Goblet, #5056, 1 oz., cordial, 3⅛", w/plain bowl | 25.00 |
| Goblet, #5056, 3½ oz., claret, 4⅝", w/plain bowl | 13.50 |
| Goblet, #5056, 3½ oz., cocktail, 4", w/plain bowl | 11.00 |
| Goblet, #5056, 4 oz., oyster cocktail, 3½", w/plain bowl | 10.00 |
| Goblet, #5056, 5½ oz., sherbet, 4⅛", w/plain bowl | 10.00 |
| Goblet, #5056, 10 oz., water, 6⅛", w/plain bowl | 12.00 |
| Hair receiver, 3" x 3" | 275.00 |
| Hat, 2⅛", (sm. ash tray) | 15.00 |
| Hat, 3" tall | 25.00 |
| Hat, 4" tall | 45.00 |
| Hat, western style | 200.00 |
| Hotel washbowl and pitcher | 2,500.00 |

* See note on new American on page 11.

8

| | *Crystal |
|---|---|
| Hurricane lamp, 12" complete | 165.00 |
| Hurricane lamp base | 52.50 |
| Ice bucket, w/tongs | 60.00 |
| Ice cream saucer (2 styles) | 55.00 |
| Ice dish for 4 oz. crab or 5 oz. tomato liner | 32.50 |
| Ice dish insert | 10.00 |
| Ice tub, w/liner, 5⅝" | 85.00 |
| Ice tub, w/liner, 6½" | 90.00 |
| Jam pot, w/cover | 50.00 |
| Jar, pickle, w/pointed cover, 6" h. | 295.00 |
| Marmalade, w/cover & chrome spoon | 50.00 |
| * Mayonnaise, div. | 15.00 |
| Mayonnaise, w/ladle, ped. ft. | 45.00 |
| Mayonnaise, w/liner & ladle | 32.50 |
| Molasses can, 11 oz., 6¾" h., 1 hdld. | 325.00 |
| * Mug, 5½ oz., "Tom & Jerry," 3¼" h. | 40.00 |
| * Mug, 12 oz., beer, 4½" h. | 65.00 |
| Mustard, w/cover | 30.00 |
| Napkin ring | 10.00 |
| Oil, 5 oz. | 35.00 |
| Oil, 7 oz. | 35.00 |
| Picture frame | 15.00 |
| Pitcher, ½ gal. w/ice lip, 8¼", flat bottom | 85.00 |
| Pitcher, ½ gal., w/o ice lip | 250.00 |
| Pitcher, ½ gal., 8", ftd. | 70.00 |
| Pitcher, 1 pt., 5⅜", flat | 27.50 |
| Pitcher, 2 pt., 7¼", ftd. | 65.00 |
| Pitcher, 3 pt., 8", ftd. | 70.00 |
| Pitcher, 3 pt., w/ice lip, 6½", ftd., "fat" | 50.00 |
| * Pitcher, 1 qt., flat | 30.00 |
| Plate, cream soup liner | 12.00 |
| Plate, 6", bread & butter | 12.00 |
| Plate, 7", salad | 10.00 |
| Plate, 7½" x 4⅜", crescent salad | 45.00 |
| Plate, 8", sauce liner, oval | 22.50 |
| Plate, 8½", salad | 12.00 |
| Plate, 9", sandwich (sm. center) | 14.00 |
| Plate, 9½", dinner | 20.00 |
| Plate, 10", cake, 2 hdld. | 25.00 |
| Plate, 10½" sandwich (sm. center) | 20.00 |
| Plate, 11½", sandwich (sm. center) | 20.00 |
| Plate, 12", cake, 3 ftd. | 22.50 |
| Plate, 13½", oval torte | 45.00 |
| Plate, 14", torte | 25.00 |
| Plate, 18", torte | 100.00 |
| Plate, 20", torte | 125.00 |
| Plate 24", torte | 200.00 |
| * Platter, 10½", oval | 40.00 |
| Platter, 12", oval | 55.00 |
| Ring holder | 200.00 |
| Salad set: 10" bowl, 14" torte, wood fork & spoon | 67.50 |
| Salt, individual | 9.00 |

| | *Crystal |
|---|---|
| Salver, 10", sq., ped. ft. (cake stand) | 70.00 |
| Salver, 10", rnd., ped. ft. (cake stand) | 60.00 |
| * Salver, 11", rnd., ped. ft. (cake stand) | 30.00 |
| Sauce boat & liner | 45.00 |
| Saucer | 3.00 |
| Set: 2 jam pots w/tray | 140.00 |
| Set: decanter, 6 - 2 oz. whiskeys on 10½" tray | 215.00 |
| Set: toddler, w/baby tumbler & bowl | 85.00 |
| Set: youth, w/bowl, hdld. mug, 6" plate | 85.00 |
| Set: condiment, 2 oils, 2 shakers, mustard w/cover & spoon w/tray | 275.00 |
| Shaker, 3", ea. | 10.00 |
| * Shaker, 3½", ea. | 7.00 |
| Shaker, 3¼", ea. | 10.00 |
| Shakers w/tray, individual, 2" | 22.00 |
| Sherbet, handled, 3½" high, 4½ oz. | 75.00 |
| Shrimp bowl, 12¼" | 335.00 |
| Spooner, 3¾" | 35.00 |
| ** Strawholder, 10", w/cover | 250.00 |
| Sugar, tea, 2¼" (#2056½) | 13.00 |
| Sugar, hdld., 3¼" h. | 12.00 |
| Sugar shaker | 50.00 |
| Sugar, w/o cover | 10.00 |
| Sugar, w/cover, no hdl., 6¼" (cover fits strawholder) | 60.00 |
| Sugar, w/cover, 2 hdld. | 20.00 |
| Syrup, 6½ oz., #2056½, Sani-cut server | 65.00 |
| Syrup, 6 oz., non pour screw top, 5¼" h. | 200.00 |
| Syrup, 10 oz., w/glass cover & 6" liner plate | 135.00 |
| Syrup, w/drip proof top | 35.00 |
| Toothpick | 22.50 |
| Tray, cloverleaf for condiment set | 145.00 |
| Tray, tid bit, w/question mark metal handle | 35.00 |
| Tray, 5" x 2½", rect. | 75.00 |
| Tray, 6" oval, hdld. | 35.00 |
| Tray, pin, oval, 5½" x 4½" | 125.00 |
| Tray, 6½" x 9" relish, 4 part | 45.00 |
| Tray, 9½", service, 2 hdld. | 30.00 |
| Tray, 10", muffin (2 upturned sides) | 30.00 |
| Tray, 10", square, 4 part | 75.00 |
| Tray, 10", square | 110.00 |
| Tray, 10½", cake, w/question mark metal hdl. | 30.00 |
| Tray, 10½" x 7½", rect. | 70.00 |
| Tray, 10½" x 5", oval hdld. | 45.00 |
| Tray, 10¾", square, 4 part | 125.00 |
| Tray, 12", sand. w/ctr. handle | 35.00 |
| Tray, 12", round | 135.00 |
| Tray, 13½", oval, ice cream | 160.00 |
| Tray for sugar & creamer, tab. hdld., 6¾" | 12.00 |

* See note on new American on page 11.

** Bottom only

| | *Crystal |
|---|---|
| Tumbler, hdld. iced tea | 200.00 |
| Tumbler, #2056, 2 oz., whiskey, 2½" h. | 11.00 |
| Tumbler, #2056, 3 oz., ftd. cone, cocktail, 2⅞" h. | 14.00 |
| Tumbler, #2056, 5 oz., ftd., juice, 4¾". | 12.00 |
| Tumbler, #2056, 6 oz., flat, old-fashioned, 3⅜" h. | 13.00 |
| Tumbler, #2056, 8 oz. flat, water, flared, 4⅛" h. | 14.00 |
| * Tumbler, #2056, 9 oz. ftd., water, 4⅞" h. | 14.00 |
| Tumbler, #2056, 12 oz., flat, tea, flared, 5¼" h. | 16.00 |
| Tumbler, #2056½, 5 oz., straight side, juice | 12.00 |
| Tumbler, #2056½, 8 oz., straight side, water, 3⅞" h. | 12.00 |
| Tumbler, #2056½, 12 oz., straight side, tea, 5" h. | 17.50 |
| Tumbler, #5056, 5 oz., ftd., juice, 4⅛" w/plain bowl | 10.00 |
| Tumbler, #5056, 12 oz., ftd., tea, 5½" w/plain bowl | 12.00 |
| Urn, 6", sq., ped. ft | 30.00 |

| | *Crystal |
|---|---|
| Urn, 7½", sq. ped. ft. | 35.00 |
| Vase, 4½", sweet pea | 70.00 |
| Vase, 6", bud, ftd. | 18.00 |
| * Vase, 6", bud, flared | 18.00 |
| Vase, 6", straight side | 35.00 |
| Vase, 6½", flared rim | 15.00 |
| Vase, 7", flared | 75.00 |
| * Vase, 8", straight side | 40.00 |
| * Vase, 8", flared | 80.00 |
| Vase, 8", porch, 5" diam. | 325.00 |
| Vase, 8½", bud, flared | 25.00 |
| Vase, 8½", bud, cupped | 25.00 |
| Vase, 9", w/sq. ped. ft. | 45.00 |
| Vase, 9½", flared | 110.00 |
| Vase, 10", cupped in top | 165.00 |
| Vase, 10", porch, 8" diam. | 300.00 |
| * Vase, 10", straight side | 90.00 |
| Vase, 10", swung | 165.00 |
| Vase, 10", flared | 90.00 |
| Vase, 12", straight side | 125.00 |
| Vase, 12", swung | 150.00 |
| Vase, 14", swung | 200.00 |
| Vase, 20", swung | 325.00 |

* Note: June 1994. Fostoria Outlet stores are continuing to stock American! I have placed an asterisk by all pieces that are being made. I do not know every piece that has been reissued, but I suspect all pieces with asterisks in my previous editions are being made since these moulds should be in working order. Lancaster Colony is having American remade at Dalzell Viking. They have even hired former Fostoria employees to get the color right!

If you live near a Fostoria "outlet" store, you might want to drop by every few months to see what is being dragged out of the mould "attic."

# APPLE BLOSSOM, Line #3400, Cambridge Glass Company, 1930's

Colors: blue, pink, light and dark green, yellow, crystal, amber

Collectors continue to make yellow Apple Blossom their number one choice. Availability is the key word in that choice! A few hardy souls search for pink, blue, and crystal; yet green Apple Blossom is the only other color in which you stand a chance of completing a set — unless you are extremely lucky and find a whole set all at once. Putting any other colored set together a piece at a time will take years. If you are up to a challenge, then go for it!

Thankfully, many of the known colors of Apple Blossom are exhibited in a pitcher collection atop page 15. You will search long and hard to round up any of these.

Stemware lines can be found with some searching, but serving pieces and unusual items are elusive. Patience is a virtue in collecting this pattern!

| | Crystal | Yellow Amber | Pink *Green |
|---|---|---|---|
| Ash tray, 6", heavy............................................... | 50.00 | 150.00 | |
| Bowl, #3025, ftd., finger, w/plate ............................ | 25.00 | 35.00 | 40.00 |
| Bowl, #3130, finger, w/plate .................................. | 30.00 | 35.00 | 40.00 |
| Bowl, 5¼", 2 hdld., bonbon.................................... | 12.50 | 25.00 | 25.00 |
| Bowl, 5½", 2 hdld., bonbon.................................... | 12.50 | 25.00 | 25.00 |
| Bowl, 5½", fruit "saucer"....................................... | 10.00 | 15.00 | 17.00 |
| Bowl, 6", 2 hdld., "basket" (sides up)...................... | 20.00 | 30.00 | 35.00 |
| Bowl, 6", cereal................................................... | 15.00 | 25.00 | 30.00 |
| Bowl, 9", pickle .................................................. | 17.00 | 32.00 | 40.00 |
| Bowl, 10", 2 hdld................................................. | 35.00 | 70.00 | 85.00 |
| Bowl, 10", baker.................................................. | 35.00 | 70.00 | 85.00 |
| Bowl, 11", fruit, tab hdld....................................... | 35.00 | 75.00 | 80.00 |
| Bowl, 11", low ftd................................................ | 30.00 | 75.00 | 90.00 |
| Bowl, 12", relish, 4 pt........................................... | 30.00 | 45.00 | 60.00 |
| Bowl, 12", 4 ftd................................................... | 40.00 | 70.00 | 85.00 |
| Bowl, 12", flat.................................................... | 35.00 | 60.00 | 65.00 |
| Bowl, 12", oval, 4 ftd. .......................................... | 40.00 | 60.00 | 85.00 |
| Bowl, 12½", console ............................................. | 35.00 | 50.00 | 55.00 |
| Bowl, 13"........................................................... | 35.00 | 60.00 | 65.00 |
| Bowl, cream soup, w/liner plate............................. | 20.00 | 27.50 | 35.00 |
| Butter w/cover, 5½".............................................. | 125.00 | 225.00 | 350.00 |
| Candelabrum, 3-lite, keyhole................................. | 27.50 | 40.00 | 50.00 |
| Candlestick, 1-lite, keyhole................................... | 17.50 | 25.00 | 27.50 |
| Candlestick, 2-lite, keyhole................................... | 22.50 | 30.00 | 35.00 |
| Candy box w/cover, 4 ftd. "bowl" ........................... | 65.00 | 85.00 | 125.00 |
| Cheese (compote) & cracker (11½" plate) .................. | 40.00 | 60.00 | 80.00 |
| Comport, 4", fruit cocktail..................................... | 12.50 | 20.00 | 25.00 |
| Comport, 7", tall ................................................. | 35.00 | 50.00 | 65.00 |
| Creamer, ftd. ..................................................... | 12.50 | 17.50 | 22.50 |
| Creamer, tall ftd.................................................. | 12.50 | 20.00 | 25.00 |
| Cup................................................................... | 15.00 | 22.00 | 26.00 |
| Cup, A.D. ........................................................... | 40.00 | 45.00 | 75.00 |
| Fruit/oyster cocktail, #3025, 4½ oz. ........................ | 12.50 | 17.50 | 20.00 |
| Mayonnaise, w/liner & ladle, (4 ftd. bowl)................. | 35.00 | 50.00 | 65.00 |
| Pitcher, 50 oz., ftd., flattened sides......................... | 125.00 | 195.00 | 250.00 |
| Pitcher, 64 oz., #3130.......................................... | 135.00 | 225.00 | 275.00 |
| Pitcher, 64 oz., #3025.......................................... | 135.00 | 235.00 | 295.00 |
| Pitcher, 67 oz., squeezed middle, loop hdld. .............. | 135.00 | 250.00 | 300.00 |
| Pitcher, 76 oz..................................................... | 145.00 | 225.00 | 295.00 |
| Pitcher, 80 oz., ball............................................. | 125.00 | 150.00 | 295.00 |
| Pitcher w/cover, 76 oz., ftd., #3135 ........................ | 195.00 | 375.00 | 475.00 |
| Plate, 6", bread/butter.......................................... | 6.00 | 7.00 | 8.00 |
| Plate, 6", sq., 2 hdld. ........................................... | 8.00 | 9.00 | 10.00 |
| Plate, 7½", tea.................................................... | 9.00 | 12.00 | 13.00 |

* Blue prices 25% to 30% more.

12

# APPLE BLOSSOM, Line #3400, Cambridge Glass Company, 1930's (continued)

| | Crystal | Yellow Amber | Pink *Green |
|---|---|---|---|
| Plate, 8½" .................................................... | 14.00 | 20.00 | 22.00 |
| Plate, 9½", dinner .......................................... | 45.00 | 65.00 | 75.00 |
| Plate, 10", grill ............................................. | 25.00 | 40.00 | 50.00 |
| Plate, sandwich, 11½", tab hdld. ..................... | 22.00 | 32.50 | 35.00 |
| Plate, sandwich, 12½", 2 hdld. ......................... | 25.00 | 35.00 | 37.50 |
| Plate, sq., bread/butter .................................. | 5.00 | 7.00 | 8.00 |
| Plate, sq., dinner .......................................... | 45.00 | 65.00 | 75.00 |
| Plate, sq., salad ............................................ | 10.00 | 12.00 | 13.00 |
| Plate, sq., service ......................................... | 17.50 | 20.00 | 22.00 |
| Platter, 11½ ................................................. | 37.50 | 60.00 | 70.00 |
| Platter, 13½" rect., w/tab handle ..................... | 40.00 | 85.00 | 95.00 |
| Salt & pepper, pr. .......................................... | 37.50 | 75.00 | 90.00 |
| Saucer ......................................................... | 4.00 | 5.00 | 5.00 |
| Saucer, A.D. ................................................. | 12.00 | 15.00 | 17.50 |
| Stem, #1066, parfait ...................................... | 65.00 | 100.00 | 140.00 |
| Stem, #3025, 7 oz., low fancy ft., sherbet ......... | 11.00 | 15.00 | 16.00 |
| Stem, #3025, 7 oz., high sherbet ...................... | 12.00 | 18.00 | 20.00 |
| Stem, #3025, 10 oz. ....................................... | 18.00 | 22.00 | 25.00 |
| Stem, #3130, 1 oz., cordial ............................. | 55.00 | 90.00 | 125.00 |
| Stem, #3130, 3 oz., cocktail ............................ | 15.00 | 24.00 | 27.50 |
| Stem, #3130, 6 oz., low sherbet ....................... | 10.00 | 15.00 | 16.00 |
| Stem, #3130, 6 oz., tall sherbet ....................... | 10.00 | 18.00 | 20.00 |
| Stem, #3130, 8 oz., water ................................ | 15.00 | 22.00 | 30.00 |
| Stem, #3135, 3 oz., cocktail ............................ | 13.00 | 24.00 | 27.50 |
| Stem, #3135, 6 oz., low sherbet ....................... | 10.00 | 15.00 | 16.00 |
| Stem, #3135, 6 oz., tall sherbet ....................... | 10.00 | 18.00 | 20.00 |
| Stem, #3135, 8 oz., water ................................ | 14.00 | 22.00 | 30.00 |
| Stem, #3400, 6 oz., ftd., sherbet ..................... | 9.00 | 15.00 | 16.00 |
| Stem, #3400, 9 oz., water ................................ | 12.50 | 22.00 | 30.00 |
| Sugar, ftd. ................................................... | 12.00 | 16.00 | 20.00 |
| Sugar, tall ftd. .............................................. | 12.00 | 18.00 | 22.50 |
| Tray, 11" ctr. hdld. sand. ................................ | 25.00 | 37.50 | 45.00 |
| Tumbler, #3025, 4 oz. ..................................... | 12.00 | 17.00 | 19.00 |
| Tumbler, #3025, 10 oz. .................................... | 15.00 | 20.00 | 22.00 |
| Tumbler, #3025, 12 oz. .................................... | 18.00 | 32.50 | 40.00 |
| Tumbler, #3130, 5 oz., ftd. .............................. | 11.00 | 20.00 | 25.00 |
| Tumbler, #3130, 8 oz., ftd. .............................. | 12.00 | 25.00 | 27.50 |
| Tumbler, #3130, 10 oz., ftd. ............................. | 13.00 | 25.00 | 27.50 |
| Tumbler, #3130, 12 oz., ftd. ............................. | 17.50 | 35.00 | 42.50 |
| Tumbler, #3135, 5 oz., ftd. .............................. | 10.00 | 20.00 | 25.00 |
| Tumbler, #3135, 8 oz., ftd. .............................. | 12.00 | 25.00 | 27.50 |
| Tumbler, #3135, 10 oz., ftd. ............................. | 13.00 | 25.00 | 27.50 |
| Tumbler, #3135, 12 oz., ftd. ............................. | 17.50 | 35.00 | 42.50 |
| Tumbler, #3400, 2½ oz., ftd. ............................ | 12.00 | 50.00 | 65.00 |
| Tumbler, #3400, 9 oz., ftd. .............................. | 12.00 | 25.00 | 27.50 |
| Tumbler, #3400, 12 oz., ftd. ............................. | 17.50 | 35.00 | 42.50 |
| Tumbler, 12 oz., flat (2 styles) - 1 mid indent to match 67 oz. pitcher ......................................... | 20.00 | 32.50 | 40.00 |
| Tumbler, 6" .................................................. | 15.00 | 30.00 | 35.00 |
| Vase, 5" ....................................................... | 25.00 | 40.00 | 45.00 |
| Vase, 6", rippled sides ................................... | 30.00 | 50.00 | 65.00 |
| Vase, 8", 2 styles .......................................... | 40.00 | 75.00 | 100.00 |
| Vase, 12", keyhole base w/neck indent .............. | 45.00 | 150.00 | 225.00 |

* Blue prices 25% to 30% more.
Note: See Pages 228-229 for stem identification.

# BAROQUE, Line #2496, Fostoria Glass Company, 1936 – 1966

Colors: crystal, "Azure" blue, "Topaz" yellow, green, pink, red, cobalt blue, black amethyst

Very few of the odd colored Baroque candlesticks are now being found; and so far, no console bowls to match those already discovered candlesticks have been reported! In the top picture on page 17 the yellow, two-handled cream soup is pictured for the first time. These are hard to find in both yellow and blue. To the left of the cream soup is a ruffled bowl. That bowl is the mayonnaise without a liner. The saucer is missing in the bottom photo also. That gives me additional pieces to search for in my travels.

The sweetmeat is the 9" tall, covered piece at the back of the bottom photograph. This is to distinguish it from the jelly that is only 7½" tall. Note the tops on the shakers. They came with both metal and glass tops, although most collectors prefer the glass lids. Metal lids were replacements when the glass ones were broken.

I sometimes forget how many new collectors are reading this book for the first time. The yellow pitcher on the top of page 17 has no ice lip while the blue one on the top of page 19 has an ice lip. Similarly, the covered jar with spoon on the top right of page 17 is a mustard and the little rounded ball shaped vase at the bottom of the same page is the rose bowl.

Notice that candlesticks come in a variety of shapes! Pictured in blue (on the top of page 19) are the 5½" single and a pair of the 4" style. The 6", 3-lite is shown in red and green at the bottom of that page.

Variations in blue are shown in the bottom photo. This is a major concern to many collectors. They tend to shy away from the green tint. If color variations do not upset you, then you will have many more choices as you search for this pattern!

Straight sided tumblers are more difficult to find than the footed ones, but many collectors seem to prefer them to the cone-shaped, footed pieces. If everyone were to like the same style, the demand would exceed the supply very quickly!

Baroque blank (#2496) was used for many of Fostoria's etched lines including Chintz and Navarre.

| | Crystal | Blue | Yellow |
|---|---|---|---|
| Ash tray | 7.50 | 15.00 | 13.00 |
| Bowl, cream soup | 35.00 | 75.00 | 75.00 |
| Bowl, ftd., punch | 350.00 | 1,250.00 | |
| Bowl, 3¾", rose | 25.00 | 55.00 | 45.00 |
| Bowl, 4", hdld. (4 styles) | 11.00 | 22.50 | 20.00 |
| Bowl, 5", fruit | 15.00 | 25.00 | 30.00 |
| Bowl, 6", cereal | 20.00 | 35.00 | 30.00 |
| Bowl, 6", sq. | 8.00 | 20.00 | 22.00 |
| Bowl, 6½", 2 pt. | 9.00 | 25.00 | 20.00 |
| Bowl, 7", 3 ftd. | 12.50 | 25.00 | 25.00 |
| Bowl, 7½", jelly, w/cover | 30.00 | 85.00 | 50.00 |
| Bowl, 8", pickle | 8.50 | 27.50 | 22.50 |
| Bowl, 8½", hdld. | 14.00 | 35.00 | 30.00 |
| Bowl, 9½", veg., oval | 25.00 | 60.00 | 45.00 |
| Bowl, 10", hdld. | 15.00 | 60.00 | 40.00 |
| Bowl, 10½", hdld., 4 ftd. | 17.50 | 47.50 | 37.50 |
| Bowl, 10" x 7½" | 25.00 | | |
| Bowl, 10", relish, 3 pt. | 20.00 | 30.00 | 22.50 |
| Bowl, 11", celery | 12.00 | 45.00 | 25.00 |
| Bowl, 11", rolled edge | 20.00 | 50.00 | 37.50 |
| Bowl, 12", flared | 21.50 | 40.00 | 32.50 |
| Candelabrum, 8¼", 2-lite, 16 lustre | 85.00 | 95.00 | 75.00 |
| Candelabrum, 9½", 3-lite, 24 lustre | 110.00 | 150.00 | 140.00 |
| Candle, 7¾", 8 lustre | 50.00 | 85.00 | 75.00 |
| Candlestick, 4" | 12.50 | 35.00 | 30.00 |
| Candlestick, 4½", 2-lite | 15.00 | 55.00 | 50.00 |

* Red $140.00
Green $110.00
Black Amethyst $135.00
Cobalt Blue $135.00

# BAROQUE, Line #2496, Fostoria Glass Company, 1936 – 1966 (continued)

| | Crystal | Blue | Yellow |
|---|---|---|---|
| Candlestick, 5½" | 9.00 | 40.00 | 35.00 |
| * Candlestick, 6", 3-lite | 17.50 | 75.00 | 60.00 |
| Candy, 3 part w/cover | 30.00 | 110.00 | 75.00 |
| Comport, 4¾" | 15.00 | 30.00 | 25.00 |
| Comport, 6½" | 17.50 | 35.00 | 30.00 |
| Creamer, 3¼", indiv. | 9.00 | 30.00 | 25.00 |
| Creamer, 3¾", ftd. | 8.00 | 14.00 | 14.00 |
| Cup | 9.00 | 30.00 | 20.00 |
| Cup, 6 oz., punch | 12.00 | 30.00 | |
| Ice bucket | 35.00 | 115.00 | 75.00 |
| Mayonnaise, 5½", w/liner | 15.00 | 55.00 | 40.00 |
| Mustard, w/cover | 22.00 | 50.00 | 37.50 |
| Oil, w/stopper, 5½" | 85.00 | 400.00 | 195.00 |
| Pitcher, 6½" | 110.00 | 700.00 | 450.00 |
| Pitcher, 7", ice lip | 110.00 | 650.00 | 400.00 |
| Plate, 6" | 3.00 | 10.00 | 8.00 |
| Plate, 7½" | 4.00 | 12.50 | 10.00 |
| Plate, 8½" | 6.00 | 20.00 | 17.50 |
| Plate, 9½" | 15.00 | 55.00 | 45.00 |
| Plate, 10", cake | 20.00 | 35.00 | 30.00 |
| Plate, 11", ctr. hdld., sand | 25.00 | | |
| Plate, 14", torte | 13.00 | 37.50 | 20.00 |
| Platter, 12", oval | 22.00 | 60.00 | 40.00 |
| Salt & pepper, pr. | 45.00 | 120.00 | 100.00 |
| Salt & pepper, indiv., pr. | 50.00 | 200.00 | 125.00 |
| Saucer | 2.00 | 5.00 | 4.00 |
| Sherbet, 3¾", 5 oz. | 10.00 | 27.50 | 17.50 |
| Stem, 6¾", 9 oz., water | 12.00 | 27.50 | 22.50 |
| Sugar, 3", indiv. | 5.00 | 27.50 | 22.50 |
| Sugar, 3½", ftd. | 6.00 | 15.00 | 11.00 |
| Sweetmeat, covered, 9" | 75.00 | 175.00 | 135.00 |
| Tray, 11", oval | 15.00 | 47.50 | 37.50 |
| Tray, 6¼" for indiv. cream/sugar | 15.00 | 25.00 | 20.00 |
| Tumbler, 3½", 6½ oz., old-fashioned | 22.50 | 80.00 | 50.00 |
| Tumbler, 3", 3½ oz., ftd., cocktail | 10.00 | 18.00 | 15.00 |
| Tumbler, 6", 12 oz., ftd., tea | 20.00 | 40.00 | 30.00 |
| Tumbler, 3¾", 5 oz., juice | 12.00 | 37.50 | 25.00 |
| Tumbler, 5½", 9 oz., ftd., water | 12.00 | 30.00 | 25.00 |
| Tumbler, 4¼", 9 oz., water | 25.00 | 50.00 | 25.00 |
| Tumbler, 5¾", 14 oz., tea | 27.50 | 70.00 | 50.00 |
| Vase, 6½" | 45.00 | 125.00 | 100.00 |
| Vase, 7" | 40.00 | 125.00 | 85.00 |

* Red $140.00
Green $110.00
Black Amethyst $135.00
Cobalt Blue $135.00

# BLACK FOREST, Possibly Paden City for Van Deman & Son, Late 1920's – Early 1930's

Colors: amber, black, ice blue, crystal, green, pink, red, cobalt

Black Forest and Deerwood patterns are often confused. Study the pattern shots of each. Black Forest depicts moose and trees; deer and trees are predominant on Deerwood. If you have trouble telling moose from deer, then you are in big trouble with these two patterns!

The question I am asked the most about Black Forest concerns goblets that were made in the 1970's. An amber one is pictured on the bottom right of page 21. These were made in amber, dark green, blue, crystal and red. They were made for an importing company in Virginia that specialized in reproductions before the current craze. Since these are newer than the original Black Forest, they are easier to find and are selling in the $25.00 range, although you may see them offered for much more by unknowing dealers. All these reproduced items have the heavy "Daisy and Button" stem shown here.

Notice the night set (pitcher and tumbler) in Black Forest. The tumbler has a molded band that will not allow it to drop down into the pitcher when turned upside down on it.

The large, footed, covered, five-part relish in the center of the top photo (page 21) is 10½" wide and stands 6¾" tall with lid. I had a report of a pink one; but no confirming picture was ever sent.

This is a pattern that will challenge your collecting abilities no matter which color you choose; but, don't let difficulty deter you from collecting! I receive hundreds of letters yearly telling me how much joy that collectors derive from owning even a piece or two of favorite patterns!

| | Amber | Black | Crystal | Green | Pink | Red |
|---|---|---|---|---|---|---|
| Batter jug | | | 125.00 | | | |
| Bowl, 4½", finger | | | | 15.00 | | |
| Bowl, 9¼", center hdld. | | | | 65.00 | 65.00 | |
| Bowl, 11", console | 50.00 | 50.00 | 35.00 | 30.00 | 30.00 | |
| Bowl, 11", fruit | | 30.00 | | 25.00 | 25.00 | |
| Bowl, 13", console | | 65.00 | | | | |
| Bowl, 3 ftd. | | | 60.00 | | | |
| Cake plate, 2" pedestal | 40.00 | 50.00 | | 40.00 | 35.00 | |
| Candlestick, mushroom style | 30.00 | 35.00 | 15.00 | 30.00 | 30.00 | |
| Candlestick double | | | 35.00 | | | |
| Candy dish, w/cover, several styles | 85.00 | 95.00 | | 75.00 | 85.00 | |
| Creamer, 2 styles | | 35.00 | 20.00 | 35.00 | 35.00 | 65.00 |
| Comport, 4", low ftd. | | | | 25.00 | 25.00 | |
| Comport, 5½", high ftd. | | 30.00 | | 28.00 | 25.00 | |
| Cup and saucer, 3 styles | | 85.00 | | 85.00 | 85.00 | 110.00 |
| Decanter, w/stopper, 8½", 28 oz., bulbous | | | | | 145.00 | |
| Decanter w/stopper, 8¾", 24 oz., straight | | | 75.00 | 125.00 | 125.00 | |
| Ice bucket | 90.00 | | | 75.00 | 75.00 | |
| Ice pail, 6", 3" high | 75.00 | | | | | |
| Ice tub, 2 styles (Ice blue $195.00) | 80.00 | 75.00 | | 75.00 | 65.00 | |
| Mayonnaise, with liner | | 60.00 | | 60.00 | 60.00 | |
| Night Set: pitcher, 6½", 42 oz. & tumbler | | | | 400.00 | 400.00 | |
| Pitcher, 8", 40 oz., (Cobalt $375.00) | | | | | | |
| Pitcher, 8", 62 oz. | | | 175.00 | | | |
| Pitcher, 9", 80 oz. | | | | | 400.00 | |
| Pitcher, 10½", 72 oz. | | | | 425.00 | 425.00 | |
| Plate, 6½", bread/butter | | 22.00 | | 22.00 | | 30.00 |
| Plate, 8", luncheon | | 25.00 | | | 25.00 | 30.00 |
| Plate, 11", 2 hdld. | | 45.00 | | 25.00 | 25.00 | |
| Relish, 10½", 5 pt. covered | | | | 175.00 | 175.00 | |
| Salt and pepper, pr. | | | 115.00 | | 150.00 | |
| Server, center hdld. | 50.00 | 40.00 | 35.00 | 35.00 | 35.00 | |
| Shot Glass, 2 oz., 2½" | 40.00 | | | | | |
| Stem, 2 oz., wine, 4¼" | | | 17.50 | 50.00 | | |
| Stem, 6 oz., champagne, 4¾" | | | 17.50 | | 30.00 | |
| Stem, 9 oz., water, 6" | | | 22.50 | | | |
| Sugar, 2 styles | | 35.00 | 20.00 | 35.00 | 35.00 | 65.00 |
| Tumbler, 3 oz., juice, flat or footed, 3½" | | | 25.00 | 20.00 | 25.00 | |
| Tumbler, 8 oz., old fashioned, 3⅞" | | | | | 30.00 | |
| Tumbler, 9 oz., ftd., 5½" | 30.00 | | | | | |
| Tumbler, 12 oz., tea, 5½" | | | | 40.00 | 40.00 | |
| Vase, 6½" (Cobalt $125.00) | | 55.00 | 45.00 | 50.00 | 50.00 | |
| Vase, 10", 2 styles in black | | 75.00 | | 65.00 | 65.00 | |
| Whipped cream pail | 75.00 | | | | | |

# BUTTERCUP, ETCHING #340, Fostoria Glass Company

Colors: crystal

I have received requests to include Buttercup in my book! It seems that people who had Buttercup as their crystal are beginning to split it up within the family, and there is no where to turn to find this glassware other than glass shows.

Vases are hard to find in Fostoria crystal patterns. The smaller vase pictured is the 6" footed #6021 and the larger is the 7½" footed #4143. The little pieces in front are an individual ash tray and a cigarette holder. That cigarette holder might make a better toothpick holder with today's concern about smoking.

| | Crystal | | Crystal |
|---|---|---|---|
| Ash tray, #2364, 2⅝", individual | 20.00 | Plate, #2337, 9½" | 37.00 |
| Bottle, #2083, salad dressing | 200.00 | Plate, #2364, 6¾", mayonnaise | 7.50 |
| Bowl, #2364, 6", baked apple | 16.00 | Plate, #2364, 7¼" x 4½", crescent salad | 35.00 |
| Bowl, #2364, 9", salad | 50.00 | Plate, #2364, 11¼", cracker | 30.00 |
| Bowl, #2364, 10½", salad | 55.00 | Plate, #2364, 11", sandwich | 35.00 |
| Bowl, #2364, 11", salad | 55.00 | Plate, #2364, 14", torte | 40.00 |
| Bowl, #2364, 12", flared | 60.00 | Plate, #2364, 16", torte | 75.00 |
| Bowl, #2364, 12", lily pond | 55.00 | Relish, #2364, 6½" x 5", 2 part | 22.50 |
| Bowl, #2364, 13", fruit | 65.00 | Relish, #2364, 10" x 7¼", 3 part | 30.00 |
| Bowl, #2594, 10", 2 hdld. | 55.00 | Saucer, #2350 | 5.00 |
| Candlestick, #2324, 4" | 15.00 | Shaker, #2364, 2⅝" | 32.50 |
| Candlestick, #2324, 6" | 27.50 | Stem, #6030, 3¾", 4 oz., oyster cocktail | 18.00 |
| Candlestick, #2594, 5½" | 25.00 | Stem, #6030, 3⅞", 1 oz., cordial | 37.50 |
| Candlestick, #2594, 8", trindle | 35.00 | Stem, #6030, 4⅜", 6 oz., low sherbet | 17.50 |
| Candlestick, #6023, 5½", duo | 32.50 | Stem, #6030, 5¼", 3½ oz., cocktail | 22.50 |
| Candy w/cover, #2364, 3¾" diameter | 90.00 | Stem, #6030, 5⅝", 6 oz., high sherbet | 20.00 |
| Celery, #2350, 11" | 27.50 | Stem, #6030, 6⅜", 10 oz., low goblet | 22.50 |
| Cheese stand, #2364, 5¾" x 2⅞" | 20.00 | Stem, #6030, 6", 3½ oz., claret-wine | 32.50 |
| Cigarette holder, #2364, 2" high | 35.00 | Stem, #6030, 7⅞", 10 oz., water goblet | 27.50 |
| Comport, # 2364, 8" | 35.00 | Sugar, #2350½, 3⅛", ftd | 13.00 |
| Comport, #6030, 5" | 30.00 | Syrup, #2586, sani-cut | 225.00 |
| Creamer, #2350½, 3¼", ftd | 14.00 | Tray, #2364, 11¼", center handled | 32.50 |
| Cup, #2350½, ftd. | 15.00 | Tumbler, #6030, 4⅝", 5 oz., ftd. juice | 20.00 |
| Mayonnaise, #2364, 5" | 25.00 | Tumbler, #6030, 6", 12 oz., ftd. ice tea | 27.50 |
| Pickle, #2350, 8" | 25.00 | Vase, #2614, 10" | 120.00 |
| Pitcher, #6011, 8⅞", 53 oz. | 250.00 | Vase, #4143, 6", ftd. | 80.00 |
| Plate, #2337, 6" | 7.00 | Vase, #4143, 7½", ftd. | 115.00 |
| Plate, #2337, 7½" | 12.00 | Vase, #6021, 6", ftd. | 65.00 |
| Plate, #2337, 8½" | 17.50 | | |

# CADENA, Tiffin Glass Company, Early 1930's

Colors: crystal, yellow; some pink

One question I field quite often is why I can't show every item in each pattern and label it as to what piece it is! One major reason is cost and another is availability! Another reason is you, the reader, wouldn't be able to afford the book or to pick it up from shear page weight. I couldn't afford to buy every piece in every pattern if I could find them. There are serious collectors of many patterns that can not find every piece regardless of how much their pocketbook holds.

We have always tried to show you as much glass as possible to whet your collecting appetite. Where feasible, we have included a close-up shot to enhance pattern identification. We try to feature different colors and pieces in each edition.

As with most Tiffin patterns, stemware can be found, but serving pieces and basic dinnerware items such as dinner plates and cups and saucers are elusive. Pitchers were sold both with and without a top. If you try to put a top on one of the pitchers sold without a top, you may be in for a big surprise since many of the topless pitchers were curved in so much that a top will not fit. Remember that the pitcher cover is plain; no pattern is etched on it.

Minute amounts of pink are being found. Cadena is rarely seen at Depression shows and that makes for fewer collectors. You will find a piece or two in your travels, but seeing a whole set for sale is perhaps a thing of the past. Obviously, Tiffin did not market this pattern as extensively as they did their Cherokee Rose, Fuchsia, and Flanders patterns, all of which are popular with today's collectors!

|  | Crystal | Pink/ Yellow |
|---|---|---|
| Bowl, cream soup | 20.00 | 30.00 |
| Bowl, finger, ftd. | 15.00 | 25.00 |
| Bowl, grapefruit, ftd. | 20.00 | 45.00 |
| Bowl, 6", hdld. | 10.00 | 22.00 |
| Bowl, 10", pickle | 15.00 | 27.50 |
| Bowl, 12", console | 25.00 | 47.50 |
| Candlestick | 17.50 | 32.50 |
| Creamer | 15.00 | 25.00 |
| Cup | 25.00 | 55.00 |
| Goblet, 4¾", sherbet | 15.00 | 22.00 |
| Goblet, 5¼", cocktail | 17.50 | 25.00 |
| Goblet, 5¼", ¾ oz., cordial | 55.00 | 85.00 |
| Goblet, 6", wine | 25.00 | 40.00 |
| Goblet, 6½", champagne | 17.00 | 30.00 |
| Goblet, 7½", water | 20.00 | 35.00 |
| Mayonnaise, ftd., w/liner | 30.00 | 50.00 |
| Oyster cocktail | 15.00 | 25.00 |
| Pitcher, ftd., w/cover | 235.00 | 350.00 |
| Plate, 6" | 5.00 | 8.00 |
| Plate, 7¾" | 7.00 | 12.00 |
| Plate, 9¼" | 30.00 | 40.00 |
| Saucer | 10.00 | 12.50 |
| Sugar | 15.00 | 23.00 |
| Tumbler, 4¼", ftd., juice | 17.50 | 27.50 |
| Tumbler, 5¼", ftd., water | 20.00 | 30.00 |
| Vase, 9" | 40.00 | 75.00 |

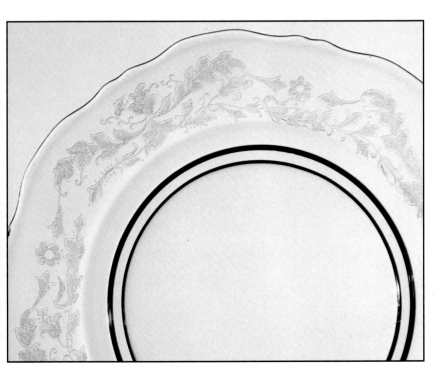

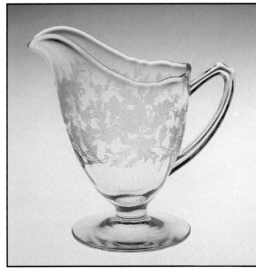

# CANDLELIGHT, Cambridge Glass Company, 1940's – Early 1950's

Colors: crystal, Crown Tuscan with gold decoration

Not one letter on Candlelight has been forthcoming in the two years since this pattern was included. I had hoped to add to my listings! Am I to assume I did it right the first time? I doubt that!

Obviously, Candlelight is not as collected as other Cambridge patterns, even though almost everyone recognizes the pattern! That bowl used as a pattern shot has a "cut" Candlelight pattern instead of acid etched. Admittedly, Candlelight pieces are rare, but even one or two pieces strategically placed can enhance a table, mantle, or entrance way.

Additional pieces with "cut" Candlelight include candlesticks to go with the bowl pictured, cocktail icer, salad plate, vase, and water goblets. There may be other pieces that are "cut," but I have not seen them. Price the "cut" Candlelight pieces **up to double** the prices of the etched.

You may find other pieces of etched Candlelight. Please let me know what you have or find.

| | Crystal | | Crystal |
|---|---|---|---|
| Bowl, 7", ftd., 2 hdld., #3900/130 | 30.00 | Relish, 12", 3 pt., #3900/126 | 52.50 |
| Bowl, 10", 4 toed, flared, #3900/54 | 55.00 | Relish, 12", 5 pt., #3900/120 | 57.50 |
| Bowl, 11", 2 hdld., #3900/34 | 60.00 | Salt & pepper, pr., #3900/1177 | 45.00 |
| Bowl, 11½", ftd., 2 hdld., #3900/28 | 65.00 | Saucer, #3900/17 | 5.00 |
| Bowl, 12", 4 toed, flared, #3900/62 | 62.50 | Stem, 1 oz., cordial, #3776 | 65.00 |
| Bowl, 12", 4 toed, oval, hdld., #3900/65 | 85.00 | Stem, 2½ oz., wine, #3776 | 30.00 |
| Candle, 5", #3900/67 | 37.50 | Stem, 2½ oz., wine, #3111 | 35.00 |
| Candle, 6", 2-lite, #3900/72 | 37.50 | Stem, 3 oz., cocktail, #3111 | 27.50 |
| Candle, 6", 3-lite, #3900/74 | 45.00 | Stem, 3 oz., cocktail, #3776 | 25.00 |
| Candy w/lid, rnd. #3900/165 | 95.00 | Stem, 4½ oz., claret, #3776 | 32.50 |
| Comport, 5⅜", blown, #3121 | 57.50 | Stem, 4½ oz., oyster cocktail, #3111 | 27.50 |
| Comport, 5½", #3900/136 | 50.00 | Stem, 4½ oz., oyster cocktail, #3776 | 22.50 |
| Creamer, #3900/41 | 20.00 | Stem, 7 oz., low sherbet, #3111 | 17.50 |
| Creamer, indiv., #3900/40 | 20.00 | Stem, 7 oz., low sherbet, #3776 | 16.50 |
| Cruet, 6 oz., w/stopper, #3900/100 | 100.00 | Stem, 7 oz., tall sherbet, #3111 | 22.50 |
| Cup, #3900/17 | 27.50 | Stem, 7 oz., tall sherbet, #3776 | 20.00 |
| Ice bucket, #3900/671 | 110.00 | Stem, 9 oz., water, #3776 | 30.00 |
| Icer, 2 pc., cocktail, #968 | 65.00 | Stem, 10 oz., water, #3111 | 30.00 |
| Lamp, hurricane, #1617 | 125.00 | Sugar, #3900/41 | 17.50 |
| Lamp, hurricane, keyhole, w/bobeche,#1603 | 175.00 | Sugar, indiv., #3900/40 | 17.50 |
| Lamp, hurricane, w/bobeche, #1613 | 265.00 | Tumbler, 5 oz., ftd., juice, #3111 | 20.00 |
| Mayonnaise, 3 pc., #3900/129 | 57.50 | Tumbler, 5 oz., juice, #3776 | 18.00 |
| Mayonnaise, div., 4 pc., #3900/111 | 65.00 | Tumbler, 12 oz., ftd., iced tea., #3111 | 25.00 |
| Mayonnaise, ftd., 2 pc., #3900/19 | 47.50 | Tumbler, 12 oz., iced tea, #3776 | 22.50 |
| Pitcher, Doulton, #3400/141 | 300.00 | Tumbler, 13 oz., #3900/115 | 35.00 |
| Plate, 6½", #3900/20 | 12.50 | Vase, 5", ftd., bud, #6004 | 35.00 |
| Plate, 8", 2 hdld., #3900/131 | 25.00 | Vase, 5", globe, #1309 | 52.50 |
| Plate, 8", salad, #3900/22 | 15.00 | Vase, 6", ftd., #6004 | 35.00 |
| Plate, 10½", dinner, #3900/24 | 65.00 | Vase, 8", ftd., #6004 | 45.00 |
| Plate, 12", 4 toed, #3900/26 | 55.00 | Vase, 9", ftd., keyhole, #1237 | 55.00 |
| Plate, 13", torte, 4 toed, #3900/33 | 55.00 | Vase, 10", bud, #274 | 42.50 |
| Plate, 13½", cake, 2 hdld., #3900/35 | 60.00 | Vase, 11", ftd. pedestal, #1299 | 105.00 |
| Plate, 14", rolled edge, #3900/166 | 65.00 | Vase, 11", ftd., #278 | 65.00 |
| Relish, 7", 2 hdld., #3900/123 | 32.50 | Vase, 12", ftd., keyhole, #1238 | 87.50 |
| Relish, 7", div., 2 hdld., #3900/124 | 35.00 | Vase, 13", ftd, #279 | 110.00 |
| Relish, 9", 3 pt., #3900/125 | 42.50 | | |

# CANDLEWICK, Line #400, Imperial Glass Company, 1936 – 1984

Colors: crystal, blue, pink, yellow, black, red, cobalt blue, green, carmel slag

For beginning collectors I need to point out a few things in the stemware and tumbler lines. In the top photo on page 29 (left front) is a cordial from the 3800 stemware line. The more commonly found 400 stemware line is shown by the cordials in the center and the floral decorated pieces on the left. The other stemware line is 400/190 and is found with a hollow stem. These can easily be seen in the ad on page 37. The 400/ was Imperial's factory listing for each piece.

The tumblers on the right at the top of page 29 that are straight sided with balls around the flattened bottom are designated 400/19 in the listings. The 400/18 are shown on the right at the bottom of page 31 and at the top of page 33 on the back left. These tumblers are distinguished by a domed foot.

Viennese Blue pieces of Candlewick (light colored blue shown below) are continuing to be purchased, but red and black pieces have been difficult to sell of late. Prices on colored Candlewick escalated very fast; but recently, those prices have slowed considerably which is usually the fate of a too rapid price rise. Ruby Red and black fancy bowls have steadied in price in the ball park of $225.00 with the Viennese Blue bringing about half of that. Ruby Red stems continue to be found in the 3400 and 3800 lines with most of these selling in the $35.00 to $55.00 range. However, cordials are selling in Ruby Red and Ritz Blue (cobalt) from $100.00 to $125.00. Other Ritz Blue stems are fetching $65.00 to $90.00. All the Viennese Blue pieces were made before 1940 as were the Ruby Red and Ritz Blue.

In the top photograph on page 29 are several etched floral designed pieces. Many of these were also gold decorated. You can see the gold decorated florals on the punch set at the bottom of page 33. At the bottom of page 29 is a setting of cut Candlewick bought in late 1939 or 1940. Unfortunately, the owner sold all the dinner plates, cups, and saucers before I had a chance to buy the set. The 7½" lily bowl shown on the right was only made in 1939 and is quite hard to find.

Page 35 shows some of the later Candlewick colors along with some Viennese Blue. I have included several advertisements from 1940's magazines.

There are unusual and rare Candlewick items shown in the three volumes of *Very Rare Glassware of the Depression Years.*

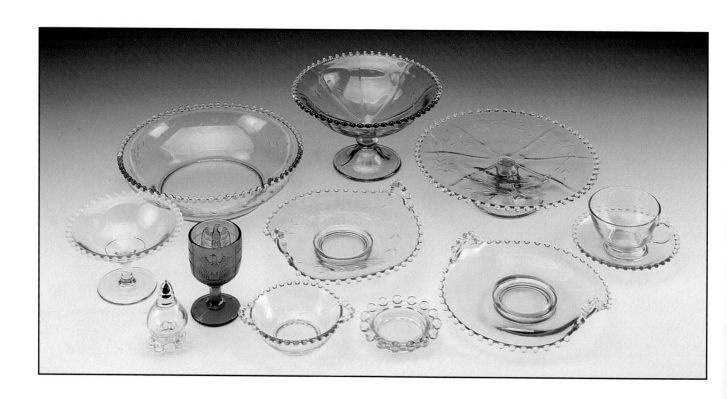

|  | Crystal |
| --- | --- |
| Ash tray, eagle, 6½", 1776/1 | 55.00 |
| Ash tray, heart, 4½", 400/172 | 9.00 |
| Ash tray, heart, 5½", 400/173 | 11.00 |
| Ash tray, heart, 6½", 400/174 | 15.00 |
| Ash tray, indiv 400/64. | 6.00 |
| Ash tray, oblong, 4½", 400/134/1 | 6.00 |
| Ash tray, round, 2¾", 400/19 | 9.00 |
| Ash tray, round, 4", 400/33 | 11.00 |
| Ash tray, round, 5", 400/133 | 8.00 |
| Ash tray, square, 3¼", 400/651 | 32.50 |
| Ash tray, square, 4½", 400/652 | 32.50 |
| Ash tray, square, 5¾", 400/653 | 37.50 |
| Ash tray, 6", matchbook holder center, 400/60 | 95.00 |
| Ash tray set, 3 pc. rnd. nest. (crys. or colors), 400/550 | 25.00 |
| Ash tray set, 3 pc. sq. nesting, 400/650 | 102.50 |
| Ash tray set, 4 pc. bridge (cig. hold at side), 400/118 | 37.50 |
| Basket, 5", beaded hdld., 400/273 | 195.00 |
| Basket, 6½", hdld., 400/40/0 | 30.00 |
| Basket, 11", hdld., 400/73/0 | 225.00 |
| Bell, 4", 400/179 | 85.00 |
| Bell, 5", 400/108 | 85.00 |
| Bottle, bitters, w/tube, 4 oz., 400/117 | 60.00 |
| Bowl, bouillon, 2 hdld., 400/126 | 40.00 |
| Bowl, #3400, finger, ftd. | 27.50 |
| Bowl, #3800, finger | 27.50 |
| Bowl, 4½", nappy, 3 ftd., 400/206 | 67.50 |
| Bowl, 4¾", round, 2 hdld., 400/42B | 10.00 |
| Bowl, 5", cream soup, 400/50 | 40.00 |
| Bowl, 5", fruit, 400/1F | 12.00 |
| Bowl, 5", heart w/hand., 400/49H | 18.00 |
| Bowl, 5", square, 400/231 | 85.00 |
| Bowl, 5½", heart, 400/53H | 20.00 |
| Bowl, 5½", jelly, w/cover, 400/59 | 60.00 |
| Bowl, 5½", sauce, deep, 400/243 | 35.00 |
| Bowl, 6", baked apple, rolled edge, 400/53X | 27.50 |
| Bowl, 6", cottage cheese, 400/85 | 25.00 |
| Bowl, 6", fruit, 400/3F | 12.00 |
| Bowl, 6", heart w/hand., 400/51H | 25.00 |
| Bowl, 6", mint w/hand., 400/51F | 20.00 |
| Bowl, 6", round, div., 2 hdld., 400/52 | 25.00 |
| Bowl, 6", 2 hdld., 400/52B | 15.00 |
| Bowl, 6", 3 ftd., 400/183 | 60.00 |
| Bowl, 6", sq., 400/232 | 110.00 |
| Bowl, 6½", relish, 2 pt., 400/84 | 25.00 |
| Bowl, 6½", 2 hdld., 400/181 | 30.00 |
| Bowl, 7", round, 400/5F | 22.00 |
| Bowl, 7", round, 2 hdld., 400/62B | 17.50 |
| Bowl, 7", relish, sq., div., 400/234 | 125.00 |
| Bowl, 7", ivy, high, bead ft., 400/188 | 175.00 |
| Bowl, 7", lily, 4 ft., 400/74J | 65.00 |
| Bowl, 7", relish, 400/60 | 25.00 |
| Bowl, 7", sq., 400/233 | 130.00 |
| Bowl, 7¼", rose, ftd. w/crimp edge, 400/132C | 235.00 |
| Bowl, 7½", pickle/celery 400/57 | 25.00 |
| Bowl, 7½", lily, bead rim, ftd., 400/75N | 135.00 |
| Bowl, 7½", belled, (console base), 400/127B | 45.00 |

|  | Crystal |
| --- | --- |
| Bowl, 8", round, 400/7F | 37.50 |
| Bowl, 8", relish, 2 pt., 400/268 | 20.00 |
| Bowl, 8", cov. veg., 400/65/1 | 265.00 |
| Bowl, 8½", rnd., 400/69 | 32.50 |
| Bowl, 8½", nappy, 4 ftd., 400/74B | 45.00 |
| Bowl, 8½", 3 ftd., 400/182 | 110.00 |
| Bowl, 8½", 2 hdld., 400/72B | 22.00 |
| Bowl, 8½", pickle/celery, 400/58 | 20.00 |
| Bowl, 8½", relish, 4 pt., 400/55 | 20.00 |
| Bowl, 9", round, 400/10F | 42.50 |
| Bowl, 9", crimp, ftd., 400/67C | 135.00 |
| Bowl, 9", sq., fancy crimp edge, 4 ft., 400/74SC | 65.00 |
| Bowl, 9", heart, 400/49H | 90.00 |
| Bowl, 9", heart w/hand., 400/73H | 115.00 |
| Bowl, 10", 400/13F | 45.00 |
| Bowl, 10", banana, 400/103E | 1,250.00 |
| Bowl, 10", 3 toed, 400/205 | 135.00 |
| Bowl, 10", belled, (punch base), 400/128B | 50.00 |
| Bowl, 10", cupped edge, 400/75F | 45.00 |
| Bowl, 10", deep, 2 hdld., 400/113A | 115.00 |
| Bowl, 10", divided, deep, 2 hdld., 400/114A | 135.00 |
| Bowl, 10", fruit, bead stem (like compote), 400/103F | 140.00 |
| Bowl, 10", relish, oval, 2 hdld., 400/217 | 40.00 |
| Bowl, 10", relish, 3 pt., 3 ft., 400/208 | 85.00 |
| Bowl, 10", 3 pt., w/cover, 400/216 | 300.00 |
| Bowl, 10½", belled, 400/63B | 60.00 |
| Bowl, 10½", butter/jam, 3 pt., 400/262 | 75.00 |
| Bowl, 10½", salad, 400/75B | 40.00 |
| Bowl, 10½", relish, 3 section, 400/256 | 30.00 |
| Bowl, 11", celery boat, oval, 400/46 | 55.00 |
| Bowl, 11", centerpiece, flared, 400/13B | 45.00 |
| Bowl, 11", float, inward rim, ftd., 400/75F | 40.00 |
| Bowl, 11", oval, 400/124A | 240.00 |
| Bowl, 11", oval w/partition, 400/125A | 265.00 |
| Bowl, 12", round, 400/92B | 40.00 |
| Bowl, 12", belled, 400/106B | 90.00 |
| Bowl, 12", float, 400/92F | 40.00 |
| Bowl, 12", hdld., 400/113B | 65.00 |
| Bowl, 12", shallow, 400/17F | 47.50 |
| Bowl, 12", relish, oblong, 4 sect., 400/215 | 115.00 |
| Bowl, 13", centerpiece, mushroom, 400/92L | 50.00 |
| Bowl, 13", float, 1½" deep, 400/101 | 60.00 |
| Bowl, 13½", relish, 5 pt., 400/209 | 77.50 |
| Bowl, 14", belled, 400/104B | 90.00 |
| Bowl, 14", oval, flared, 400/131B | 175.00 |
| Butter and jam set, 5 piece, 400/204 | 245.00 |
| Butter, w/ cover, rnd., 5½", 400/144 | 32.50 |
| Butter, w/ cover, no beads, California, 400/276 | 115.00 |
| Butter, w/ bead top, ¼ lb., 400/161 | 30.00 |
| Cake stand, 10", low foot, 400/67D | 52.50 |
| Cake stand, 11", high foot, 400/103D | 67.50 |
| Calendar, 1947, desk | 175.00 |
| Candleholder, 3 way, beaded base, 400/115 | 105.00 |
| Candleholder, 2-lite, 400/100 | 20.00 |
| Candleholder, flat, 3½", 400/280 | 20.00 |
| Candleholder, 3½", rolled edge, 400/79R | 10.50 |
| Candleholder, 3½", w/fingerhold, 400/81 | 42.50 |
| Candleholder, flower, 4", 2 bead stem, 400/66F | 45.00 |
| Candleholder, flower, 4½", 2 bead stem, 400/66C | 60.00 |

| | Crystal |
|---|---|
| Candleholder, 4½", 3 toed, 400/207 | 40.00 |
| Candleholder, 3-lite on cir. bead. ctr., 400/147 ... | 25.00 |
| Candleholder, 5", hdld./bowled up base, 400/90.................................................... | 45.00 |
| Candleholder, 5" heart shape, 400/40HC.......... | 45.00 |
| Candleholder, 5½", 3 bead stems, 400/224 ....... | 85.00 |
| Candleholder, flower, 5", (epergne inset), 400/40CV.................................................. | 95.00 |
| Candleholder, 5", flower, 400/40C | 27.50 |
| Candleholder, 6½", tall, 3 bead stems, 400/175 ... | 75.00 |
| Candleholder, flower, 6", round, 400/40F......... | 17.50 |
| Candleholder, urn, 6", holders on cir. ctr. bead, 400/129R.......................................... | 115.00 |
| Candleholder, flower, 6½", square, 400/40S ..... | 25.00 |
| Candleholder, mushroom, 400/86.................... | 22.00 |
| Candleholder, flower 9" centerpiece, 400/196FC.................................................. | 135.00 |
| Candy box, round, 5½", 400/59 ..................... | 45.00 |
| Candy box, sq., 6½", rnd. lid, 400/245 ............. | 150.00 |
| Candy box, w/ cover, 7", 400/259................... | 135.00 |
| Candy box, w/ cover, 7" partitioned, 400/110 .. | 65.00 |
| Candy box, w/ cover, round, 7", 3 sect., 400/158.................................................... | 165.00 |
| Candy box, w/ cover, beaded, ft., 400/140....... | 225.00 |
| Cigarette box w/cover, 400/134 ...................... | 30.00 |
| Cigarette holder, 3", bead ft., 400/44 ............... | 40.00 |
| Cigarette set: 6 pc., (cigarette box & 4 rect. ash trays), 400/134/6.................................... | 67.50 |
| Clock, 4", round ...................................... | 265.00 |
| Coaster, 4", 400/78 ................................... | 6.00 |
| Coaster, w/spoon rest, 400/226 .................... | 13.00 |
| Cocktail, seafood w/bead ft., 400/190 ............. | 52.50 |
| Cocktail set: 2 pc., plate w/indent; cocktail, 400/97.................................................... | 35.00 |
| Compote, 4½", 400/63B............................... | 25.00 |
| Compote, 5", 3 bead stems, 400/220 ............... | 55.00 |
| Compote, 5½", 4 bead stem, 400/45 ............... | 22.00 |
| Compote, 5½, low, plain stem, 400/66B.......... | 18.00 |
| Compote, 5½", 2 bead stem, 400/66B ............. | 18.00 |
| Compote, 8", bead stem, 400/48F................... | 77.50 |
| Compote, 10", ftd. fruit, crimped, 40/103C...... | 120.00 |
| Compote, ft. oval, 400/137........................... | 850.00 |
| Condiment set: 4 pc., (2 squat bead ft. shakers, marmalade), 400/1786 ............................. | 67.50 |
| Console sets: 3 pc. (14" oval bowl, two 3-lite candles), 400/1531B................................ | 275.00 |
| 3 pc. (mushroom bowl, w/mushroom candles), 400/8692L.................................. | 105.00 |
| Creamer, domed foot, 400/18 ........................ | 115.00 |
| Creamer, 6 oz., bead handle, 400/30 ............... | 8.00 |
| Creamer, indiv. bridge, 400/122 .................... | 7.50 |
| Creamer, plain ft., 400/31 ............................ | 9.00 |
| Creamer, flat, bead handle, 400/126............... | 32.50 |
| Cup, after dinner, 400/77............................. | 17.50 |
| Cup, coffee, 400/37 ................................... | 7.50 |
| Cup, punch, 400/211 .................................. | 7.50 |
| Cup, tea, 400/35 ....................................... | 8.00 |
| Decanter, w/stopper, 15 oz. cordial, 400/82/2 .. | 295.00 |
| Decanter w/stopper, 18 oz., 400/18 ................ | 365.00 |
| Decanter w/stopper, 26 oz., 400/163 .............. | 295.00 |
| Deviled egg server, 12", ctr. hdld., 400/154...... | 100.00 |
| Egg cup, bead. ft., 400/19............................ | 47.50 |

| | Crystal |
|---|---|
| Fork & spoon, set, 400/75 .............................. | 35.00 |
| Hurricane lamp, 2 pc. candle base, 400/79....... | 120.00 |
| Hurricane lamp, 2 pc. hdld. candle base, 400/76 | 150.00 |
| Hurricane lamp, 3 pc. flared & crimped edge globe, 400/152 ........................................ | 150.00 |
| Ice tub, 5½" deep, 8" diam., 400/63................. | 85.00 |
| Ice tub, 7", 2 hdld., 400/168......................... | 195.00 |
| Icer, 2 pc., seafood/fruit cocktail, 400/53/3 ...... | 95.00 |
| Icer, 2 pc., seafood/fruit cocktail #3800 line, one bead stem........................................ | 65.00 |
| Jam set, 5 pc., oval tray w/2 marmalade jars w/ladles, 400/1589................................... | 115.00 |
| Jar tower, 3 sect., 400/655............................ | 300.00 |
| Knife, butter, 4000.................................... | 250.00 |
| Ladle, marmalade, 3 bead stem, 400/130......... | 10.00 |
| Ladle, mayonnaise, 6¼", 400/135.................... | 10.00 |
| Marmalade set, 3 pc., beaded ft. w/cover & spoon, 400/1989...................................... | 40.00 |
| Marmalade set, 3 pc. tall jar, domed bead ft., lid, spoon, 400/8918................................ | 65.00 |
| Marmalade set, 4 pc., liner saucer, jar, lid, spoon, 400/89.......................................... | 42.50 |
| Mayonnaise set, 2 pc. scoop side bowl, spoon, 400/23.................................................. | 37.50 |
| Mayonnaise set, 3 pc. hdld. tray/hdld. bowl/ladle, 400/52/3................................... | 45.00 |
| Mayonnaise set, 3 pc. plate, heart bowl, spoon, 400/49.................................................. | 33.00 |
| Mayonnaise set, 3 pc. scoop side bowl, spoon, tray, 400/496.......................................... | 40.00 |
| Mayonnaise 4 pc., plate, divided bowl, 2 ladles, 400/84.......................................... | 40.00 |
| Mirror, 4½", rnd., standing........................... | 95.00 |
| Mustard jar, w/spoon, 400/156...................... | 30.00 |
| Oil, 4 oz., bead base, 400/164....................... | 55.00 |
| Oil, 6 oz., bead base, 400/166....................... | 65.00 |
| Oil, 4 oz., bulbous bottom, 400/274 ................ | 45.00 |
| Oil, 4 oz., hdld., bulbous bottom, 400/278 ....... | 65.00 |
| Oil, 6 oz., hdld., bulbous bottom, 400/279 ....... | 80.00 |
| Oil, 6 oz., bulbous bottom, 400/275 ................ | 55.00 |
| Oil, w/stopper, etched "Oil," 400/121 .............. | 65.00 |
| Oil, w/stopper, etched "Vinegar," 400/121 ....... | 65.00 |
| Party set, 2 pc., oval plate w/indent for cup, 400/98.................................................. | 30.00 |
| Pitcher, 14 oz., short rnd., 400/330 ................. | 125.00 |
| Pitcher, 16 oz., low ft., 400/19...................... | 210.00 |
| Pitcher, 16 oz., no ft., 400/16....................... | 175.00 |
| Pitcher, 20 oz., plain, 400/416...................... | 40.00 |
| Pitcher, 40 oz., juice/cocktail, 400/19.............. | 175.00 |
| Pitcher, 40 oz., manhattan, 400/18................. | 225.00 |
| Pitcher, 40 oz., plain, 400/419...................... | 40.00 |
| Pitcher, 64 oz., plain, 400/424...................... | 50.00 |
| Pitcher, 80 oz., plain, 400/424...................... | 55.00 |
| Pitcher, 80 oz., 400/24................................ | 130.00 |
| Pitcher, 80 oz., beaded ft., 400/18.................. | 225.00 |
| Plate, 4½", 400/34..................................... | 6.00 |
| Plate, 5½", 2 hdld., 400/42D......................... | 10.00 |
| Plate, 6", bread/butter, 400/1D...................... | 8.00 |
| Plate, 6", canape w/off ctr. indent, 400/36........ | 11.00 |
| Plate, 6¾", 2 hdld. crimped, 400/52C................ | 25.00 |
| Plate, 7", salad, 400/3D............................... | 8.00 |

|  | Crystal |
|---|---|
| Plate, 7½", 2 hdld., 400/52D | 10.00 |
| Plate, 7½", triangular, 400/266 | 85.00 |
| Plate, 8", oval, 400/169 | 22.50 |
| Plate, 8", salad, 400/5D | 9.00 |
| Plate, 8", w/indent, 400/50 | 11.00 |
| Plate, 8¼", crescent salad, 400/120 | 45.00 |
| Plate, 8½", 2 hdld., crimped, 400/62C | 20.00 |
| Plate, 8½", 2 hdld., 400/62D | 12.00 |
| Plate, 8½", salad, 400/5D | 10.00 |
| Plate, 8½", 2 hdld. (sides upturned), 400/62E | 25.00 |
| Plate, 9", luncheon, 400/7D | 13.50 |
| Plate, 9", oval, salad, 400/38 | 37.50 |
| Plate, 9", w/indent, oval, 400/98 | 15.00 |
| Plate, 10", 2 hdld., sides upturned, 400/72E | 22.50 |
| Plate, 10", 2 hdld. crimped, 400/72C | 30.00 |
| Plate, 10", 2 hdld., 400/72D | 17.50 |
| Plate, 10½", dinner, 400/10D | 35.00 |
| Plate, 12", 2 hdld., 400/145D | 27.50 |
| Plate, 12", 2 hdld. crimp., 400/145C | 32.50 |
| Plate, 12", service, 400/13D | 30.00 |
| Plate, 12½", cupped edge, torte, 400/75V | 27.50 |
| Plate, 12½", oval, 400/124 | 75.00 |
| Plate, 13½", cupped edge, serving, 400/92V | 37.50 |
| Plate, 14" birthday cake (holes for 72 candles), 400/160 | 395.00 |
| Plate, 14", 2 hdld., sides upturned, 400/113E | 35.00 |
| Plate, 14", 2 hdld., torte, 400/113D | 30.00 |
| Plate, 14", service, 400/92D | 30.00 |
| Plate, 14", torte, 400/17D | 42.50 |
| Plate, 17", cupped edge, 400/20V | 42.50 |
| Plate, 17", torte, 400/20D | 45.00 |
| Platter, 13", 400/124D | 90.00 |
| Platter, 16", 400/131D | 175.00 |
| Punch ladle, 400/91 | 22.50 |
| Punch set, family, 8 demi cups, ladle, lid, 400/139/77 | 425.00 |
| Punch set, 15 pc. bowl on base, 12 cups, ladle, 400/20 | 235.00 |
| Relish & dressing set, 4 pc. (10½" 4 pt. relish w/marmalade), 400/1112 | 90.00 |
| Salad set, 4 pc., buffet; lg. rnd. tray, div. bowl, 2 spoons, 400/17 | 100.00 |
| Salad set, 4 pc. (rnd. plate, flared bowl, fork, spoon), 400/75B | 85.00 |
| Salt & pepper pr., bead ft., straight side, chrome top, 400/247 | 16.00 |
| Salt & pepper pr., bead ft., bulbous, chrome top, 400/96 | 15.00 |
| Salt & pepper pr., bulbous w/bead stem, plastic top, 400/116 | 42.50 |
| Salt & pepper, pr., indiv., 400/109 | 10.00 |
| Salt & pepper, pr., ftd. bead base, 400/190 | 47.50 |
| Salt dip, 2", 400/61 | 9.00 |
| Salt dip, 2¼", 400/19 | 9.00 |
| Salt spoon, 3, 400/616 | 9.00 |
| Salt spoon, w/ribbed bowl, 4000 | 9.00 |
| Sauce boat, 400/169 | 100.00 |
| Sauce boat liner, 400/169 | 35.00 |
| Saucer, after dinner, 400/77AD | 5.00 |
| Saucer, tea or coffee, 400/35 or 400/37 | 2.50 |

|  | Crystal |
|---|---|
| Set: 2 pc. hdld. cracker w/cheese compote, 400/88 | 37.50 |
| Set: 2 pc. rnd. cracker plate w/indent; cheese compote, 400/145 | 45.00 |
| Snack jar w/cover, bead ft., 400/139/1 | 425.00 |
| Stem, 1 oz., cordial, 400/190 | 70.00 |
| Stem, 4 oz., cocktail, 400/190 | 18.00 |
| Stem, 5 oz., tall sherbet, 400/190 | 15.00 |
| Stem, 5 oz., wine, 400/190 | 22.50 |
| Stem, 6 oz., sherbet, 400/190 | 14.00 |
| Stem, 10 oz., water 400/190 | 18.00 |
| Stem, #3400, 1 oz., cordial | 37.50 |
| Stem, #3400, 4 oz., cocktail | 14.00 |
| Stem, #3400, 4 oz. oyster cocktail | 14.00 |
| Stem, #3400, 4 oz., wine | 24.00 |
| Stem, #3400, 5 oz., claret | 45.00 |
| Stem, #3400, 5 oz., low sherbet | 10.00 |
| Stem, #3400, 6 oz., parfait | 50.00 |
| Stem, #3400, 6 oz., sherbet/saucer champagne | 17.50 |
| Stem, #3400, 9 oz., goblet, water | 15.00 |
| Stem, #3800, low sherbet | 25.00 |
| Stem, #3800, brandy | 27.50 |
| Stem, #3800, 1 oz. cordial | 42.50 |
| Stem, #3800, 4 oz., cocktail | 25.00 |
| Stem, #3800, 4 oz. wine | 27.50 |
| Stem, #3800, 6 oz., champagne/sherbet | 25.00 |
| Stem, #3800, 9 oz. water goblet | 25.00 |
| Stem, #3800, claret | 30.00 |
| Stem, #4000, 1¼ oz., cordial | 30.00 |
| Stem, #4000, cocktail | 22.00 |
| Stem, #4000, 5 oz., wine | 25.00 |
| Stem, #4000, 6 oz., tall sherbet | 14.00 |
| Stem, #4000, 11 oz., goblet | 18.00 |
| Stem, #4000, 12 oz., tea | 20.00 |
| Strawberry set, 2 pc. (7" plate/sugar dip bowl), 400/83 | 50.00 |
| Sugar, domed foot, 400/18 | 115.00 |
| Sugar, 6 oz., bead hdld., 400/30 | 7.00 |
| Sugar, flat, bead handle, 400/126 | 40.00 |
| Sugar, indiv. bridge, 400/122 | 6.00 |
| Sugar, plain ft., 400/31 | 6.50 |
| Tete-a-tete 3 pc. brandy, a.d. cup, 6½" oval tray, 400/111 | 57.50 |
| Tid bit server, 2 tier, cupped, 400/2701 | 45.00 |
| Tid bit set, 3 pc., 400/18TB | 165.00 |
| Toast, w/cover, set, 7¾", 400/123 | 245.00 |
| Tray, 5½", hdld., upturned handles, 400/42E | 18.00 |
| Tray, 5½", lemon, ctr. hdld., 400/221 | 30.00 |
| Tray, 5¼" x 9¼", condiment, 400/148 | 42.50 |
| Tray, 6½", 400/29 | 15.00 |
| Tray, 6", wafer, handle bent to ctr. of dish, 400/51T | 22.00 |
| Tray, 10½", ctr. hdld. fruit, 400/68F | 55.00 |
| Tray, 11½", ctr. hdld. party, 400/68D | 30.00 |
| Tray, 13½", 2 hdld. celery, oval, 400/105 | 30.00 |
| Tray, 13", relish, 5 sections, 400/102 | 65.00 |
| Tray, 14", hdld., 400/113E | 40.00 |
| Tumbler, 3½ oz., cocktail, 400/18 | 40.00 |
| Tumbler, 5 oz., juice, 400/18 | 37.50 |
| Tumbler, 6 oz., sherbet, 400/18 | 40.00 |

| | Crystal | | Crystal |
|---|---|---|---|
| Tumbler, 7 oz., old-fashioned 400/18.............. | 32.50 | Vase, 6", flat, crimped edge, 400/287C............ | 20.00 |
| Tumbler, 7 oz., parfait, 400/18........................ | 45.00 | Vase, 6", ftd., flared rim, 400/138B.................. | 80.00 |
| Tumbler, 9 oz., water, 400/18 ........................... | 40.00 | Vase, 6" diam., 400/198................................... | 195.00 |
| Tumbler, 12 oz., tea, 400/18 ........................... | 42.50 | Vase, 6" fan, 400/287 F................................... | 27.50 |
| Tumbler, 3 oz., ftd., cocktail, 400/19.............. | 15.00 | Vase, 7", ftd., bud, 400/186........................... | 225.00 |
| Tumbler, 3 oz., ftd., wine, 400/19.................... | 16.00 | Vase, 7", ftd., bud, 400/187 ........................... | 200.00 |
| Tumbler, 5 oz., low sherbet, 400/19 ................. | 15.00 | Vase, 7", ivy bowl, 400/74J ........................... | 50.00 |
| Tumbler, 5 oz., juice, 400/19.......................... | 10.00 | Vase, 7", rolled rim w/bead hdld., 400/87 R..... | 35.00 |
| Tumbler, 7 oz., old-fashioned, 400/19.............. | 32.50 | Vase, 7", rose bowl, 400/142 K ........................ | 125.00 |
| Tumbler, 10 oz., 400/19 ................................... | 12.00 | Vase, 7¼", ftd., rose bowl, crimped top, | |
| Tumbler, 12 oz., 400/19 ................................... | 22.00 | 400/132C ...................................................... | 250.00 |
| Tumbler, 14 oz., 400/19, tea .......................... | 22.00 | Vase, 7½", ftd., rose bowl, 400/132.................. | 165.00 |
| Tumbler, #3400, 5 oz., ft., juice ......................... | 15.00 | Vase, 8", fan, w/bead hdld., 400/87F................ | 35.00 |
| Tumbler, #3400, 9 oz., ftd. ........................... | 14.00 | Vase, 8", flat, crimped edge, 400/143C............ | 65.00 |
| Tumbler, #3400, 10 oz., ftd. ........................... | 14.00 | Vase, 8", fluted rim w/bead hdlds., 400/87C .... | 27.50 |
| Tumbler, #3400, 12 oz., ftd. ........................... | 16.00 | Vase, 8½", bead ft., bud, 400/28C ................... | 75.00 |
| Tumbler, #3800, 5 oz., juice............................ | 25.00 | Vase, 8½", bead ft., flared rim, 400/21............ | 125.00 |
| Tumbler, #3800, 9 oz............................... | 25.00 | Vase, 8½", bead ft., inward rim, 400/27 ........... | 125.00 |
| Tumbler, #3800, 12 oz............................... | 25.00 | Vase, 8½", hdld. (pitcher shape), 400/227........ | 350.00 |
| Vase, 4", bead ft., sm. neck, ball, 400/25 ........... | 42.50 | Vase, 10", bead ft., straight side, 400/22........... | 150.00 |
| Vase, 5¾", bead ft., bud, 400/107..................... | 45.00 | Vase, 10", ftd., 400/193 ................................... | 165.00 |
| Vase, 5¾", bead ft., mini bud, 400/107............. | 40.00 | | |

IMPERIAL GLASS CORPORATION
BELLAIRE, OHIO

*Easter Dinner*
## IMPERIAL CANDLEWICK
*Family Style*

A beautiful table crystal to express your joy in living—and dining . . . to reflect the rich colors of the awakening season and help you make your table an invitation to good company as well as to complement your Easter cuisine. Each piece of this extensive and varied service is designed for functional use . . . superbly hand-crafted crystal for daily family appreciation as well as for your most memorable occasions.

*Imperial Candlewick is an open stock pattern. Add to your collection as your need and budget permits, for a perfect, scintillating table service.*

HAND-CRAFTED AT IMPERIAL GLASS CORPORATION, BELLAIRE, OHIO

# CANTERBURY NO. 115, Duncan & Miller Glass Company, 1937

Color: crystal, Sapphire blue, Cape Cod blue, Chartreuse, Ruby, Cranberry pink, Jasmine yellow

Canterbury is another pattern that I have been requested to include in my book over the years — so I did. Included in the pictures are some of the colors made in the Canterbury pattern. However, I am only pricing crystal at present. Don't miss the four pages of catalogue reprints on pages 42-45.

Duncan's light blue was called Sapphire and the opalescent blue was called Cape Cod blue. The yellowish-green was called Chartreuse and the red was Ruby. Although not pictured, you may find opalescent pieces in pink or yellow. These were called Cranberry pink and Jasmine yellow.

If you know of additional pieces or wish to help in pricing colored pieces, just drop me a postcard!

| | Crystal | | Crystal |
|---|---|---|---|
| Ash tray, 3".................................................... | 6.00 | Candle, 3", low...................................... | 12.50 |
| Ash tray, 3", club ........................................ | 8.00 | Candle, 3½"............................................. | 12.50 |
| Ash tray, 4½", club ..................................... | 10.00 | Candlestick, 6", 3 light ......................... | 25.00 |
| Ash tray, 5"................................................... | 12.00 | Candlestick, 6"........................................ | 22.50 |
| Ash tray, 5½", club ..................................... | 15.00 | Candlestick, 7", w/U prisms................... | 45.00 |
| Basket, 3" x 3" x 3¼", oval, hdld. ...................... | 20.00 | Candy and cover, 8" x 3½", 3 hdld., 3 part ........ | 32.50 |
| Basket, 3" x 4", crimped, hdld........................... | 27.50 | Candy, 6½", w/5" lid............................... | 32.50 |
| Basket, 3½", crimped, hdld ............................. | 30.00 | Celery and relish, 10½" x 6¾" x 1¼", 2 hdld., | |
| Basket, 3½", oval, hdld .................................. | 25.00 | 2 part .............................................................. | 30.00 |
| Basket, 4½" x 4¾" x 4¾", oval, hdld ................ | 35.00 | Celery and relish, 10½" x 6¾" x 1¼", 2 hdld., | |
| Basket, 4½" x 5" x 5", crimped, hdld................ | 40.00 | 3 part .............................................................. | 32.50 |
| Basket, 9¼" x 10" x 7¼"................................ | 60.00 | Celery, 9" x 4" x 1¼", 2 hdld................. | 20.00 |
| Basket, 10" x 4¼" x 7", oval, hdld. ................ | 60.00 | Cheese stand, 5½" x 3½" high................ | 10.00 |
| Basket, 10" x 4½" x 8", oval, hdld. ................ | 65.00 | Cigarette box w/cover, 3½" x 4½"........... | 18.00 |
| Basket, 11½", oval, hdld. ............................... | 70.00 | Cigarette jar w/cover, 4"......................... | 20.00 |
| Bowl, 4¼" x 2", finger .................................. | 9.00 | Comport, high, 6" x 5½" high................... | 20.00 |
| Bowl, 5" x 3¼", 2 part, salad dressing.............. | 12.50 | Comport, low, 6" x 4½" high.................... | 18.00 |
| Bowl, 5" x 3¼", salad dressing ....................... | 12.50 | Creamer, 2¾", 3 oz., individual............... | 9.00 |
| Bowl, 5½" x 1¾", one hdld. heart .................... | 9.00 | Creamer, 3¾", 7 oz. ............................... | 7.50 |
| Bowl, 5½" x 1¾", one hdld. square ................... | 9.00 | Cup........................................................... | 10.00 |
| Bowl, 5½" x 1¾", one hdld. star ...................... | 10.00 | Decanter w/stopper, 12", 32 oz. ............. | 40.00 |
| Bowl, 5½" x 1¾", one hdld., fruit ..................... | 7.00 | Ice bucket or vase, 7"............................. | 35.00 |
| Bowl, 5½" x 1¾", one hdld., round ................... | 7.00 | Ice bucket or vase, 6"............................. | 32.50 |
| Bowl, 5", fruit nappy ..................................... | 8.00 | Lamp, hurricane, w/prisms, 15"............... | 65.00 |
| Bowl, 6" x 2", 2 hdld., round........................... | 10.00 | Marmalade, 4½" x 2¾", crimped ............. | 12.00 |
| Bowl, 6" x 2", 2 hdld.., sweetmeat, star ........... | 15.00 | Mayonnaise, 5" x 3¼" .............................. | 15.00 |
| Bowl, 6" x 3¼", 2 part, salad dressing.............. | 14.00 | Mayonnaise, 5½" x 3¼", crimped............. | 17.50 |
| Bowl, 6" x 3¼", salad dressing ........................ | 14.00 | Mayonnaise, 6" x 3¼"............................. | 17.50 |
| Bowl, 6" x 5¼" x 2¼", oval olive..................... | 10.00 | Pitcher, 9¼", 32 oz., hdld., martini .......... | 45.00 |
| Bowl, 7½" x 2¼", crimped ............................. | 15.00 | Pitcher, 9¼", 32 oz., martini .................... | 40.00 |
| Bowl, 7½" x 2¼", gardenia.............................. | 15.00 | Plate, 6½", one hdld., fruit ..................... | 6.00 |
| Bowl, 8" x 2¾", crimped ................................ | 19.00 | Plate, 6", finger bowl liner...................... | 6.00 |
| Bowl, 8" x 2½", flared ................................... | 17.50 | Plate, 7½".............................................. | 9.00 |
| Bowl, 8½" x 4"............................................... | 22.00 | Plate, 7½", 2 hdld., mayonnaise............. | 9.00 |
| Bowl, 9" x 2", gardenia .................................. | 25.00 | Plate, 8½".............................................. | 10.00 |
| Bowl, 9" x 4¼", crimped ................................ | 27.50 | Plate, 11¼", dinner ................................ | 25.00 |
| Bowl, 9" x 6" x 3", oval ................................. | 25.00 | Plate, 11", 2 hdld. w/ring, cracker .......... | 20.00 |
| Bowl, 10" x 5", salad...................................... | 25.00 | Plate, 11", 2 hdld., sandwich ................. | 22.00 |
| Bowl, 10" x 8½" x 5", oval ............................. | 27.50 | Plate, 13½", cake, hdld. ......................... | 25.00 |
| Bowl, 10¾" x 4¾".......................................... | 27.50 | Plate, 14", cake...................................... | 25.00 |
| Bowl, 10½" x 5", crimped............................... | 30.00 | Relish, 6" x 2", 2 hdld., 2 part, round .......... | 12.00 |
| Bowl, 11½" x 8¼", oval .................................. | 30.00 | Relish, 6" x 2", 2 hdld., 2 part, star .......... | 12.00 |
| Bowl, 12" x 2¾", gardenia............................... | 30.00 | Relish, 7" x 5¼" x 2¼", 2 hdld., 2 part, oval....... | 15.00 |
| Bowl, 12" x 3½", flared .................................. | 30.00 | Relish, 8" x 1¾", 3 hdld., 3 part.............. | 17.50 |
| Bowl, 12" x 3¾", crimped ............................... | 32.50 | Relish, 9" x 1½", 3 hdld., 3 part.............. | 19.00 |
| Bowl, 13" x 8½" x 3 ¼", oval, flared ................ | 35.00 | Rose bowl, 5" .......................................... | 20.00 |
| Bowl, 13" x 10" x 5", crimped, oval ................. | 37.50 | Rose bowl, 6" .......................................... | 22.50 |
| Bowl, 15" x 2¾", shallow salad ........................ | 40.00 | Salt and pepper ...................................... | 22.50 |

# CANTERBURY NO. 115, Duncan & Miller Glass Company, 1937

| | Crystal | | Crystal |
|---|---|---|---|
| Sandwich tray, 12" x 5¼", center handle ........... | 35.00 | Tumbler, 5½", 9 oz., ftd., luncheon goblet ......... | 12.50 |
| Saucer ................................................................. | 3.00 | Tumbler, 5¾", 12 oz., ftd., ice tea, #5115 ........... | 14.00 |
| Sherbet, crimped, 4½", 2¾" high ........................ | 10.00 | Tumbler, 6¼", 13 oz., flat, ice tea ...................... | 15.00 |
| Sherbet, crimped, 5½", 2¾" high ........................ | 12.00 | Tumbler, 6¼", 13 oz., ftd., ice tea ...................... | 15.00 |
| Stem, 3¾", 6 oz., ice cream................................ | 6.00 | Urn, 4½" x 4½" .................................................... | 15.00 |
| Stem, 4", 4½ oz., oyster cocktail ....................... | 12.50 | Vase, 3", crimped violet...................................... | 15.00 |
| Stem, 4½", 6 oz., saucer champagne ................. | 9.00 | Vase, 3½", clover leaf ........................................ | 15.00 |
| Stem, 4¼", 1 oz., cordial, #5115 ........................ | 25.00 | Vase, 3½", crimped ............................................ | 15.00 |
| Stem, 4¼", 3½ oz., cocktail............................... | 10.00 | Vase, 3½", crimped violet.................................... | 15.00 |
| Stem, 5½", 5 oz., saucer champagne, #5115 ...... | 12.00 | Vase, 3½", oval .................................................. | 15.00 |
| Stem, 5¼", 3 oz., cocktail, #5115 ...................... | 14.00 | Vase, 4", clover leaf............................................ | 17.50 |
| Stem, 5", 4 oz., claret or wine .......................... | 20.00 | Vase, 4", crimped ............................................... | 17.50 |
| Stem, 6¾", 5 oz., claret, #5115 ......................... | 25.00 | Vase, 4", flared rim ........................................... | 17.50 |
| Stem, 6", 3½ oz., wine, #5115 ........................... | 27.50 | Vase, 4", oval ..................................................... | 17.50 |
| Stem, 6", 9 oz., water........................................ | 14.00 | Vase, 4½" x 4¾" ................................................. | 15.00 |
| Stem, 7¼", 10 oz., water, #5115 ........................ | 17.50 | Vase, 4½", clover leaf ......................................... | 17.50 |
| Sugar, 2½", 3 oz., individual ............................. | 8.00 | Vase, 4½", crimped violet.................................... | 17.50 |
| Sugar, 3", 7 oz. .................................................. | 7.50 | Vase, 4½", oval .................................................. | 17.50 |
| Top hat, 3"......................................................... | 15.00 | Vase, 5" x 5", crimped........................................ | 17.50 |
| Tray, 9", individual cr/sug................................. | 10.00 | Vase, 5", clover leaf............................................ | 20.00 |
| Tray, 9" x 4" x 1¼", 2 part, pickle and olive ...... | 17.50 | Vase, 5", crimped ............................................... | 17.50 |
| Tumbler, 2½", 5 oz., ftd., ice cream, #5115........ | 10.00 | Vase, 5½", crimped ............................................ | 20.00 |
| Tumbler, 3¼", 4 oz., ftd., oyster cocktail, #5115 | 15.00 | Vase, 5½", flower arranger ................................. | 27.50 |
| Tumbler, 3¾", 5 oz., flat, juice........................... | 8.00 | Vase, 6½", clover leaf......................................... | 30.00 |
| Tumbler, 4¼", 5 oz., ftd., juice........................... | 7.50 | Vase, 7", crimped ............................................... | 30.00 |
| Tumbler, 4¼", 5 oz., ftd., juice, #5115................ | 10.00 | Vase, 7", flower arranger.................................... | 35.00 |
| Tumbler, 4½", 9 oz., flat, table, straight ............ | 12.00 | Vase, 8½" x 6" .................................................... | 45.00 |
| Tumbler, 4½", 10 oz., ftd., water, #5115............. | 12.50 | Vase, 12", flared ................................................ | 60.00 |

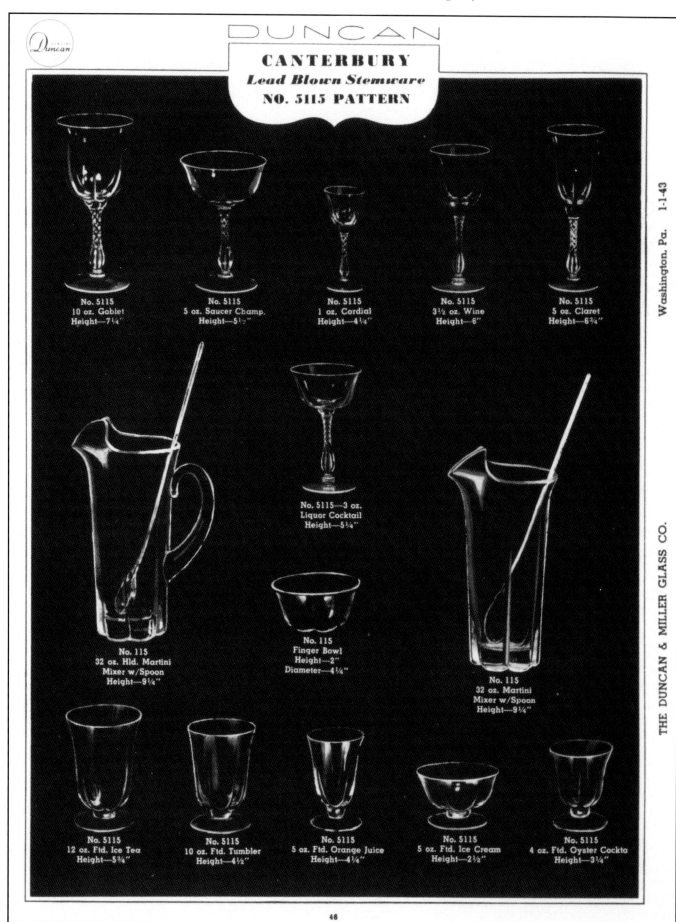

**DUNCAN**

**CANTERBURY**
*Lead Blown Stemware*
**NO. 5115 PATTERN**

No. 5115
10 oz. Goblet
Height—7¼"

No. 5115
5 oz. Saucer Champ.
Height—5½"

No. 5115
1 oz. Cordial
Height—4¾"

No. 5115
3½ oz. Wine
Height—6"

No. 5115
5 oz. Claret
Height—6¾"

No. 5115—3 oz.
Liquor Cocktail
Height—5¼"

No. 115
32 oz. Hld. Martini
Mixer w/Spoon
Height—9¼"

No. 115
Finger Bowl
Height—2"
Diameter—4¼"

No. 115
32 oz. Martini
Mixer w/Spoon
Height—9¼"

No. 5115
12 oz. Ftd. Ice Tea
Height—5¾"

No. 5115
10 oz. Ftd. Tumbler
Height—4½"

No. 5115
5 oz. Ftd. Orange Juice
Height—4¼"

No. 5115
5 oz. Ftd. Ice Cream
Height—2½"

No. 5115
4 oz. Ftd. Oyster Cockta
Height—3¼"

Washington, Pa.     1-1-43

THE DUNCAN & MILLER GLASS CO.

46

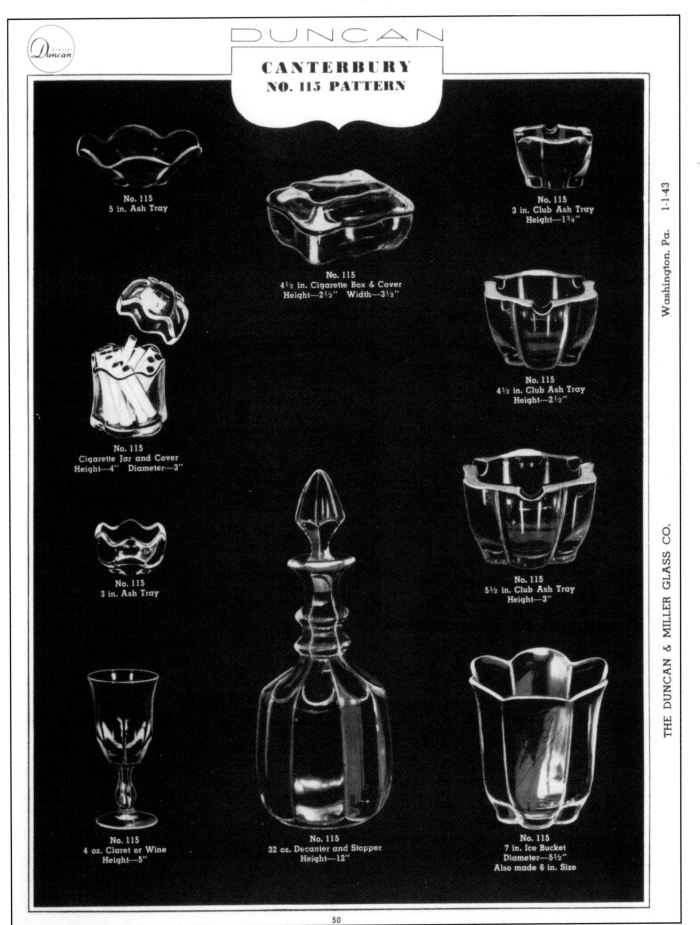

No. 115
5 in. Ash Tray

No. 115
4½ in. Cigarette Box & Cover
Height—2½"   Width—3½"

No. 115
3 in. Club Ash Tray
Height—1¾"

No. 115
Cigarette Jar and Cover
Height—4"   Diameter—3"

No. 115
4½ in. Club Ash Tray
Height—2½"

No. 115
3 in. Ash Tray

No. 115
5½ in. Club Ash Tray
Height—3"

No. 115
4 oz. Claret or Wine
Height—5"

No. 115
32 oz. Decanter and Stopper
Height—12"

No. 115
7 in. Ice Bucket
Diameter—5½"
Also made 6 in. Size

Washington, Pa.   1-1-43

THE DUNCAN & MILLER GLASS CO.

50

**CANTERBURY NO. 115 PATTERN**

No. 115
3 Light Candlestick
Height—6"  Width—10"

No. 115
6 in. Candlestick
1 Light

No. 115
3 in. Low Candlestick

No. 115
1 Light Candelabrum W/U Prisms
Height—7"

No. 115
3 Light Candelabrum W/U Prisms
3 Bobeches
Height—7"  Width—11"

No. 115
3 Light Candelabrum W/U Prisms
2 Bobeches
Height—7"  Width—11"

Washington, Pa.   1-1-43

THE DUNCAN & MILLER GLASS CO.

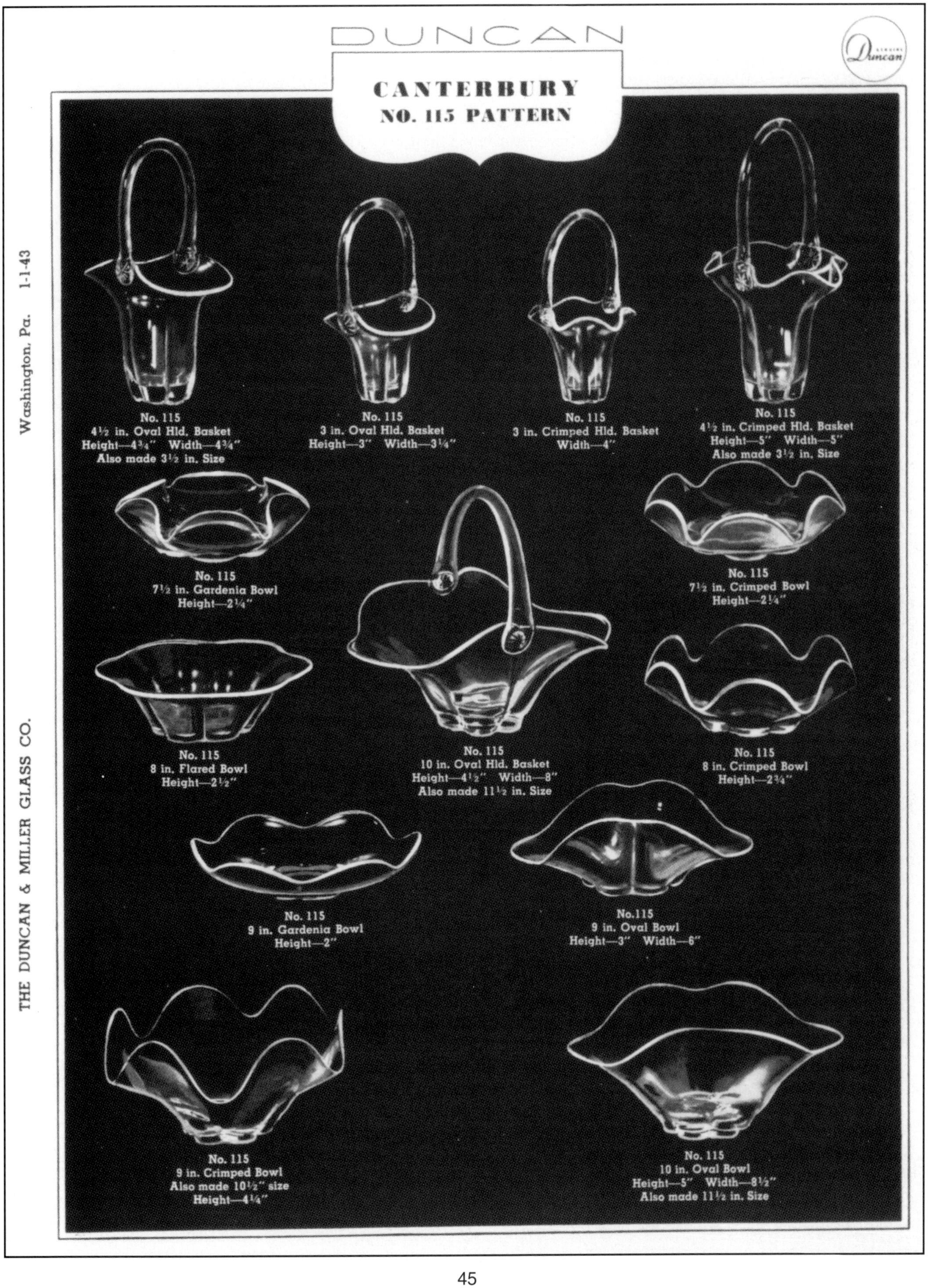

DUNCAN

Genuine Duncan

CANTERBURY
NO. 115 PATTERN

Washington, Pa. 1-1-43

No. 115
4½ in. Oval Hld. Basket
Height—4¾" Width—4¾"
Also made 3½ in. Size

No. 115
3 in. Oval Hld. Basket
Height—3" Width—3¼"

No. 115
3 in. Crimped Hld. Basket
Width—4"

No. 115
4½ in. Crimped Hld. Basket
Height—5" Width—5"
Also made 3½ in. Size

No. 115
7½ in. Gardenia Bowl
Height—2¼"

No. 115
7½ in. Crimped Bowl
Height—2¼"

No. 115
8 in. Flared Bowl
Height—2½"

No. 115
10 in. Oval Hld. Basket
Height—4½" Width—8"
Also made 11½ in. Size

No. 115
8 in. Crimped Bowl
Height—2¾"

No. 115
9 in. Gardenia Bowl
Height—2"

No.115
9 in. Oval Bowl
Height—3" Width—6"

No. 115
9 in. Crimped Bowl
Also made 10½" size
Height—4¼"

No. 115
10 in. Oval Bowl
Height—5" Width—8½"
Also made 11½ in. Size

THE DUNCAN & MILLER GLASS CO.

# CAPE COD, Imperial Glass Company, 1932 – 1984

Colors: amber, crystal, blue, cobalt blue, red, green, black, milk glass, pink

Colored Cape Cod has begun to pique the interest of a few collectors. Several of these colors are shown on page 47. The top row shows Imperial's green called Verde; the darker green in row 2 was called Evergreen. Imperial's pink, called Azalea, is depicted in row 2. The blue color shown in rows 3 and 4 was called Antique Blue. Row 3 shows black, milk glass, and Ruby. Ritz Blue (cobalt blue, not pictured) and Ruby are the colors that are most in demand. These two colors are selling 50% to 200% more than crystal, depending upon the piece. Prices for other colors are a little more than crystal with most of them selling at reasonable prices – if at all! If a consistent market is established for colors, I will list them in the next edition. The only thing I can say now with certainty about colored Cape Cod is that its prices are inconsistent.

A whimsy vase is on the bottom row of page 47. Evidently, some factory worker played around with a goblet or tumbler while it was still hot. Many collectors love to add these unusual pieces to their accumulations.

A pitcher in the **Tradition** pattern that was also made by Imperial is shown in the bottom picture on page 49. Notice the round rings with no diamonds around the rings as is on Cape Cod. Many new collectors get these similar patterns confused; so I wanted to point out the difference.

The advertisements shown on page 50 and 51 were taken from 1940's magazines. Although Imperial advertised Cape Cod through national campaigns as it did Candlewick, there was never the demand generated for Cape Cod as there was for Candlewick. This is true with collectors today! Rarely found pieces of Cape Cod sell one-half or less than the prices of rare Candlewick. I have no idea why!

| | Crystal | | Crystal |
|---|---|---|---|
| Ash tray, 4", 160/134/1 | 14.00 | Bowl, 12", oval, 160/131B | 70.00 |
| Ash tray, 5½", 160/150 | 17.50 | Bowl, 12", oval crimped, 160/131C | 80.00 |
| Basket, 9", handled, crimped, 160/221/0 | 175.00 | Bowl, 12", punch, 160/20B | 60.00 |
| Basket, 11" tall, handled, 160/40 | 110.00 | Bowl, 13", console, 160/75L | 42.50 |
| Bottle, bitters, 4 oz., 160/235 | 55.00 | Bowl, 15", console, 160/10L | 67.50 |
| Bottle, cologne, w/stopper, 1601 | 55.00 | Butter, 5", w/cover, handled, 160/144 | 30.00 |
| Bottle, condiment, 6 oz., 160/224 | 65.00 | Butter, w/cover, ¼ lb., 160/161 | 45.00 |
| Bottle, cordial, 18 oz., 160/256 | 115.00 | Cake plate, 10", 4 toed, 160/220 | 90.00 |
| Bottle, decanter, 26 oz., 160/244 | 105.00 | Cake stand, 10½", footed, 160/67D | 40.00 |
| Bottle, ketchup, 14 oz., 160/237 | 150.00 | Cake stand, 11", 160/103D | 75.00 |
| Bowl, 3", handled mint, 160/183 | 20.00 | Candleholder, twin, 160/100 | 55.00 |
| Bowl, 3", jelly, 160/33 | 12.00 | Candleholder, 3", single, 160/170 | 17.50 |
| Bowl, 4" finger, 1602 | 12.00 | Candleholder, 4", 160/81 | 25.00 |
| Bowl, 4½", finger, 1604½A | 12.00 | Candleholder, 4", Aladdin style, 160/90 | 115.00 |
| Bowl, 4½", handled spider, 160/180 | 22.50 | Candleholder, 4½", saucer, 160/175 | 22.50 |
| Bowl, 4½", dessert, tab handled, 160/197 | 23.00 | Candleholder, 5", 160/80 | 20.00 |
| Bowl, 5", dessert, heart shape, 160/49H | 17.50 | Candleholder, 5", flower, 160/45B | 55.00 |
| Bowl, 5", flower, 1605N | 25.00 | Candleholder, 5½", flower, 160/45N | 65.00 |
| Bowl, 5½", fruit, 160/23B | 10.00 | Candleholder, 6", centerpiece, 160/48BC | 70.00 |
| Bowl, 5½", handled spider, 160/181 | 22.50 | Candy, w/cover, 160/110 | 65.00 |
| Bowl, 5½", tab handled, soup, 160/198 | 15.00 | Carafe, wine, 26 oz., 160/185 | 145.00 |
| Bowl, 6", fruit, 160/3F | 10.00 | Celery, 8", 160/105 | 30.00 |
| Bowl, 6", baked apple, 160/53X | 9.00 | Celery, 10½", 160/189 | 45.00 |
| Bowl, 6", handled, round mint, 160/51F | 22.00 | Cigarette box, 4½", 160/134 | 40.00 |
| Bowl, 6", handled heart, 160/40H | 20.00 | Cigarette holder, ftd., 1602 | 12.50 |
| Bowl, 6", handled mint, 160/51H | 22.00 | Cigarette holder, Tom & Jerry mug, 160/200 | 32.50 |
| Bowl, 6", handled tray, 160/51T | 20.00 | Cigarette lighter, 1602 | 30.00 |
| Bowl, 6½", handled portioned spider, 160/187 | 27.50 | Coaster, w/spoon rest, 160/76 | 10.00 |
| Bowl, 6½", handled spider, 160/182 | 32.50 | Coaster, 3", square, 160/85 | 12.50 |
| Bowl, 6½", tab handled, 160/199 | 25.00 | Coaster, 4", round, 160/78 | 12.50 |
| Bowl, 7", nappy, 160/5F | 22.00 | Coaster, 4½", flat, 160/1R | 9.00 |
| Bowl, 7½", 160/7F | 22.00 | Comport, 5¼", 160F | 27.50 |
| Bowl, 7½", 2-handled, 160/62B | 27.50 | Comport, 5¾", 160X | 30.00 |
| Bowl, 8¾", 160/10F | 27.50 | Comport, 6", 160/45 | 25.00 |
| Bowl, 9", footed fruit, 160/67F | 62.50 | Comport, 6", w/cover, ftd., 160/140 | 60.00 |
| Bowl, 9½", 2-handled, 160/145B | 37.50 | Comport, 7", 160/48B | 35.00 |
| Bowl, 9½", crimped, 160/221C | 75.00 | Comport, 11¼", oval, 1602, 6½" tall | 125.00 |
| Bowl, 9½", float, 160/221F | 65.00 | Creamer, 160/190 | 30.00 |
| Bowl, 10", footed, 160/137B | 70.00 | Creamer, 160/30 | 8.00 |
| Bowl, 10", oval, 160/221 | 70.00 | Creamer, ftd., 160/31 | 15.00 |
| Bowl, 11", flanged edge, 1608X | 100.00 | Cruet, w/stopper, 4 oz., 160/119 | 22.50 |
| Bowl, 11", oval, 160/124 | 70.00 | Cruet, w/stopper, 5 oz., 160/70 | 25.00 |
| Bowl, 11", oval divided, 160/125 | 75.00 | Cruet, w/stopper, 6 oz., 160/241 | 37.50 |
| Bowl, 11", round, 1608A | 65.00 | Cup, tea, 160/35 | 7.00 |
| Bowl, 11", salad, 1608D | 40.00 | Cup, coffee, 160/37 | 7.00 |
| Bowl, 11¼", oval, 1602 | 70.00 | Cup, bouillon, 160/250 | 30.00 |
| Bowl, 12", 160/75B | 40.00 | Decanter, bourbon, 160/260 | 70.00 |

| | Crystal |
|---|---|
| Decanter, rye, 160/260 | 70.00 |
| Decanter w/stopper, 30 oz., 160/163 | 57.50 |
| Decanter w/stopper, 24 oz., 160/212 | 65.00 |
| Egg cup, 160/225 | 32.50 |
| Epergne, 2 pc., plain center, 160/196 | 195.00 |
| Fork, 160/701 | 12.00 |
| Gravy bowl, 18 oz., 160/202 | 55.00 |
| Horseradish, 5 oz. jar, 160/226 | 67.50 |
| Ice bucket, 6½", 160/63 | 125.00 |
| Icer, 3 pc., bowl, 2 inserts, 160/53/3 | 45.00 |
| Jar, 12 oz., hdld. peanut w/lid, 160/210 | 55.00 |
| Jar, 10", "Pokal," 160/133 | 75.00 |
| Jar, 11", "Pokal," 160/128 | 80.00 |
| Jar, 15", "Pokal," 160/132 | 125.00 |
| Jar, candy w/lid, wicker hand., 5" h., 160/194 | 75.00 |
| Jar, cookie, w/lid, wicker hand., 6½" h., 160/195 | 95.00 |
| Jar, peanut butter w/lid, wicker hand., 4" h., 160/193 | 65.00 |
| Ladle, marmalade, 160/130 | 10.00 |
| Ladle, mayonnaise, 160/165 | 10.00 |
| Ladle, punch | 25.00 |
| Lamp, hurricane, 2 pc., 5" base, 160/79 | 75.00 |
| Lamp, hurricane, 2 pc., bowl-like base, 1604 | 75.00 |
| Marmalade, 3 pc. set, 160/89/3 | 32.50 |
| Marmalade, 4 pc. set, 160/89 | 40.00 |
| Mayonnaise, 3 pc. set, 160/52H | 37.50 |
| Mayonnaise, 3 pc., 160/23 | 27.50 |
| Mayonnaise, 12 oz., hdld., spouted, 160/205 | 47.50 |
| Mug, 12 oz., handled, 160/188 | 42.50 |
| Mustard, w/cover & spoon, 160/156 | 20.00 |
| Nut dish, 3", hdld., 160/183 | 20.00 |
| Nut dish, 4", hdld., 160/184 | 20.00 |
| Pepper mill, 160/236 | 25.00 |
| Pitcher, milk, 1 pt., 160/240 | 45.00 |
| Pitcher, ice lipped, 40 oz., 160/19 | 75.00 |
| Pitcher, martini, blown, 40 oz., 160/178 | 175.00 |
| Pitcher, ice lipped, 2 qt., 160/239 | 90.00 |
| Pitcher, 2 qt., 160/24 | 80.00 |
| Pitcher, blown, 5 pt., 160/176 | 150.00 |
| Plate, 4½" butter, 160/34 | 8.00 |
| Plate, 6", cupped, (liner for 160/208 salad dressing), 160/209 | 20.00 |
| Plate, 6½", bread & butter, 160/1D | 7.00 |
| Plate, 7", 160/3D | 8.00 |
| Plate, 7", cupped (liner for 160/205 Mayo), 160/206 | 30.00 |
| Plate, 8", center handled tray, 160/149D | 35.00 |
| Plate, 8", crescent salad, 160/12 | 45.00 |
| Plate, 8", cupped, (liner for gravy), 160/203 | 35.00 |
| Plate, 8", salad, 160/5D | 9.00 |
| Plate, 8½", 2-handled, 160/62D | 30.00 |
| Plate, 9", 160/7D | 20.00 |
| Plate, 9½", 2 hdld., 160/62D | 40.00 |
| Plate, 10", dinner, 160/10D | 35.00 |
| Plate, 11½", 2-handled, 160/145D | 35.00 |
| Plate, 12½" bread, 160/222 | 65.00 |
| Plate, 13", birthday, 72 candle holes, 160/72 | 325.00 |
| Plate, 13", cupped torte, 1608V | 35.00 |
| Plate, 13", torte, 1608F | 37.50 |
| Plate, 14", cupped, 160/75V | 35.00 |
| Plate, 14", flat, 160/75D | 35.00 |
| Plate, 16", cupped, 160/20V | 55.00 |
| Plate, 17", 2 styles, 160/10D or 20D | 45.00 |

| | Crystal |
|---|---|
| Platter, 13½", oval, 160/124D | 47.50 |
| Puff Box, w/cover, 1601 | 37.50 |
| Relish, 8", hdld., 2 part. 160/223 | 37.50 |
| Relish, 9½", 4 pt., 160/56 | 35.00 |
| Relish, 9½", oval, 3 part, 160/55 | 35.00 |
| Relish, 11", 5 part, 160/102 | 55.00 |
| Relish, 11¼", 3 part, oval, 1602 | 65.00 |
| Salad dressing, 6 oz., hdld., spouted, 160/208 | 42.50 |
| Salad set, 14" plate, 12" bowl, fork & spoon, 160/75 | 95.00 |
| Salt & pepper, individual, 160/251 | 15.00 |
| Salt & pepper, pr., ftd., 160/116 | 20.00 |
| Salt & pepper, pr., ftd., stemmed, 160/243 | 35.00 |
| Salt & pepper, pr., 160/96 | 15.00 |
| Salt & pepper, pr. square, 160/109 | 20.00 |
| Salt dip, 160/61 | 15.00 |
| Salt spoon, 1600 | 8.00 |
| Saucer, tea, 160/35 | 2.00 |
| Saucer, coffee, 160/37 | 2.00 |
| Server, 12", ftd. or turned over, 160/93 | 85.00 |
| Spoon, 160/701 | 12.00 |
| Stem, 1½ oz., cordial, 1602 | 10.00 |
| Stem, 3 oz., wine, 1602 | 8.00 |
| Stem, 3½ oz., cocktail, 1602 | 8.00 |
| Stem, 5 oz., claret, 1602 | 12.50 |
| Stem, 6 oz., low sundae, 1602 | 7.00 |
| Stem, 6 oz., parfait, 1602 | 12.00 |
| Stem, 6 oz., sherbet, 1600 | 15.00 |
| Stem, 6 oz., tall sherbet, 1602 | 8.50 |
| Stem, 9 oz., water, 1602 | 9.50 |
| Stem, 10 oz., water, 1600 | 20.00 |
| Stem, 11 oz., dinner goblet, 1602 | 10.00 |
| Stem, 14 oz., goblet, magnum, 160 | 30.00 |
| Stem, oyster cocktail, 1602 | 10.00 |
| Sugar, 160/190 | 30.00 |
| Sugar, 160/30 | 7.00 |
| Sugar, ftd., 160/31 | 15.00 |
| Toast, w/cover, 160/123 | 135.00 |
| Tom & Jerry footed punch bowl, 160/200 | 300.00 |
| Tray, square covered sugar & creamer, 160/25/26 | 150.00 |
| Tray, 7", for creamer/sugar, 160/29 | 15.00 |
| Tray, 11", pastry, center handle, 160/68D | 65.00 |
| Tumbler, 2½ oz., whiskey, 160 | 12.50 |
| Tumbler, 6 oz., ftd., juice, 1602 | 9.00 |
| Tumbler, 6 oz., juice, 1600 | 10.00 |
| Tumbler, 7 oz., old-fashioned, 160 | 12.50 |
| Tumbler, 10 oz., ftd., water, 1602 | 10.00 |
| Tumbler, 10 oz., water, 160 | 10.00 |
| Tumbler, 12 oz., ftd., ice tea, 1602 | 12.00 |
| Tumbler, 12 oz., ftd., tea, 1600 | 17.50 |
| Tumbler, 12 oz., ice tea, 160 | 12.50 |
| Tumbler, 14 oz., double old-fashioned, 160 | 22.50 |
| Tumbler, 16 oz., 160 | 30.00 |
| Vase, 6¼", ftd., 160/22 | 35.00 |
| Vase, 6½", ftd., 160/110B | 65.00 |
| Vase, 7½", ftd., 160/22 | 40.00 |
| Vase, 8", fan, 160/87F | 85.00 |
| Vase, 8½", flip, 160/143 | 50.00 |
| Vase, 8½", ftd., 160/28 | 42.50 |
| Vase, 10", cylinder, 160/192 | 75.00 |
| Vase, 10½", hdld., urn, 160/186 | 125.00 |
| Vase, 11", flip, 1603 | 125.00 |
| Vase, 11½", ftd., 160/21 | 60.00 |

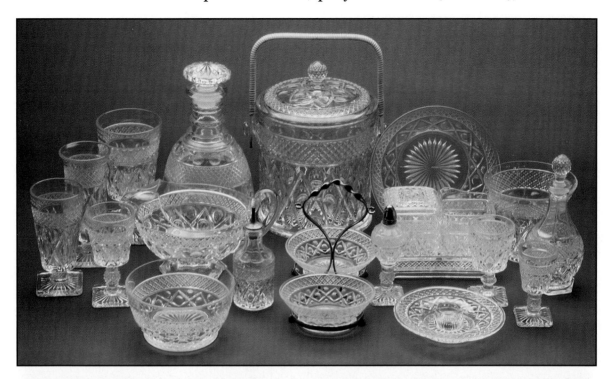

# CAPE COD, Imperial Glass Company, 1932 – 1984

MARTIN BRUEHL

*Mission Accomplished*

Farewell to the old order, hail to the new standard of fine things and a manner of joyous living! Captured prize for this, as for *every* happy occasion, is the diamond-like brilliance of our Cape Cod Crystal table service. There is a tradition in this design; it delighted your Grandmother and your great Grandmother when it graced proud tables of yesterdays. For *your* table today Imperial craftsmen have given the Cape Cod pattern a new grace, balance and sparkling fire as they blow, mould and finish each piece by hand. Cape Cod is crystal tableware to be proudly possessed, used every day, cherished always. Available in fine stores everywhere; crafted by THE IMPERIAL GLASS CORPORATION, BELLAIRE, OHIO.

MARTIN BRUEHL

*A Bountiful*
# HARVEST TABLE

An American tradition, as old as Thanksgiving, but Imperial gives you a wonderful *new* way to serve it this year! Table crystal in the Cape Cod pattern, transparent in loveliness, sturdy for constant use. All these pieces and many, many more. A leading dealer near you will have everything you need for a complete table service, and for gifts, too! Cape Cod hand-crafted crystal is open stock, priced for budget keeping. Made skillfully by master crystal craftsmen and patent protected by the Imperial Glass Corporation, Bellaire, Ohio.

# CAPRICE, Cambridge Glass Company, 1940's – 1957

Colors: crystal, Moonlight Blue, white, amber, amethyst, pink, emerald green, pink, cobalt blue, milk glass

A major collector of blue Caprice sent me a listing of vases that I did not have! Thanks to him, my listing of Caprice has expanded quite a bit. Prices on the more commonly found pieces have remained rather steady. Having just returned from the West Coast, I was more than surprised at the asking prices of the larger bowls that we have a difficult time selling in the East. Most of the other pieces seemed to be in line with prices here.

Many newer collectors who decided to collect pink have already given that up. There just isn't enough of the color available to encourage them to continue. Prices for pink have caught up with those of blue in basic pieces and are selling a little above blue in harder to find pieces. Those prices are now listed with the blue. There were enough items made in pink to assemble a set; yet a set of pink will be lacking many of the pieces found in blue and crystal!

The covered cracker jar (shown in the back of the photo atop page 53) has now been found in blue. The Caprice pieces with satinized panels are called Alpine. Some collectors gleefully seek these while others avoid them. It depends upon what you like!

Many Caprice items are not being found on the market at any price including 2½ oz. footed whiskies, 5 oz. moulded sherbets, clarets (both blown and moulded), finger bowls, and the moulded, straight side 9 and 12 oz. tumblers. There are other hard-to-find items, but those items are on most collector's want lists.

There are collectors of crystal also, but they are helped by more reasonable prices. Crystal candle reflectors and punch bowls are rarely found; and there is a strong demand for them when they do turn up!

Most other colors of Caprice are purchased by collectors looking for colored additions to their sets of Caprice. As far as I know, colors other than blue, crystal, and pink can not be collected into completed sets. Prices for other colors of Caprice follow along the lines of blue. There is little demand for amber or amethyst and prices for those particular colors are more closely reflected by the prices for crystal.

*Moulds owned by Summit Art Glass and many of these pieces have been reproduced.

| | Crystal | Blue, Pink | | Crystal | Blue, Pink |
|---|---|---|---|---|---|
| Ash tray, 2¾", 3 ftd., shell, #213 | 7.00 | 14.00 | Cake plate, 13", ftd., #36 | 150.00 | 325.00 |
| * Ash tray, 3", #214 | 6.00 | 12.00 | Candle reflector, #73 | 250.00 | |
| * Ash tray, 4", #215 | 7.00 | 14.00 | Candlestick, 2½", ea., #67 | 13.00 | 27.50 |
| * Ash tray, 5", #216 | 10.00 | 20.00 | Candlestick, 2-lite, keyhole, 5", #647 | 16.00 | 50.00 |
| Bonbon, 6", oval, ftd., #155 | 20.00 | 40.00 | Candlestick, 3-lite, #74 | 35.00 | 115.00 |
| Bonbon, 6", sq., 2 hdld., #154 | 14.00 | 35.00 | Candlestick, 3-lite, keyhole, #638 | 25.00 | 60.00 |
| Bonbon, 6", sq., ftd., #133 | 15.00 | 40.00 | Candlestick, 3-lite, #1338 | 30.00 | 75.00 |
| Bottle, 7 oz., bitters, #186 | 175.00 | 350.00 | Candlestick, 5-lite, #1577 | 75.00 | |
| Bowl, 2", 4 ftd., almond #95 | 25.00 | 50.00 | Candlestick, 5", ea. keyhole #646 | 20.00 | 55.00 |
| * Bowl, 5", 2 hdld., jelly, #151 | 15.00 | 30.00 | Candlestick, 6", 2-lite, ea., #72 | 40.00 | 95.00 |
| Bowl, 5", fruit, #18 | 30.00 | 60.00 | Candlestick, 7", ea. w/prism, #70 | 22.00 | 65.00 |
| Bowl, 5", fruit, crimped, #19 | 22.00 | 45.00 | Candlestick, 7½", dbl., ea., #69 | 150.00 | 500.00 |
| Bowl, 8", 4 ftd., #49 | 40.00 | 115.00 | Candy, 6", 3 ftd. w/cover, #165 | 42.50 | 110.00 |
| Bowl, 8", sq., 4 ftd., #50 | 40.00 | 125.00 | Candy, 6", w/cover (divided), | | |
| * Bowl, 8", 3 pt., relish, #124 | 20.00 | 40.00 | #168 | 55.00 | 120.00 |
| Bowl, 9½", crimped, 4 ftd., #52 | 40.00 | 115.00 | Celery & relish, 8½", 3 pt., #124 | 20.00 | 40.00 |
| Bowl, 9", pickle, #102 | 25.00 | 60.00 | Cigarette box, w/cover, 3½" x 2¼", | | |
| Bowl, 10", salad, 4 ftd., #57 | 40.00 | 125.00 | #207 | 20.00 | 45.00 |
| Bowl, 10", sq., 4 ftd., #58 | 35.00 | 115.00 | Cigarette box, w/cover, 4½" x 3½", | | |
| Bowl, 10½", belled, 4 ftd. | 35.00 | 75.00 | #208 | 22.00 | 75.00 |
| Bowl, 10½", crimped, 4 ftd., | | | Cigarette holder, 2" x 2¼", | | |
| #53 | 40.00 | 110.00 | triangular, #205 | 18.00 | 65.00 |
| Bowl, 11", crimped, 4 ftd., #60 | 35.00 | 115.00 | Cigarette holder, 3" x 3", | | |
| * Bowl, 11", 2 hdld., oval, 4 ftd., | | | triangular, #204 | 22.00 | 55.00 |
| #65 | 40.00 | 115.00 | Coaster, 3½", #13 | 15.00 | 35.00 |
| Bowl, 11½", shallow, 4 ftd., #81 | 35.00 | 100.00 | Comport, 6", low ftd., #130 | 22.00 | 45.00 |
| * Bowl, 12", 4 pt. relish, oval, #126 | 65.00 | 195.00 | Comport, 7", low ftd., #130 | 24.00 | 50.00 |
| * Bowl, 12", relish, 3 pt., | | | Comport, 7", tall, #136 | 40.00 | 100.00 |
| rectangular, #125 | 45.00 | 135.00 | Cracker jar & cover, #202 | 250.00 | 900.00 |
| Bowl, 12½", belled, 4 ftd., #62 | 35.00 | 90.00 | * Creamer, large, #41 | 13.00 | 25.00 |
| Bowl, 12½", crimped, 4 ftd., #61 | 35.00 | 100.00 | * Creamer, medium, #38 | 11.00 | 22.00 |
| Bowl, 13", cupped, salad, #80 | 75.00 | 175.00 | * Creamer, ind., #40 | 12.00 | 27.50 |
| Bowl, 13", crimped, 4 ftd., #66 | 40.00 | 125.00 | Cup, #17 | 14.00 | 35.00 |
| Bowl, 13½", 4 ftd., shallow | | | Decanter, w/stopper, 35 oz., #187 | 150.00 | 425.00 |
| cupped #82 | 40.00 | 110.00 | Finger bowl & liner, #16 | 40.00 | 125.00 |
| Bowl, 15", salad, shallow, #84 | 50.00 | 135.00 | Finger bowl and liner, blown, #300 | 40.00 | 125.00 |
| Bridge set: | | | Ice bucket, #201 | 60.00 | 165.00 |
| *Cloverleaf, 6½", #173 | 25.00 | 85.00 | Marmalade, w/cover, 6 oz., #89 | 65.00 | 210.00 |
| *Club, 6½", #170 | 25.00 | 85.00 | * Mayonnaise, 6½", 3 pc. set, #129 | 35.00 | 115.00 |
| Diamond, 6½", #171 | 25.00 | 85.00 | * Mayonnaise, 8", 3 pc. set, #106 | 50.00 | 120.00 |
| *Heart, 6½", #169 | 30.00 | 100.00 | Mustard, w/cover, 2 oz., #87 | 55.00 | 165.00 |
| *Spade, 6½", #172 | 25.00 | 85.00 | Nut Dish, 2½", #93 | 22.00 | 35.00 |
| * Butterdish, ¼ lb., #52 | 225.00 | | Nut Dish, 2½", divided, #94 | 25.00 | 45.00 |

# CAPRICE, Cambridge Glass Company, 1940's – 1957 (continued)

| | Crystal | Blue, Pink |
|---|---|---|
| * Oil, 3 oz., w/stopper, #101 | 30.00 | 90.00 |
| * Oil, 5 oz., w/stopper, #100 | 70.00 | 185.00 |
| Pitcher, 32 oz., ball shape, #179 | 85.00 | 315.00 |
| Pitcher, 80 oz., ball shape, #183 | 100.00 | 310.00 |
| Pitcher, 90 oz., tall Doulton style, #178 | 700.00 | 4,250.00 |
| Plate, 5½", bread & butter, #20 | 12.00 | 25.00 |
| Plate, 6½", bread & butter, #21 | 11.00 | 24.00 |
| Plate, 6½", hdld., lemon, #152 | 11.00 | 20.00 |
| Plate, 7½", salad, #23 | 15.00 | 27.50 |
| Plate, 8½", luncheon, #22 | 14.00 | 32.50 |
| * Plate, 9½", dinner, #24 | 40.00 | 125.00 |
| Plate, 11", cabaret, 4 ftd., #32 | 30.00 | 75.00 |
| Plate, 11½", cabaret, #26 | 30.00 | 75.00 |
| Plate, 14", cabaret, 4 ftd., #33 | 40.00 | 100.00 |
| Plate, 14", 4 ftd., #28 | 40.00 | 100.00 |
| Plate, 15", 4ftd. | 40.00 | 110.00 |
| Plate, 16", #30 | 40.00 | 110.00 |
| Punch bowl, ftd. | 2,000.00 | |
| * Salad dressing, 3 pc., ftd. & hdld., 2 spoons, #112 | 190.00 | 465.00 |
| Salt & pepper, pr., ball, #91 | 40.00 | 115.00 |
| * Salt & pepper, pr., flat, #96 | 28.00 | 100.00 |
| Salt & pepper, indiv., ball, pr., #90 | 45.00 | 145.00 |
| Salt & pepper, indiv., flat, pr., #92 | 40.00 | 135.00 |
| Salver, 13", 2 pc. (cake atop pedestal), #31 | 165.00 | 450.00 |
| Saucer, #17 | 2.50 | 5.50 |
| Stem, #300, blown, 1 oz., cordial | 42.00 | 130.00 |
| Stem, #300, blown, 2½ oz., wine | 27.50 | 62.50 |
| Stem, #300, blown, 3 oz., cocktail | 22.00 | 42.50 |
| Stem, #300, blown, 4½ oz., claret | 50.00 | 200.00 |
| Stem, #300, blown, 4½ oz., low oyster cocktail | 18.00 | 47.50 |
| Stem, #300, blown, 5 oz., parfait | 80.00 | 245.00 |
| Stem, #300, blown, 6 oz., low sherbet | 10.00 | 16.00 |
| Stem, #300, blown, 6 oz., tall sherbet | 12.00 | 24.00 |
| Stem, #300, blown, 9 oz. water | 18.00 | 37.50 |
| Stem, #301, blown, 1 oz., cordial | 37.50 | |
| Stem, #301, blown, 2½ oz., wine | 27.50 | |
| Stem, #301, blown, 3 oz., cocktail | 20.00 | |
| Stem, #301, blown, 4½ oz., claret | 45.00 | |
| Stem, #301, blown, 6 oz., sherbet | 13.00 | |
| Stem, #301, blown, 9 oz., water | 17.50 | |
| * Stem, 3 oz., wine, #6 | 35.00 | 125.00 |
| * Stem, 3½ oz., cocktail, #3 | 25.00 | 55.00 |
| * Stem, 4½ oz., claret, #5 | 40.00 | 200.00 |
| Stem, 4½ oz., fruit cocktail, #7 | 30.00 | 75.00 |
| Stem, 5 oz., low sherbet, #4 | 22.00 | 85.00 |
| * Stem, 7 oz., tall sherbet, #2 | 17.50 | 35.00 |
| Stem, 10 oz., water, #1 | 27.50 | 47.50 |
| * Sugar, large, #41 | 11.00 | 22.00 |
| * Sugar, medium, #38 | 10.00 | 20.00 |
| * Sugar, indiv., #40 | 12.00 | 25.00 |
| * Tray, for sugar & creamer, #37 | 17.50 | 40.00 |
| Tray, 9" oval, #42 | 22.00 | 50.00 |
| * Tumbler, 2 oz., flat, #188 | 22.00 | 65.00 |
| Tumbler, 3 oz., ftd., #12 | 22.00 | 47.50 |
| Tumbler, 5 oz., ftd., #11 | 20.00 | 45.00 |
| Tumbler, 5 oz., flat, #180 | 22.00 | 50.00 |
| Tumbler, #300, 2½ oz., whiskey | 40.00 | 210.00 |
| Tumbler, #300, 5 oz., ftd., juice | 18.00 | 32.50 |
| Tumbler, #300, 10 oz., ftd. water | 20.00 | 40.00 |

| | Crystal | Blue, Pink |
|---|---|---|
| Tumbler, #300, 12 oz., ftd. tea | 20.00 | 40.00 |
| Tumbler, #301, blown, 4½ oz., low oyster cocktail | 15.00 | |
| Tumbler, #301, blown, 5 oz., juice | 13.00 | |
| Tumbler, #301, blown, 12 oz., tea | 17.00 | |
| * Tumbler, 9 oz., straight side, #14 | 32.50 | 87.50 |
| * Tumbler, 10 oz., ftd., #10 | 18.00 | 40.00 |
| Tumbler, 12 oz., flat., #184 | 16.00 | 35.00 |
| Tumbler, 12 oz., ftd., #9 | 22.50 | 47.50 |
| * Tumbler, 12 oz., straight side, #15 | 37.50 | 90.00 |
| Tumbler, #310, 5 oz., flat, juice | 15.00 | 40.00 |
| Tumbler, #310, 7 oz., flat, old-fashioned | 35.00 | 125.00 |
| Tumbler, #310, 10 oz., flat, table | 15.00 | 35.00 |
| Tumbler, #310, 11 oz., flat, tall, 4¹³/₁₆" | 25.00 | 80.00 |
| Tumbler, #310, 12 oz., flat, tea | 30.00 | 125.00 |
| Vase, 3½", #249 | 55.00 | 195.00 |
| Vase, 4", blown, #251, blown | 55.00 | 195.00 |
| Vase, 4¼", #241, ball | 40.00 | 115.00 |
| Vase, 4½", #237, ball | 60.00 | 150.00 |
| Vase, 4½", #252, blown | 40.00 | 150.00 |
| Vase, 4½", #337, crimped top | 55.00 | 110.00 |
| Vase, 4½", #344, crimped top | 85.00 | 185.00 |
| Vase, 4½", #244 | 40.00 | 150.00 |
| Vase, 5", ivy bowl, #232 | 60.00 | 180.00 |
| Vase, 5½", #245 | 45.00 | 160.00 |
| Vase, 5½", #345, crimped top | 55.00 | 200.00 |
| Vase, 6", #242, ftd. | 35.00 | 140.00 |
| Vase, 6", blown, #254 | 175.00 | 350.00 |
| Vase, 6", #342, crimped top | 60.00 | 200.00 |
| Vase, 6", #235, ftd., rose bowl | 50.00 | 125.00 |
| Vase, 6½", #238, ball | 40.00 | 155.00 |
| Vase, 6½", #338, crimped top | 100.00 | 225.00 |
| Vase, 7½", #246 | 55.00 | 175.00 |
| Vase, 7½", #346, crimped top | 110.00 | 250.00 |
| Vase, 8", #236, ftd., rose bowl | 60.00 | 165.00 |
| Vase, 8½", #243 | 50.00 | 185.00 |
| Vase, 8½", #239, ball | 50.00 | 175.00 |
| Vase, 8½", #339, crimped top | 60.00 | 225.00 |
| Vase, 8½", #343, crimped top | 140.00 | 325.00 |
| Vase, 9¼" #240, ball | 140.00 | 275.00 |
| Vase, 9½" #340, crimped top | 160.00 | 375.00 |

*Moulds owned by Summit Art Glass and many of these pieces have been reproduced.

# CARIBBEAN, Line #112, Duncan Miller Glass Company, 1936 – 1955

Colors: blue, crystal, amber, red

An enthusiastic collector of blue Caribbean sold me one of his six cordials for my collection back in 1980, as we were photographing for the first Elegant book. He accosted me at a recent show and wanted to know if I would be willing to sell it back to him!

He had bought those years ago as part of a set and no one has ever seen another one. He collects a setting of twelve and I promised him the one he sold me if he ever finds eleven! I hope my cordial is safe for now! I do know a buyer if you find some!

Blue dinnerware pieces such as dinner plates, cups and saucers have almost vanished from the collecting scene. Some collectors have begun buying crystal Caribbean since they are not finding blue. Mixing colors and patterns is becoming the "in" thing with collectors.

The crystal punch set with colored handled cups and ladle sells for about $40.00 more than the plain crystal set. Red handled pieces are more desirable than amber!

Caribbean is the most difficult pattern to price in this book since there is never enough seen at shows to establish a fairly representative price!

| | Crystal | Blue |
|---|---|---|
| Ash tray, 6", 4 indent | 15.00 | 32.50 |
| Bowl, 3¾" x 5", folded side, hdld. | 16.00 | 35.00 |
| Bowl, 4½", finger | 16.00 | 32.00 |
| Bowl, 5", fruit nappy (takes liner), hdld. | 12.00 | 25.00 |
| Bowl, 5" x 7", folded side, hdld. | 16.00 | 37.50 |
| Bowl, 6½", soup (takes liner) | 16.00 | 37.50 |
| Bowl, 7", hdld. | 25.00 | 45.00 |
| Bowl, 7¼", ftd., hdld., grapefruit | 20.00 | 40.00 |
| Bowl, 8½" | 27.50 | 65.00 |
| Bowl, 9", salad | 30.00 | 70.00 |
| Bowl, 9¼", veg., flared edge | 30.00 | 65.00 |
| Bowl, 9¼", veg., hdld. | 30.00 | 75.00 |
| Bowl, 9½", epergne, flared edge | 37.50 | 85.00 |
| Bowl, 10", 6¼ qt., punch | 87.50 | 425.00 |
| Bowl, 10", 6¼ qt. punch, flared top | 87.50 | 475.00 |
| Bowl, 10¾", oval, flower, hdld. | 35.00 | 80.00 |
| Bowl, 12", console, flared edge | 40.00 | 90.00 |
| Candelabrum, 4¾", 2-lite | 35.00 | 75.00 |
| Candlestick, 7¼", 1-lite, w/bl. prisms | 60.00 | 160.00 |
| Candy dish w/cover, 4" x 7" | 40.00 | 95.00 |
| Cheese/cracker crumbs, 3½" h., plate 11", hdld. | 39.50 | 80.00 |
| Cigarette holder, (stack ash tray top) | 35.00 | 80.00 |
| Cocktail shaker, 9", 33 oz. | 75.00 | 175.00 |
| Creamer | 14.00 | 25.00 |
| Cruet | 37.50 | 85.00 |
| Cup, tea | 15.00 | 60.00 |
| Cup, punch | 8.00 | 22.50 |
| Epergne, 4 pt., flower (12" bowl; 9½" bowl; 7¾" vase; 14" plate) | 185.00 | 400.00 |
| Ice bucket, 6½", hdld. | 70.00 | 150.00 |
| Ladle, punch | 32.50 | 95.00 |
| Mayonnaise, w/liner, 5¾", 2 pt., 2 spoons, hdld. | 42.50 | 95.00 |
| Mayonnaise, w/liner, 5¾", hdld., 1 spoon | 35.00 | 80.00 |
| Mustard, 4", w/slotted cover | 32.00 | 60.00 |
| Pitcher, 4¼", 9 oz., syrup | 60.00 | 135.00 |
| Pitcher, 4¾" 16 oz., milk | 90.00 | 225.00 |
| Pitcher, w/ice lip, 9", 72 oz., water | 185.00 | 450.00 |
| Plate, 6", hdld., fruit nappy liner | 4.00 | 12.00 |
| Plate 6¼", bread/butter | 5.00 | 12.00 |
| Plate, 7¼", rolled edge, soup liner | 5.00 | 12.50 |
| Plate, 7½", salad | 10.00 | 20.00 |

## CARIBBEAN, Line #112, Duncan Miller Glass Company, 1936 – 1955 (continued)

| | Crystal | Blue |
|---|---|---|
| Plate, 8", hdld., mayonnaise liner | 6.00 | 14.00 |
| Plate, 8½", luncheon | 14.00 | 32.50 |
| Plate, 10½", dinner | 47.50 | 115.00 |
| Plate, 11", hdld., cheese/cracker liner | 20.00 | 42.50 |
| Plate, 12", salad liner, rolled edge | 22.00 | 50.00 |
| Plate, 14" | 22.00 | 55.00 |
| Plate, 16", torte | 32.50 | 80.00 |
| Plate, 18", punch underliner | 37.50 | 90.00 |
| Relish, 6", round, 2 pt. | 12.00 | 25.00 |
| Relish, 9½", 4 pt., oblong | 30.00 | 65.00 |
| Relish, 9½", oblong | 27.50 | 60.00 |
| Relish, 12¾", 5 pt., rnd. | 40.00 | 90.00 |
| Relish, 12¾", 7 pt., rnd. | 40.00 | 90.00 |
| Salt dip, 2½" | 9.00 | 20.00 |
| Salt & pepper, 3", metal tops | 32.00 | 75.00 |
| Salt & pepper, 5", metal tops | 37.50 | 90.00 |
| Saucer | 4.00 | 8.00 |
| Server, 5¾", ctr. hdld. | 13.00 | 45.00 |
| Server, 6½", ctr. hdld. | 22.00 | 50.00 |
| Stem, 3", 1 oz., cordial | 65.00 | 150.00 |
| Stem, 3½", 3½ oz., ftd., ball stem, wine | 20.00 | 40.00 |
| Stem, 3⅝", 2½ oz., wine (egg cup shape) | 22.50 | 35.00 |
| Stem, 4", 6 oz., ftd., ball stem, champagne | 14.00 | 27.50 |
| Stem, 4¼", ftd., sherbet | 8.00 | 17.50 |
| Stem, 4¾", 3 oz., ftd., ball stem, wine | 20.00 | 47.50 |
| Stem, 5¾", 8 oz., ftd., ball stem | 18.00 | 40.00 |
| Sugar | 11.00 | 22.00 |
| Syrup, metal cutoff top | 75.00 | 165.00 |
| Tray, 6¼", hand., mint, div. | 14.00 | 30.00 |
| Tray, 12¾", rnd. | 25.00 | 50.00 |
| Tumbler, 2¼", 2 oz., shot glass | 25.00 | 55.00 |
| Tumbler, 3½", 5 oz., flat | 20.00 | 40.00 |
| Tumbler, 5¼" 11½ oz., flat | 20.00 | 40.00 |
| Tumbler, 5½", 8½ oz., ftd. | 22.00 | 45.00 |
| Tumbler, 6½", 11 oz., ftd., ice tea | 27.50 | 55.00 |
| Vase, 5¾", ftd., ruffled edge | 22.00 | 50.00 |
| Vase, 7¼", ftd., flared edge, ball | 27.50 | 55.00 |
| Vase, 7½", ftd., flared edge, bulbous | 32.50 | 65.00 |
| Vase, 7¾", flared edge, epergne | 35.00 | 75.00 |
| Vase, 8", ftd., straight side | 37.50 | 80.00 |
| Vase, 9", ftd., ruffled top | 47.50 | 165.00 |
| Vase, 10", ftd. | 52.50 | 130.00 |

# CENTURY, Line #2630, Fostoria Glass Company

Colors: crystal

This is one of the patterns that will be moved into my *Collectible Glassware from the 40's, 50's, 60's...* because it actually falls within that time frame. I am trying to eliminate duplications in my books; so I am warning you that from now on, Century will not be included in this book! I used that warning on patterns in my *Collector's Encyclopedia of Depression Glass* when I split it into two time periods and some collectors did not heed my warning and wondered why their patterns disappeared.

Catalogue listings for plates are different from the actual measurements by one-half inch. I have included actual measurements for all Fostoria patterns in this book. This has been an extreme problem for people ordering through the mail.

There are two sizes of dinner plates as happens in most of Fostoria's patterns. The larger plate (usually listed as a service plate) is the harder to find. They were priced higher originally, and many people did without the larger plates. One problem with this pattern is scratches. Since all the pieces are very plain in the center, scratches show up even more than on patterns with designs in the center.

There is confusion between the candy and the covered preserve. The candy with cover stands 7" tall, but the preserve with cover only stands 6" tall. The taller candy is more in demand. The oval vase is found in front of the ice bucket in the bottom photo on the next page. That vase is often sold as an ice bucket. It is harder to find than the metal handled ice bucket!

Fostoria used the Century blank for most of its Heather line that is also included in this book.

| | Crystal | | Crystal |
|---|---|---|---|
| Ash tray, 2¾" | 10.00 | Pitcher, 7⅛", 48 oz. | 95.00 |
| Basket, 10¼" x 6½", wicker hdld. | 70.00 | Plate, 6", bread/butter | 6.00 |
| Bowl, 4½", hdld. | 12.00 | Plate, 7½", salad | 8.00 |
| Bowl, 5", fruit | 14.00 | Plate, 7½", crescent salad | 35.00 |
| Bowl, 6", cereal | 22.50 | Plate, 8", party, w/indent for cup | 22.50 |
| Bowl, 6¼", snack, ftd. | 13.00 | Plate, 8½", luncheon | 12.50 |
| Bowl, 7⅛", 3 ftd., triangular | 15.00 | Plate, 9½", small dinner | 22.50 |
| Bowl, 7¼", bonbon, 3 ftd. | 20.00 | Plate, 10", hdld., cake | 22.00 |
| Bowl, 8", flared | 25.00 | Plate, 10½", dinner | 30.00 |
| Bowl, 8½", salad | 25.00 | Plate, 14", torte | 30.00 |
| Bowl, 9", lily pond | 30.00 | Platter, 12" | 47.50 |
| Bowl, 9½", hdld., serving bowl | 35.00 | Preserve, w/cover, 6" | 35.00 |
| Bowl, 9½", oval, serving bowl | 32.50 | Relish, 7⅜", 2 part | 15.00 |
| Bowl, 10", oval, hdld. | 32.50 | Relish, 11⅛", 3 part | 22.50 |
| Bowl, 10½", salad | 30.00 | Salt and pepper, 2⅜", individual, pr. | 15.00 |
| Bowl, 10¾", ftd., flared | 35.00 | Salt and pepper, 3⅛", pr. | 20.00 |
| Bowl, 11, ftd., rolled edge | 40.00 | Salver, 12¼", ftd. (like cake stand) | 50.00 |
| Bowl, 11¼", lily pond | 32.50 | Saucer | 3.50 |
| Bowl, 12", flared | 35.00 | Stem, 3½ oz., cocktail, 4⅛" | 20.00 |
| Butter, w/cover, ¼ lb. | 35.00 | Stem, 3½ oz., wine, 4½" | 30.00 |
| Candy, w/cover, 7" | 35.00 | Stem, 4½ oz., oyster cocktail, 3¾" | 20.00 |
| Candlestick, 4½" | 17.50 | Stem, 5½" oz., sherbet, 4½" | 12.00 |
| Candlestick, 7", double | 30.00 | Stem, 10 oz., goblet, 5¾" | 22.50 |
| Candlestick, 7¾", triple | 40.00 | Sugar, 4", ftd. | 9.00 |
| Comport, 2¾", cheese | 15.00 | Sugar, individual | 9.00 |
| Comport, 4⅜" | 20.00 | Tid bit, 8⅛", 3 ftd., upturned edge | 18.00 |
| Cracker plate, 10¾" | 30.00 | Tid bit, 10¼", 2 tier, metal hdld. | 25.00 |
| Creamer, 4¼" | 9.00 | Tray, 4¼", for ind. salt/pepper | 14.00 |
| Creamer, individual | 9.00 | Tray, 7⅛", for ind. sug/cr | 14.00 |
| Cup, 6 oz., ftd. | 15.00 | Tray, 9⅛", hdld., utility | 25.00 |
| Ice Bucket | 65.00 | Tray, 9½", hdld., muffin | 30.00 |
| Mayonnaise, 3 pc. | 30.00 | Tray, 11½", center hdld. | 30.00 |
| Mayonnaise, 4 pc., div. w/2 ladles | 35.00 | Tumbler, 5 oz., ftd., juice, 4¾" | 22.50 |
| Mustard, w/spoon, cover | 27.50 | Tumbler, 12 oz., ftd., tea, 5⅞" | 27.50 |
| Oil, w/stopper, 5 oz. | 45.00 | Vase, 6", bud | 18.00 |
| Pickle, 8¾" | 15.00 | Vase, 7½", hdld. | 67.50 |
| Pitcher, 6⅛", 16 oz. | 50.00 | Vase, 8½", oval | 65.00 |

# CHANTILLY, Cambridge Glass Company, Late 1940's – Early 1950's

Colors: crystal

Chantilly is most often collected on stemware line #3625. You can see a better depiction of this stem on page 229 in the back of the book. On pages 228-229 I have shown most of the popular Cambridge stemware lines. If you have trouble determining what stem you have, refer to those pages. As with other Cambridge patterns, there are several blanks and hundreds of items that can be collected in Chantilly.

Most of the pieces found with Chantilly etching can also be seen in Rose Point. There is a more comprehensive listing for Rose Point in this book since there are so many more known pieces (and collectors) of that pattern. Prices for Rose Point items are higher due to collector demand!

Rare Chantilly items pictured include the crescent salad plate, quarter pound butter, hurricane shades, and etched bobeches in the top photograph.

|  | Crystal |
|---|---|
| Bowl, 7", bonbon, 2 hdld., ftd. | 17.50 |
| Bowl, 7", relish/pickle, 2 pt. | 18.00 |
| Bowl, 7", relish/pickle | 20.00 |
| Bowl, 9", celery/relish, 3 pt. | 25.00 |
| Bowl, 10", 4 ftd., flared | 40.00 |
| Bowl, 11", tab hdld. | 35.00 |
| Bowl, 11½", tab hdld. ftd. | 35.00 |
| Bowl, 12", celery/relish, 3 pt. | 35.00 |
| Bowl, 12", 4 ftd., flared | 35.00 |
| Bowl, 12", 4 ftd., oval | 37.50 |
| Bowl, 12", celery/relish, 5 pt. | 40.00 |
| Butter, w/cover, round | 125.00 |
| Butter, ¼ lb. | 210.00 |
| Candlestick, 5" | 17.50 |
| Candlestick, 6", 2-lite, "fleur-de-lis" | 32.50 |
| Candlestick, 6", 3-lite | 37.50 |
| Candy box, w/cover, ftd. | 125.00 |
| Candy box, w/cover, rnd. | 60.00 |
| Cocktail icer, 2 pc. | 55.00 |
| Comport, 5½" | 30.00 |
| Comport, 5⅜", blown | 37.50 |
| Creamer | 14.50 |
| Creamer, indiv., #3900, scalloped edge | 12.50 |
| Cup | 17.50 |
| Decanter, ftd. | 150.00 |
| Decanter, ball | 185.00 |
| Hat, small | 150.00 |
| Hat, large | 200.00 |
| Hurricane lamp, candlestick base | 110.00 |
| Hurricane lamp, keyhole base w/prisms | 150.00 |
| Ice bucket, w/chrome handle | 65.00 |
| Marmalade & cover | 55.00 |
| Mayonnaise, (sherbet type bowl w/ladle) | 25.00 |
| Mayonnaise, div. w/liner & 2 ladles | 40.00 |
| Mayonnaise, w/liner & ladle | 37.50 |
| Mustard & cover | 50.00 |
| Oil, 6 oz., hdld., w/stopper | 60.00 |
| Pitcher, ball | 120.00 |
| Pitcher, Doulton | 265.00 |
| Pitcher, upright | 175.00 |
| Plate, crescent, salad | 80.00 |
| Plate, 6½", bread/butter | 6.50 |
| Plate, 8", salad | 12.50 |
| Plate, 8", tab hdld., ftd., bonbon | 15.00 |
| Plate, 10½", dinner | 57.50 |
| Plate, 12", 4 ftd., service | 30.00 |
| Plate, 13", 4 ftd. | 30.00 |
| Plate 13½", tab hdld., cake | 32.50 |
| Plate, 14", torte | 35.00 |
| Salad dressing bottle | 85.00 |
| Salt & pepper, pr., flat | 27.50 |
| Salt & pepper, footed | 30.00 |
| Salt & pepper, handled | 30.00 |

|  | Crystal |
|---|---|
| Saucer | 3.00 |
| Stem, #3600, 1 oz., cordial | 50.00 |
| Stem, #3600, 2½ oz., cocktail | 24.00 |
| Stem #3600, 2½ oz., wine | 30.00 |
| Stem, #3600, 4½ oz., claret | 40.00 |
| Stem, #3600, 4½ oz., low oyster cocktail | 15.00 |
| Stem, #3600, 7 oz., tall sherbet | 17.50 |
| Stem, #3600, 7 oz., low sherbet | 15.00 |
| Stem, #3600, 10 oz., water | 20.00 |
| Stem, #3625, 1 oz., cordial | 50.00 |
| Stem, #3625, 3 oz., cocktail | 27.50 |
| Stem, #3625, 4½ oz., claret | 40.00 |
| Stem, #3625, 4½ oz., low oyster cocktail | 16.00 |
| Stem, #3625, 7 oz., low sherbet | 16.00 |
| Stem, #3625, 7 oz., tall sherbet | 18.00 |
| Stem, #3625, 10 oz., water | 25.00 |
| Stem, #3775, 1 oz., cordial | 50.00 |
| Stem, #3775, 2½ oz., wine | 30.00 |
| Stem, #3775, 3 oz., cocktail | 25.00 |
| Stem, #3775, 4½ oz., claret | 40.00 |
| Stem, #3775, 4½ oz., oyster cocktail | 15.00 |
| Stem, #3775, 6 oz., low sherbet | 15.00 |
| Stem, #3775, 6 oz., tall sherbet | 17.50 |
| Stem, #3779, 1 oz., cordial | 60.00 |
| Stem, #3779, 2½ oz., wine | 30.00 |
| Stem, #3779, 3 oz., cocktail | 25.00 |
| Stem, #3779, 4½ oz., claret | 40.00 |
| Stem, #3779, 4½ oz., low oyster cocktail | 15.00 |
| Stem, #3779, 6 oz., tall sherbet | 17.50 |
| Stem, #3779, 6 oz., low sherbet | 15.00 |
| Stem, #3779, 9 oz., water | 20.00 |
| Sugar | 13.50 |
| Sugar, indiv., #3900, scalloped edge | 11.00 |
| Tumbler, #3600, 5 oz., ftd., juice | 15.00 |
| Tumbler, #3600, 12 oz., ftd., tea | 20.00 |
| Tumbler, #3625, 5 oz., ftd., juice | 15.00 |
| Tumbler, #3625, 10 oz., ftd., water | 17.50 |
| Tumbler, #3625, 12 oz., ftd., tea | 22.00 |
| Tumbler, #3775, 5 oz., ftd., juice | 14.00 |
| Tumbler, #3775, 10 oz., ftd., water | 15.00 |
| Tumbler, #3775, 12 oz., ftd., tea | 20.00 |
| Tumbler, #3779, 5 oz., ftd., juice | 15.00 |
| Tumbler, #3779, 12 oz., ftd., tea | 20.00 |
| Tumbler, 13 oz. | 22.00 |
| Vase, 5", globe | 30.00 |
| Vase, 6", high ftd., flower | 22.00 |
| Vase, 8", high ftd., flower | 30.00 |
| Vase, 9", keyhole base | 35.00 |
| Vase, 10", bud | 30.00 |
| Vase, 11", ftd., flower | 45.00 |
| Vase, 11", ped. ftd., flower | 50.00 |
| Vase, 12", keyhole base | 55.00 |
| Vase, 13", ftd., flower | 75.00 |

Note: See Pages 228-229 for stem identification.

# CHARTER OAK, #3362 A.H. Heisey Co., 1926 – 1935

Colors: crystal, Flamingo, Moongleam, Hawthorne, Marigold

Charter Oak was a new Heisey entry for the fifth edition of this book. Since then, there are a number of collectors looking for this pattern with acorns in the design. One collector commented that he had never considered any Heisey pattern before because they all looked alike to him until he saw Charter Oak in the last book.

I have only shown Flamingo, but there are several other colors of Charter Oak that can be collected. Yeoman cup and saucers are used with this set since there were no cups and saucers made in this pattern. One is pictured here, but only priced under Yeoman. I mention that since several collectors have wanted to know why I didn't price the cup and saucer. Hopefully, they will venture to read my commentary this time!

The #4262 Charter Oak lamp was produced from 1928-1931. It looks like a blown comport with an acorn in the stem. It has a diamond optic font that was filled with water to magnify the design and to stabilize the lamp.

The #130 one lite candleholder base is an oak leaf with stem curled up having an acorn for the candle cup! Have you seen one?

| | Crystal | Flamingo | Moongleam | Hawthorne | Marigold |
|---|---|---|---|---|---|
| Bowl, 11" floral #116 (oak leaf) | 30.00 | 45.00 | 47.50 | 75.00 | |
| Bowl, finger #3362 | 10.00 | 17.50 | 20.00 | | |
| Candleholder, 1-lite, #130 "Acorn" | 100.00 | 125.00 | 135.00 | | |
| Candlestick, 3", #116 (oak leaf) | 25.00 | 30.00 | 35.00 | 125.00 | |
| Candlestick, 5", 3-lite, #129 "Tricorn" | | 65.00 | 85.00 | 125.00 | 150.00 |
| Comport, 6" low ft., #3362 | 45.00 | 50.00 | 55.00 | 70.00 | 100.00 |
| Comport, 7" ftd., #3362 | 50.00 | 55.00 | 60.00 | 160.00 | 175.00 |
| Lamp #4262 (blown comport/water filled to magnify design & stabilize lamp) | 400.00 | 700.00 | 850.00 | | |
| Pitcher, flat #3362 | | 85.00 | 95.00 | | |
| Plate, 6" salad #1246 (Acorn & Leaves) | 5.00 | 10.00 | 12.50 | 20.00 | |
| Plate, 7" luncheon/salad #1246 (Acorn & Leaves) | 8.00 | 12.00 | 17.50 | 22.50 | |
| Plate, 8" luncheon #1246 (Acorn & Leaves) | 10.00 | 15.00 | 20.00 | 25.00 | |
| Plate, 10½" dinner #1246 (Acorn & Leaves) | 27.50 | 35.00 | 45.00 | 65.00 | |
| Stem, 3 oz. cocktail #3362 | 10.00 | 15.00 | 20.00 | 45.00 | 40.00 |
| Stem, 3½ oz. low ft., oyster cocktail #3362 | 8.00 | 10.00 | 15.00 | 40.00 | 35.00 |
| Stem, 4½ oz parfait #3362 | 15.00 | 25.00 | 30.00 | 60.00 | 50.00 |
| Stem, 6 oz. saucer champagne #3362 | 10.00 | 15.00 | 20.00 | 50.00 | 40.00 |
| Stem, 6 oz. sherbet, low ft. #3362 | 10.00 | 15.00 | 20.00 | 50.00 | 40.00 |
| Stem, 8 oz. goblet, high ft. #3362 | 15.00 | 30.00 | 35.00 | 95.00 | 60.00 |
| Stem, 8 oz. luncheon goblet, low ft. #3362 | 15.00 | 30.00 | 35.00 | 95.00 | 60.00 |
| Tumbler, 10 oz. flat #3362 | 10.00 | 15.00 | 20.00 | 35.00 | 30.00 |
| Tumbler, 12 oz. flat #3362 | 12.50 | 17.50 | 22.50 | 40.00 | 35.00 |

# CHEROKEE ROSE, Tiffin Glass Company, 1940's – 1950's

Colors: crystal

Cherokee Rose is a pattern that showed up better in black and white photographs, however my publisher squashed the decision to use black and white photos after their trial in the fifth edition. I asked for readers input and only received one negative vote. The writer commented that he understood what we were doing, but he didn't like black and white. Neither did Collector Books!

As with most Tiffin patterns, stems are the pieces most often seen. In my travels around the country I mostly see the stemware line #17399. This is the tear drop style that is shown on most of the stemware in the picture. The other stem (#17403) is represented by the cordial on the far right in the top photograph. There is no distinction in stemware line prices at present.

Cups and saucers are apparently nonexistent; I doubt if any will show up at this point. The little bowl shown in the foreground of the top picture is the mayonnaise. It should have a liner and spoon, but I bought it without those parts.

|  | Crystal |
|---|---|
| Bowl, 5", finger. | 22.50 |
| Bowl, 6", fruit or nut | 20.00 |
| Bowl, 7", salad | 30.00 |
| Bowl, 10", deep salad | 45.00 |
| Bowl, 10½", celery, oblong | 32.50 |
| Bowl, 12", crimped | 45.00 |
| Bowl, 12½" centerpiece, flared | 45.00 |
| Bowl, 13", centerpiece | 50.00 |
| Cake plate, 12½", center hdld. | 45.00 |
| Candlesticks, pr., double branch | 85.00 |
| Comport, 6" | 35.00 |
| Creamer | 20.00 |
| Mayonnaise, liner and ladle | 50.00 |
| Pitcher | 325.00 |
| Plate, 6", sherbet | 6.00 |
| Plate, 8", luncheon | 12.50 |
| Plate, 13½", turned-up edge, lily | 35.00 |
| Plate, 14", sandwich | 35.00 |
| Relish, 6½", 3 pt. | 25.00 |
| Relish, 12½", 3 pt. | 45.00 |
| Stem, 1 oz., cordial | 55.00 |

|  | Crystal |
|---|---|
| Stem, 2 oz., sherry | 35.00 |
| Stem, 3½ oz., cocktail | 20.00 |
| Stem, 3½ oz., wine | 35.00 |
| Stem, 4 oz., claret | 45.00 |
| Stem, 4½ oz., parfait | 40.00 |
| Stem, 5½ oz., sherbet/champagne | 20.00 |
| Stem, 9 oz., water | 25.00 |
| Sugar | 20.00 |
| Table bell | 65.00 |
| Tumbler, 4½ oz., oyster cocktail | 20.00 |
| Tumbler, 5 oz., ftd., juice | 20.00 |
| Tumbler, 8 oz., ftd., water | 22.50 |
| Tumbler, 10½ oz., ftd., ice tea | 32.50 |
| Vase, 6", bud | 25.00 |
| Vase, 8", bud | 35.00 |
| Vase, 8½", tear drop | 55.00 |
| Vase, 9¼", tub | 65.00 |
| Vase, 10", bud | 40.00 |
| Vase, 11", bud | 45.00 |
| Vase, 11", urn | 95.00 |
| Vase, 12", flared | 95.00 |

# CHINTZ, (Plate Etching #338), Fostoria Glass Company

Colors: crystal

Fostoria's Chintz was added to my *Collectible Glassware from the 40's, 50's, 60's...* because it fit the parameters of that book. As with Century, I will be dropping Chintz from this book and putting it only in the 50's book with the next edition. New listings for this book are the 9½" oval vegetable bowl, 9¼" footed bowl and a cigarette box.

Several pieces of Chintz are proving to be elusive. They include the cream soup, finger bowl, salad dressing bottle, syrup, and those newly listed items. Stemware abounds as it does for many patterns of this time. Evidently, people purchased stemware whether or not they purchased the serving pieces.

The regularly found oval sauce boat (Fostoria's rendition of a gravy) has no divider. Note that many Chintz pieces are found on the #2496 blank (known as Baroque).

| | Crystal | | Crystal |
|---|---|---|---|
| Bell, dinner | 110.00 | Plate, #2496, 8½", luncheon | 21.00 |
| Bowl, #869, 4½", finger | 50.00 | Plate, #2496, 9½", dinner | 50.00 |
| Bowl, #2496, 4⅝", tri-cornered | 20.00 | Plate, #2496, 10", hdld., cake | 42.50 |
| Bowl, #2496, cream soup | 67.50 | Plate, #2496, 11", cracker | 40.00 |
| Bowl, #2496, 5", fruit | 30.00 | Plate, #2496, 14", upturned edge | 50.00 |
| Bowl, #2496, 5", hdld. | 25.00 | Plate, #2496, 16", torte, plain edge | 110.00 |
| Bowl, #2496, 7⅝", bonbon | 32.50 | Platter, #2496, 12" | 95.00 |
| Bowl, #2496, 8½", hdld. | 52.50 | Relish, #2496, 6", 2 part, square | 32.50 |
| Bowl, 9¼", ftd. | 375.00 | Relish, #2496, 10" x 7½", 3 part | 40.00 |
| Bowl, #2496, 9½", oval vegetable | 185.00 | Relish, #2419, 5 part | 40.00 |
| Bowl, #2496, 9½", vegetable | 70.00 | Salad dressing bottle, #2083, 6½" | 300.00 |
| Bowl, #2484, 10", hdld. | 60.00 | Salt and pepper, #2496, 2¾", flat, pr. | 90.00 |
| Bowl, #2496, 10½" hdld. | 65.00 | Sauce boat, #2496, oval | 70.00 |
| Bowl, #2496, 11½", flared | 60.00 | Sauce boat, #2496, oval, divided | 70.00 |
| Bowl, #6023, ftd | 37.50 | Sauce boat liner, #2496, oval | 30.00 |
| Candlestick, #2496, 3½", double | 30.00 | Saucer, #2496 | 5.00 |
| Candlestick, #2496, 4" | 18.00 | Stem, #6026, 1 oz., cordial, 3⅞" | 47.50 |
| Candlestick, #2496, 5½" | 30.00 | Stem, #6026, 4 oz., cocktail, 5" | 26.00 |
| Candlestick, #2496, 6", triple | 42.50 | Stem, #6026, 4 oz., oyster cocktail, 3⅜" | 27.50 |
| Candlestick, #6023, double | 37.50 | Stem, #6026, 4½ oz., claret-wine, 5⅜" | 40.00 |
| Candy, w/cover, #2496, 3 part | 125.00 | Stem, #6026, 6 oz., low sherbet, 4⅜" | 20.00 |
| Celery, #2496, 11" | 35.00 | Stem, #6026, 6 oz., saucer champagne, 5½" | 22.00 |
| Comport, #2496, 3¼", cheese | 25.00 | Stem, #6026, 9 oz., water goblet, 7⅝" | 32.50 |
| Comport, #2496, 4¾" | 32.50 | Sugar, #2496, 3½", ftd. | 16.00 |
| Comport, #2496, 5½" | 37.50 | Sugar, #2496½, individual | 21.00 |
| Creamer, #2496, 3¾", ftd. | 17.50 | Syrup, #2586, sani-cut | 325.00 |
| Creamer, #2496½, individual | 22.50 | Tid bit, #2496, 8¼", 3 ftd., upturned edge. | 26.00 |
| Cup, #2496, ftd. | 21.00 | Tray, #2496½, 6½", for ind. sugar/creamer. | 22.00 |
| Ice bucket, #2496 | 130.00 | Tray, #2375, 11", center hdld. | 40.00 |
| Jelly, w/cover, #2496, 7½" | 82.50 | Tumbler, #6026, 5 oz., juice, ftd. | 27.50 |
| Mayonnaise, #2496½, 3 piece | 57.50 | Tumbler, #6026, 9 oz., water or low goblet | 27.50 |
| Oil, w/stopper, #2496, 3½ oz. | 100.00 | Tumbler, #6026, 13 oz., tea, ftd. | 32.50 |
| Pickle, #2496, 8" | 32.50 | Vase, #4108, 5" | 85.00 |
| Pitcher, #5000, 48 oz., ftd. | 350.00 | Vase, #4128, 5" | 85.00 |
| Plate, #2496, 6", bread/butter | 10.00 | Vase, #4143, 6", ftd. | 100.00 |
| Plate, #2496, 7½", salad | 15.00 | Vase, #4143, 7½", ftd. | 135.00 |

# CHINTZ, #1401 (Empress Blank) and CHINTZ #3389 (Duquesne Blank) A.H. Heisey Co., 1931 – 1938

Colors: crystal, "Sahara" yellow, "Moongleam" green, "Flamingo" pink, and "Alexandrite" orchid

Quite a few pieces in Alexandrite Chintz appeared on the market a few years ago. It did not take long for them to disappear into collections. Even so, prices for the Alexandrite Chintz are not established enough to list at this time!

Pieces with the encircled flowers are known as "formal" Chintz. The pattern shot, one of the cream soups and the individual sugar are all "formal" Chintz.

Don't confuse this pattern with Fostoria's Chintz, and learn to specify the company name when you ask for a pattern named Chintz. It was a popular name used by several companies!

| | Crystal | Sahara |
|---|---|---|
| Bowl, finger, #4107 | 8.00 | 15.00 |
| Bowl, 5½", ftd., preserve, hdld. | 15.00 | 27.00 |
| Bowl, 6", ftd., mint | 18.00 | 30.00 |
| Bowl, 6", ftd., 2 hdld., jelly | 15.00 | 30.00 |
| Bowl, 7", triplex relish | 16.00 | 35.00 |
| Bowl, 7½", Nasturtium | 16.00 | 30.00 |
| Bowl, 8½", ftd., 2 hdld., floral | 32.00 | 65.00 |
| Bowl, 11", dolphin ft., floral | 40.00 | 110.00 |
| Bowl, 13", 2 pt., pickle & olive | 15.00 | 35.00 |
| Comport, 7", oval | 40.00 | 85.00 |
| Creamer, 3 dolphin ft. | 20.00 | 45.00 |
| Creamer, individual | 12.00 | 25.00 |
| Grapefruit, ftd., #3389, Duquesne | 30.00 | 60.00 |
| Ice bucket, ftd. | 85.00 | 135.00 |
| Mayonnaise, 5½", dolphin ft. | 35.00 | 65.00 |
| Oil, 4 oz. | 60.00 | 125.00 |
| Pitcher, 3 pint, dolphin ft. | 125.00 | 235.00 |
| Plate, 6", square, bread | 6.00 | 15.00 |
| Plate, 7", square, salad | 8.00 | 18.00 |
| Plate, 8", square, luncheon | 10.00 | 22.00 |
| Plate, 10½", square, dinner | 40.00 | 85.00 |
| Plate, 12", two hdld., | 25.00 | 45.00 |
| Plate, 13", hors d' oeuvre, two hdld. | 20.00 | 37.50 |
| Platter, 14", oval | 30.00 | 65.00 |
| Stem, #3389, Duquesne, 1 oz., cordial | 115.00 | 235.00 |
| Stem, #3389, 2½ oz., wine | 17.50 | 45.00 |
| Stem, #3389, 3 oz., cocktail | 15.00 | 35.00 |
| Stem, #3389, 4 oz., claret | 20.00 | 45.00 |
| Stem, #3389, 4 oz., oyster cocktail | 10.00 | 20.00 |
| Stem, #3389, 5 oz., parfait | 14.00 | 35.00 |
| Stem, #3389, 5 oz., saucer champagne | 11.00 | 22.50 |
| Stem, #3389, 5 oz., sherbet | 8.00 | 17.50 |
| Stem, #3389, 9 oz., water | 15.00 | 30.00 |
| Sugar, 3 dolphin ft. | 20.00 | 42.50 |
| Sugar, individual | 12.00 | 28.00 |
| Tray, 10", celery | 14.00 | 27.50 |
| Tray, 12", sq., ctr. hdld., sandwich | 35.00 | 65.00 |
| Tray, 13", celery | 18.00 | 26.00 |
| Tumbler, #3389, 5 oz., ftd., juice | 11.00 | 22.00 |
| Tumbler, #3389, 8 oz., soda | 12.00 | 24.00 |
| Tumbler, #3389, 10 oz., ftd., water | 13.00 | 25.00 |
| Tumbler, #3389, 12 oz., iced tea | 14.00 | 30.00 |
| Vase, 9", dolphin ft. | 95.00 | 185.00 |

# CLASSIC, Tiffin Glass Company, 1913 – 1930's

Colors: crystal, pink

Classic stems abound and other items are rarely seen. Cathy started buying this pattern a few years ago, and we have found enough pieces to start a listing for it. You will assuredly find additional pieces of Classic; let me hear what you discover.

Pink stems are found on the #17024 line that is also seen in Tiffin's Flanders pattern. Crystal stemmed items seem to all appear on the #14185 line. There are some size discrepancies within these stemware lines. We have measured both colors and noted the differences in these price listings.

| | Crystal | Pink |
|---|---|---|
| Bowl, 2 hdld., 8"x9¼" ............................................. | 95.00 | |
| Comport, 6" wide, 3¼" tall................................ | 50.00 | |
| Creamer, flat ....................................................... | 35.00 | 55.00 |
| Creamer,. ftd. ..................................................... | 35.00 | |
| Finger bowl, ftd.................................................. | 17.50 | 25.00 |
| Pitcher, 61 oz..................................................... | 250.00 | 395.00 |
| Pitcher, 61 oz., w/cover ...................................... | 300.00 | 450.00 |
| Plate, 6⅜", champagne liner............................ | 10.00 | |
| Plate, 8" ............................................................. | 12.50 | 15.00 |
| Sherbet, 3⅛", 6½ oz., short ........................... | 17.50 | 27.50 |
| Stem, 3⅞", 1 oz., cordial................................. | 45.00 | |
| Stem, 4¹⁵⁄₁₆", 3 oz., wine ................................. | 32.50 | 47.50 |
| Stem, 4⅞", 3¾ oz., cocktail............................ | 40.00 | |
| Stem, 4⅞", 4 oz., cocktail............................... | 27.50 | |
| Stem, 6½, 5 oz., parfait.................................... | 35.00 | 50.00 |
| Stem, 6", 7½ oz., saucer champagne ..................... | 22.50 | 32.50 |
| Stem, 8¼", 9 oz., water .................................... | 30.00 | 45.00 |
| Sugar, flat........................................................... | 35.00 | 55.00 |
| Sugar, ftd. .......................................................... | 35.00 | |
| Tumbler, 3½", 5 oz., ftd., juice........................ | 17.50 | |
| Tumbler, 4½", 8½ oz., ftd., water...................... | 20.00 | |
| Tumbler, 4⅛", 10½ oz., flat, water ....................... | 25.00 | |
| Tumbler, 5⁹⁄₁₆", 14 oz., ftd., tea....................... | 30.00 | |
| Tumbler, 6", 13 oz., ftd., iced tea........................... | | 40.00 |
| Tumbler, 6¹⁄₁₆", 14 oz., ftd., iced tea..................... | 30.00 | |
| Tumbler, 6¼", 6½ oz., ftd., Pilsner ....................... | 32.50 | |
| Vase, bud, 6½"..................................................... | 27.50 | |
| Vase, bud, 10½".................................................. | 42.50 | |

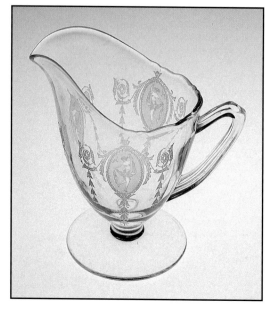
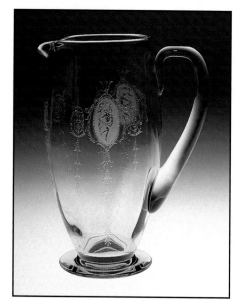

73

# CLEO, Cambridge Glass Company, Introduced 1930

Colors: amber, blue, crystal, green, pink, yellow

Cleo can be collected in sets of pink or green, but with great difficulty and also in blue with lots of patience and a "deep" pocket. There are several collectors who have amassed large sets of blue, but it has taken years to do that. One recently told me he was glad he had started when the prices were more reasonable than they are today. There are a multitude of pieces made in Cleo, but it seems that all the unusual items are found in amber or crystal instead of blue, pink, or green. Few collectors today search for amber colored pieces, but those who do have quite an array of Cleo pattern from which to choose.

In the foreground atop page 77 are three exceptional pieces. The wafer tray now has a home in Seattle. They are rarely found. The smaller footed item next to it is a salt dip and the larger footed piece is an individual almond!

Two styles of icers are pictured bottom left, page 77. Notice that Decagon style icers have a plain insert, but the other does not!

| | Blue | Pink/ Green/ Yellow/ Amber |
|---|---|---|
| Almond, 2½", individual ............ | 85.00 | 70.00 |
| Basket, 7", 2 hdld. (upturned sides) DECAGON .................... | 35.00 | 22.00 |
| Basket, 11", 2 hdld. (upturned sides) DECAGON .................... | 50.00 | 30.00 |
| Bouillon cup, w/saucer, 2 hdld., DECAGON ............................ | 45.00 | 30.00 |
| Bowl, 2 pt., relish ...................... | 40.00 | 22.00 |
| Bowl, 5½", fruit........................ | 25.00 | 15.00 |
| Bowl, 5½" 2 hdld., bonbon, DECAGON ............................ | 30.00 | 20.00 |
| Bowl, 6", 4 ft., comport .............. | 50.00 | 35.00 |
| Bowl, 6", cereal, DECAGON....... | 35.00 | 22.00 |
| Bowl, 6½", 2 hdld., bonbon DECAGON ............................ | 35.00 | 22.00 |
| Bowl, 6½", cranberry ................. | 40.00 | 27.50 |
| Bowl, 7½", tab hdld., soup ......... | 45.00 | 32.00 |
| Bowl, 8", miniature console........ | | 135.00 |
| Bowl, 8½" ................................ | 65.00 | 40.00 |
| Bowl, 8½" 2 hdld., DECAGON.... | 70.00 | 40.00 |
| Bowl, 9", covered vegetable ........ | | 150.00 |
| Bowl, 9½", oval veg., DECAGON | 90.00 | 45.00 |
| Bowl, 9", pickle, DECAGON ....... | 60.00 | 30.00 |
| Bowl, 10", 2 hdld., DECAGON.... | 75.00 | 40.00 |
| Bowl, 11", oval........................ | 95.00 | 40.00 |
| Bowl, 11½", oval...................... | 95.00 | 40.00 |
| Bowl, 12", console.................... | 75.00 | 40.00 |
| Bowl, 15½", oval, DECAGON...... | | 175.00 |
| Bowl, cream soup w/saucer, 2 hdld., DECAGON ................ | 50.00 | 30.00 |
| Bowl, finger w/liner, #3077 ........ | 50.00 | 30.00 |
| Bowl, finger w/liner, #3115 ........ | 50.00 | 30.00 |
| Candlestick, 1-lite, 2 styles ........ | 35.00 | 22.00 |
| Candlestick, 2-lite...................... | 75.00 | 35.00 |
| Candlestick, 3-lite..................... | 100.00 | 65.00 |
| Candy box w/lid........................ | | 125.00 |
| Candy & cover, tall .................... | | 145.00 |
| Comport, 7", tall, #3115 ............. | 75.00 | 40.00 |
| Creamer, DECAGON................... | 27.50 | 17.50 |
| Creamer, ewer style, 6"............... | | 75.00 |
| Creamer, ftd. ............................ | 30.00 | 20.00 |
| Cup, DECAGON ........................ | 25.00 | 15.00 |
| Decanter, w/stopper .................. | | 225.00 |

| | Blue | Pink/ Green/ Yellow/ Amber |
|---|---|---|
| Gravy boat, w/liner plate, DECAGON ............................ | 250.00 | 150.00 |
| Ice pail ................................... | 125.00 | 60.00 |
| Ice tub ................................... | 110.00 | 50.00 |
| Mayonnaise, w/liner and ladle, DECAGON ............................ | 95.00 | 45.00 |
| Mayonnaise, ftd. ........................ | 55.00 | 35.00 |
| Oil, 6 oz., w/stopper, DECAGON | | 135.00 |
| Pitcher, 3½ pt., #38................... | | 195.00 |
| Pitcher, w/cover, 22 oz. .............. | | 175.00 |
| Pitcher, w/cover, 60 oz., #804 ..... | | 250.00 |
| Pitcher, w/cover, 62 oz., #955 ..... | | 250.00 |
| Pitcher, w/cover, 63 oz., #3077 ... | | 275.00 |
| Pitcher, w/cover, 68 oz., #937 ..... | | 295.00 |
| Plate, 7"................................. | 15.00 | 12.00 |
| Plate, 7", 2 hdld., DECAGON ...... | 20.00 | 14.00 |
| Plate, 9½", dinner, DECAGON .... | 95.00 | 65.00 |
| Plate, 11", 2 hdld., DECAGON .... | 110.00 | 30.00 |
| Platter, 12".............................. | 150.00 | 100.00 |
| Platter, 15".............................. | 275.00 | 175.00 |
| Platter, w/cover, oval (toast) ....... | | 325.00 |
| Platter, asparagus, indented, w/sauce & spoon ..................... | | 325.00 |
| Salt dip, 1½" .............................. | 100.00 | 70.00 |
| Saucer, DECAGON ..................... | 5.00 | 3.00 |
| Server, 12", ctr. hand. ................ | 65.00 | 35.00 |
| Stem, #3077, 1 oz., cordial.......... | 165.00 | 125.00 |
| Stem, #3077, 2½ oz., cocktail...... | 45.00 | 27.50 |
| Stem, #3077, 3½ oz., wine ......... | 95.00 | 60.00 |
| Stem, #3077, 6 oz., low sherbet .. | 27.50 | 15.00 |
| Stem, #3077, 6 oz., tall sherbet... | 35.00 | 17.50 |
| Stem, #3115, 9 oz. .................... | | 30.00 |
| Stem, #3115, 3½ oz., cocktail...... | | 25.00 |
| Stem, #3115, 6 oz., fruit ............. | | 15.00 |
| Stem, #3115, 6 oz., low sherbet .. | | 15.00 |
| Stem, #3115, 6 oz., tall sherbet... | | 17.00 |
| Stem, #3115, 9 oz. .................... | | 27.50 |
| Sugar cube tray........................ | | 175.00 |
| Sugar, DECAGON ..................... | 25.00 | 17.50 |
| Sugar, ftd................................ | 30.00 | 20.00 |
| Sugar sifter, ftd., 6¾" ............... | | 275.00 |
| Syrup pitcher, drip cut............... | | 150.00 |

# CLEO, Cambridge Glass Company, Introduced 1930

| | Blue | Pink/Green/Yellow/Amber |
|---|---|---|
| Syrup pitcher, glass lid .............. | | 165.00 |
| Toast & cover, round................... | | 350.00 |
| Tobacco humidor....................... | | 350.00 |
| Tray, 12", handled serving.......... | | 150.00 |
| Tray, 12", oval service DECAGON ............................ | 175.00 | 135.00 |
| Tray, creamer & sugar, oval ........ | | 50.00 |
| Tumbler, #3077, 2½ oz., ftd........ | 95.00 | 60.00 |
| Tumbler, #3077, 5 oz., ftd. ......... | 50.00 | 20.00 |
| Tumbler, #3077, 8 oz., ftd. ......... | 50.00 | 25.00 |
| Tumbler, #3077, 10 oz., ftd. ....... | 55.00 | 27.50 |

| | Blue | Pink/Green/Yellow/Amber |
|---|---|---|
| Tumbler, #3022, 12 oz., ftd. ........ | 75.00 | 35.00 |
| Tumbler, #3115, 2½ oz., ftd........ | | 50.00 |
| Tumbler, #3115, 5 oz., ftd. ......... | | 25.00 |
| Tumbler, #3115, 8 oz., ftd. ......... | | 25.00 |
| Tumbler, #3115, 10 oz., ftd. ........ | | 37.50 |
| Tumbler, #3115, 12 oz., ftd. ........ | | 35.00 |
| Tumbler, 12 oz., flat................... | | 35.00 |
| Vase, 5½"............................... | | 65.00 |
| Vase, 9½"............................... | | 110.00 |
| Vase, 11"............................... | | 130.00 |
| Wafer tray ................................. | | 225.00 |

# COLONY, Line #2412, Fostoria Glass Company, 1920's – 1970's

Colors: crystal; some yellow, blue, green, white amber, red in 1980's

Colony evolved from an earlier Fostoria pattern called Queen Ann, represented by the amber flat bowl shown in the middle of the bottom photograph. The candlesticks and oval bowl shown in the rear were made in the early 1980's under the name "Maypole."

Cream soups, cigarette boxes, 48 oz., ice lipped, pitcher, flat teas, and the 12" vase all persist in being hard to locate. Mint condition dinner plates (without scratched centers) also haunt collectors wanting perfect pieces. Otherwise this pattern was very durable and more of it seems to be emerging of late, a hopeful sign for collectors.

Red vases, candlesticks, and bowls being seen were a product of Viking made for Fostoria in the early 1980's. Do not be too surprised to see these again since Dalzell Viking is currently making red for Lancaster Colony who now owns the Fostoria name.

| | Crystal | | Crystal |
|---|---|---|---|
| Ash tray, 3", round | 7.00 | Comport, cover, 6½" | 35.00 |
| Ash tray, 3½" | 10.00 | Creamer, 3¼" indiv. | 6.50 |
| Ash tray, 4½", round | 12.50 | Creamer, 3¾" | 6.00 |
| Ash tray, 6", round | 17.50 | Cup, 6 oz., ftd. | 7.50 |
| Bowl, 2¾" ftd., almond | 15.00 | Cup, punch | 12.50 |
| Bowl, 4½", rnd. | 7.00 | Ice bucket | 65.00 |
| Bowl, 4¾", finger | 14.00 | Ice bucket, plain edge | 110.00 |
| Bowl, 4¾", hdld. | 8.00 | Lamp, electric | 135.00 |
| Bowl, 5", bonbon | 9.00 | Mayonnaise, 3 pc. | 35.00 |
| Bowl, 5", cream soup | 45.00 | Oil w/stopper, 4½ oz. | 37.50 |
| Bowl, 5", hdld. | 9.00 | Pitcher, 16 oz., milk | 70.00 |
| Bowl, 5½", sq. | 10.00 | Pitcher, 48 oz., ice lip | 190.00 |
| Bowl, 5¾", high ft. | 15.00 | Pitcher, 2 qt., ice lip | 100.00 |
| Bowl, 5", rnd. | 12.00 | Plate, ctr. hdld., sandwich | 27.50 |
| Bowl, 6", rose | 25.00 | Plate, 6", bread & butter | 4.00 |
| Bowl, 7", bonbon, 3 ftd. | 12.00 | Plate, 6½", lemon, hdld. | 12.00 |
| Bowl, 7", olive, oblong | 12.00 | Plate, 7", salad | 8.00 |
| Bowl, 7¾", salad | 22.50 | Plate, 8", luncheon | 10.00 |
| Bowl, 8", cupped | 32.50 | Plate, 9", dinner | 25.00 |
| Bowl, 8", hdld. | 32.50 | Plate, 10", hdld., cake | 22.00 |
| Bowl, 9", rolled console | 32.50 | Plate, 12", ftd., salver | 65.00 |
| Bowl, 9½", pickle | 15.00 | Plate, 13", torte | 27.50 |
| Bowl, 9¾", salad | 35.00 | Plate, 15", torte | 50.00 |
| Bowl, 10", fruit | 32.50 | Plate, 18", torte | 80.00 |
| Bowl, 10½", low ft. | 70.00 | Platter, 12" | 45.00 |
| Bowl, 10½", high ft. | 90.00 | Relish, 10½", hdld., 3 part | 20.00 |
| Bowl, 10½", oval | 30.00 | Salt, 2½" indiv. | 12.00 |
| Bowl, 10½", oval, 2 part | 32.50 | Salt & pepper, pr., 3⅝" | 12.50 |
| Bowl, 11", oval, ftd. | 37.50 | Saucer | 2.00 |
| Bowl, 11", flared | 35.00 | Stem, 3⅜", 4 oz., oyster cocktail | 12.00 |
| Bowl, 11½", celery | 30.00 | Stem, 3⅝", 5 oz., sherbet | 9.00 |
| Bowl, 13", console | 35.00 | Stem, 4", 3½ oz., cocktail | 11.00 |
| Bowl, 13¼", punch, ftd. | 350.00 | Stem, 4¼", 3¼ oz., wine | 25.00 |
| Bowl, 14", fruit | 40.00 | Stem, 5¼", 9 oz., goblet | 16.00 |
| Butter dish, ¼ lb. | 32.50 | Sugar, 2¾", indiv. | 6.00 |
| Candlestick, 3½" | 11.00 | Sugar, 3½" | 5.00 |
| Candlestick, 6½", double | 22.50 | Tray for indiv. sugar/cream | 10.00 |
| Candlestick, 7" | 20.00 | Tumbler, 3⅝", 5 oz., juice | 18.00 |
| Candlestick, 7½", w/8 prisms | 60.00 | Tumbler, 3⅞", 9 oz., water | 16.00 |
| Candlestick, 9" | 30.00 | Tumbler, 4⅞", 12 oz., tea | 25.00 |
| Candlestick, 9¾", w/prisms | 80.00 | Tumbler, 4½", 5 oz., ftd. | 13.00 |
| Candlestick, 14½", w/10 prisms | 150.00 | Tumbler, 5¾", 12 oz., ftd. | 17.00 |
| Candy w/cover, 6½" | 35.00 | Vase, 6", bud, flared | 14.00 |
| Candy, w/cover, ftd., ½ lb. | 65.00 | Vase, 7", cupped | 35.00 |
| Cheese & cracker | 50.00 | Vase, 7½", flared | 40.00 |
| Cigarette box | 40.00 | Vase, 9", cornucopia | 55.00 |
| Comport, 4" | 15.00 | Vase, 12", straight | 175.00 |

# CRYSTOLITE, Blank #1503, A.H. Heisey & Co.

Colors: crystal, Zircon/Limelight, Sahara and rare in amber

I am most often asked about the swan handled pitcher in this pattern which is extremely rare. You will never mistake it should you get the opportunity to see one! The cocktail shaker pictured here is missing from many collections. Crystolite is an easily recognized pattern and since most pieces are marked, you will rarely find a bargain. The cordial is the only stem shown. You won't see many of them either!

Additional pieces rarely seen are the 6" basket, rye bottle, and iced tea tumblers; but other items are also beginning to disappear. Don't hesitate on buying any of these pieces!

Although the punch set is not rare, it is a practical piece for people to use and display!

| | Crystal | | Crystal |
|---|---|---|---|
| Ash tray, 3½", square | 4.00 | Jar, covered cherry | 90.00 |
| Ash tray, 4½", square | 4.50 | Jam jar, w/cover | 50.00 |
| Ash tray, 5", w/book match holder | 25.00 | Ladle, glass, punch | 25.00 |
| Ash tray (coaster), 4", rnd. | 6.00 | Ladle, plastic | 7.50 |
| Basket, 6", hdld. | 400.00 | Mayonnaise, 5½", shell, 3 ft. | 32.00 |
| Bonbon, 7", shell | 17.00 | Mayonnaise, 6", oval, hdld. | 26.00 |
| Bonbon, 7½", 2 hdld. | 15.00 | Mayonnaise ladle | 9.00 |
| Bottle, 1 qt., rye, #107 stopper | 250.00 | Mustard & cover | 37.00 |
| Bottle, 4 oz., bitters, w/short tube | 175.00 | Oil bottle, 3 oz. | 40.00 |
| Bottle, 4 oz., cologne w/#108 stopper | 65.00 | Oil bottle, w/stopper, 2 oz. | 30.00 |
| w/drip stop | 150.00 | Oval creamer, sugar, w/tray, set | 47.50 |
| Bottle, syrup w/drip & cut top | 85.00 | Pitcher, ½ gallon, ice, blown | 110.00 |
| Bowl, 7½ quart, punch | 120.00 | Pitcher, 2 quart swan, ice lip | 700.00 |
| Bowl, 2", indiv. swan nut (or ash tray) | 18.00 | Plate, 7", salad | 9.00 |
| Bowl, 3", indiv. nut, hdld. | 15.00 | Plate, 7", shell | 24.00 |
| Bowl, 4½", dessert (or nappy) | 8.00 | Plate, 7", underliner for 1000 island dressing | |
| Bowl, 5", preserve | 12.00 | bowl | 10.00 |
| Bowl, 5", 1000 island dressing, ruffled top | 18.00 | Plate, 7½", coupe | 20.00 |
| Bowl, 5½", dessert | 12.00 | Plate, 8", oval, mayonnaise liner | 14.00 |
| Bowl, 6", oval jelly, 4 ft. | 16.00 | Plate, 8½", salad | 15.00 |
| Bowl, 6", preserve, 2 hdld. | 13.00 | Plate, 10½", dinner | 80.00 |
| Bowl, 7", shell praline | 35.00 | Plate, 11", ftd., cake salver | 300.00 |
| Bowl, 8", dessert (sauce) | 30.00 | Plate, 11", torte | 24.00 |
| Bowl, 8", 2 pt. conserve, hdld. | 16.00 | Plate, 12", sand. | 35.00 |
| Bowl, 9", leaf pickle | 20.00 | Plate, 13", shell torte | 75.00 |
| Bowl, 10", salad, rnd. | 47.50 | Plate, 14", sand. | 40.00 |
| Bowl, 11", w/attached mayonnaise (chip 'n dip) | 175.00 | Plate, 14", torte | 35.00 |
| Bowl, 12", gardenia, shallow | 30.00 | Plate, 20", buffet or punch liner | 100.00 |
| Bowl, 13", oval floral, deep | 30.00 | Puff box, w/cover, 4¾" | 60.00 |
| Candle block, 1-lite, sq. | 15.00 | Salad dressing set, 3 pc. | 38.00 |
| Candle block, 1-lite, swirl | 15.00 | Salt & pepper, pr. | 30.00 |
| Candlestick, 1-lite, ftd. | 15.00 | Saucer | 5.00 |
| Candlestick, 1-lite, w/#4233, 5", vase | 25.00 | Stem, 1 oz., cordial, wide optic, blown, #5003 | 120.00 |
| Candlestick, 2-lite | 25.00 | Stem, 3½ oz., cocktail, w.o., blown, #5003 | 20.00 |
| Candlestick, 2-lite, bobeche & 10 "D" prisms | 50.00 | Stem, 3½ oz., claret, w.o., blown, #5003 | 25.00 |
| Candlestick sans vase, 3-lite | 20.00 | Stem, 3½ oz., oyster cocktail, w.o. blown, #5003 | 18.00 |
| Candlestick w/#4233, 5", vase, 3-lite | 45.00 | Stem, 6 oz., sherbet/saucer champagne, #5003 | 14.00 |
| Candy, 6½", swan | 35.00 | Stem, 10 oz., water, #1503, pressed | 480.00 |
| Candy box, w/cover, 5½" | 50.00 | Stem, 10 oz., w.o., blown, #5003 | 24.00 |
| Candy box, w/cover, 7" | 55.00 | Sugar, indiv. | 15.00 |
| Cheese, 5½", ftd. | 20.00 | Sugar, reg. | 20.00 |
| Cigarette box, w/cover, 4" | 17.00 | Syrup pitcher, drip cut | 100.00 |
| Cigarette box, w/cover, 4½" | 20.00 | Tray, 5½", oval, liner indiv. creamer/sugar set | 40.00 |
| Cigarette holder, ftd. | 17.50 | Tray, 9", 4 pt., leaf relish | 25.00 |
| Cigarette holder, oval | 17.50 | Tray, 10", 5 pt., rnd. relish | 35.00 |
| Cigarette holder, rnd. | 17.50 | Tray, 12", 3 pt., relish | 25.00 |
| Cigarette lighter | 30.00 | Tray, 12", rect., celery | 35.00 |
| Coaster, 4" | 6.00 | Tray, 12", rect., celery/olive | 35.00 |
| Cocktail shaker, 1 qt. w/#1 strainer; #86 stopper | 250.00 | Tumbler, 5 oz., ftd., juice, w.o., blown, #5003 | 27.00 |
| Comport, 5", fed., deep, #5003, blown rare | 275.00 | Tumbler, 8 oz., pressed, #5003 | 60.00 |
| Creamer, indiv. | 17.00 | Tumbler, 10 oz., pressed | 70.00 |
| Creamer, reg. | 20.00 | Tumbler, 10 oz., iced tea, w.o., blown, #5003 | 30.00 |
| Cup | 20.00 | Tumbler, 12 oz., ftd., iced tea, w.o., blown #5003 | 24.00 |
| Cup, punch or custard | 7.00 | Urn, 7", flower | 75.00 |
| Hurricane block, 1-lite, sq. | 17.50 | Vase, 3", short stem | 20.00 |
| Hurricane block, w/#4061, 10" plain globe, | | Vase, 6", ftd. | 22.50 |
| 1-lite, sq. | 90.00 | Vase, 12" | 225.00 |
| Ice tub, w/silver plate handle | 75.00 | | |

# DECAGON, Cambridge Glass Company, 1930's – 1940's

Colors: green, pink, red, cobalt blue, amber, Moonlight blue, black

Cambridge had a plain pattern on which many of its famous etchings are found. That pattern is Decagon. Cleo, Rosalie, and Imperial Hunt Scene are better known than this Decagon blank on which they are etched! Some of the stems pictured are etched, but, Decagon pattern itself actually had no etching at all. The Royal blue (cobalt) and Moonlight blue are the colors most collected although others are more plentiful. Pattern availability is only one determining factor in collecting! Color plays another major role and blue usually wins out.

I need one blue relish insert to finish that tray pictured. An insert was broken ten years ago and I have never found another!

| | Pastel Colors | Red Blue | | Pastel Colors | Red Blue |
|---|---|---|---|---|---|
| Basket, 7", 2 hdld. (upturned sides) | 12.00 | 22.50 | Mayonnaise, w/liner & ladle | 18.00 | 80.00 |
| Bowl, bouillon, w/liner | 7.50 | 15.00 | Oil, 6 oz., tall, w/hdld. & stopper | 50.00 | 90.00 |
| Bowl, cream soup, w/liner | 10.00 | 27.50 | Plate, 6¼", bread/butter | 3.00 | 5.00 |
| Bowl, 2½", indiv., almond | 20.00 | 35.00 | Plate, 7", 2 hdld. | 9.00 | 15.00 |
| Bowl, 3¾", flat rim, cranberry | 15.00 | 20.00 | Plate, 7½" | 4.00 | 10.00 |
| Bowl, 3½" belled, cranberry | 15.00 | 20.00 | Plate, 8½", salad | 6.00 | 10.00 |
| Bowl, 5½", 2 hdld., bonbon | 10.00 | 17.00 | Plate, 9½", dinner | 25.00 | 35.00 |
| Bowl, 5½", belled, fruit | 5.50 | 10.00 | Plate, 10", grill | 8.00 | 14.00 |
| Bowl, 5¾", flat rim, fruit | 6.00 | 11.00 | Plate, 10", service | 25.00 | 30.00 |
| Bowl, 6", belled, cereal | 10.00 | 15.00 | Plate, 12½", service | 9.00 | 17.50 |
| Bowl, 6", flat rim, cereal | 10.00 | 15.00 | Relish, 6 inserts | 75.00 | 110.00 |
| Bowl, 6", ftd., almond | 22.00 | 40.00 | Salt dip, 1½", ftd. | 15.00 | 22.50 |
| Bowl, 6¼", 2 hdld., bonbon | 10.00 | 17.00 | Sauce boat & plate | 45.00 | 75.00 |
| Bowl, 8½", flat rim, soup "plate" | 12.50 | 25.00 | Saucer | 1.00 | 2.50 |
| Bowl, 9", rnd., veg. | 14.00 | 24.00 | Server, center hdld. | 12.00 | 20.00 |
| Bowl, 9", 2 pt., relish | 9.00 | 15.00 | Stem, 1 oz., cordial | 40.00 | 65.00 |
| Bowl, 9½", oval, veg. | 12.00 | 27.50 | Stem, 3½ oz., cocktail | 12.00 | 20.00 |
| Bowl, 10", berry | 12.00 | 20.00 | Stem, 6 oz., low sherbet | 9.00 | 15.00 |
| Bowl, 10½", oval, veg. | 17.50 | 30.00 | Stem, 6 oz., high sherbet | 10.00 | 20.00 |
| Bowl, 11", rnd. veg. | 17.00 | 30.00 | Stem, 9 oz., water | 15.00 | 30.00 |
| Bowl, 11", 2 pt., relish | 10.00 | 17.50 | Sugar, lightning bolt handles | 7.00 | 12.00 |
| Comport, 5¾" | 12.50 | 20.00 | Sugar, ftd. | 9.00 | 20.00 |
| Comport, 6½", low ft. | 15.00 | 25.00 | Sugar, scalloped edge | 9.00 | 20.00 |
| Comport, 7", tall | 20.00 | 35.00 | Sugar, tall, lg. ft. | 8.00 | 18.00 |
| Creamer, ftd. | 9.00 | 20.00 | Tray, 8", 2 hdld., flat pickle | 10.00 | 17.00 |
| Creamer, scalloped edge | 8.00 | 18.00 | Tray, 9", pickle | 10.00 | 17.50 |
| Creamer, lightning bolt handles | 7.00 | 12.00 | Tray, 11", oval, service | 8.00 | 15.00 |
| Creamer, tall, lg. ft. | 10.00 | 22.00 | Tray, 11", celery | 10.00 | 20.00 |
| Cup | 6.00 | 10.00 | Tray, 12", center handled | 15.00 | 25.00 |
| French dressing bottle, "Oil/Vinegar" | 65.00 | 95.00 | Tray, 12", oval, service | 10.00 | 20.00 |
| Gravy boat, w/2 hdld. liner (like spouted cream soup) | 70.00 | 110.00 | Tray, 13", 2 hdld., service | 20.00 | 30.00 |
| Ice bucket | 35.00 | 60.00 | Tray, 15", oval, service | 20.00 | 40.00 |
| Ice tub | 30.00 | 45.00 | Tumbler, 2½ oz., ftd. | 15.00 | 25.00 |
| Mayonnaise, 2 hdld., w/2 hdld. liner and ladle | 25.00 | 40.00 | Tumbler, 5 oz., ftd. | 10.00 | 18.00 |
| | | | Tumbler, 8 oz., ftd. | 12.00 | 22.00 |
| | | | Tumbler, 10 oz., ftd. | 15.00 | 25.00 |
| | | | Tumbler, 12 oz., ftd. | 20.00 | 35.00 |

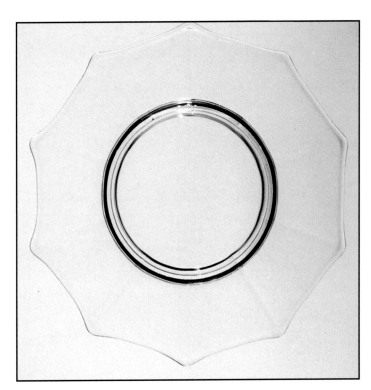

# "DEERWOOD" or "BIRCH TREE," U.S. Glass Company, Late 1920's – Early 1930's

Colors: light amber, green, pink, black, crystal

See the Black Forest pattern shot if you confuse these two patterns. Deer and trees are the dominant theme of Deerwood, whereas Black Forest depicts moose and trees.

More black Deerwood is being found, and prices being asked for it are running up to fifty percent more than the pink. It will take a little while to see how much black is actually available. Several pieces are shown this time. Notice how the gold decorated pieces really make the pattern stand out!

The flat, three-part pink candy looks more like a Paden City blank than it does U.S. Glass. There is no mayonnaise listed although I have had several reports of one. It was listed in old catalogues as a whipped cream pail instead of a mayonnaise. Terminology of the old glass companies often differs.

There is some catalogue documentation for Deerwood which is not the case with Black Forest. All the information for Black Forest is from measuring actual pieces! If you know of other pieces, please send documentation.

| | Black | Amber | Green | Pink |
|---|---|---|---|---|
| Bowl, 10", straight edge | | | | 35.00 |
| Bowl, 12", console | | | 55.00 | 55.00 |
| Bowl, 10", footed | 100.00 | | | |
| Cake plate, low pedestal | | | 55.00 | 55.00 |
| Candlestick, 2½" | 50.00 | | 35.00 | |
| Candlestick, 4" | | | | 45.00 |
| Candy dish, w/cover, 3 part, flat | | | | 85.00 |
| Candy jar, w/cover, ftd. cone | | | 90.00 | 90.00 |
| Celery, 12" | | | 50.00 | |
| Cheese and cracker | | | 75.00 | 75.00 |
| Comport, 10", low, ftd., flared | | | | 45.00 |
| Creamer, 2 styles | 60.00 | | 40.00 | 40.00 |
| Cup | | | | 65.00 |
| Plate, 5½" | | | 12.00 | 12.00 |
| Plate, 7½", salad | | | | 22.00 |
| Plate, 9½", dinner | | | | 60.00 |
| Saucer | | | | 17.50 |
| Server, center hdld. | | | 40.00 | 40.00 |
| Stem, 2 oz., wine, 4½" | | | | 30.00 |
| Stem, 6 oz., sherbet, 4¾" | | | 27.50 | |
| Stem, 6 oz., cocktail, 5" | | | 32.50 | |
| Stem, 9 oz., water, 7" | | | 40.00 | |
| Sugar, 2 styles | 60.00 | | 40.00 | 40.00 |
| Tumbler, 9 oz. | | | 37.50 | 37.50 |
| Tumbler, 12 oz., tea, 5½" | | 45.00 | | |
| Vase, 7", sweet pea, rolled edge | | | 75.00 | 75.00 |
| Vase, 10", ruffled top | | | 90.00 | 80.00 |
| Whipped cream pail, w/ladle | | | 45.00 | 45.00 |
| Vase, 12", 2 handles | 110.00 | | | |

## U.S. Glass Company, Late 1920's – Early 1930's, "DEERWOOD" or "BIRCH TREE"

# DIANE, Cambridge Glass Company, 1934 – Early 1950's

Colors: crystal; some pink, yellow, blue, Heatherbloom, Emerald green, amber, Crown Tuscan

Diane is one Cambridge pattern that we have had difficulty capturing on film. Too, one of the problems for new collectors is identifying pieces in the pictures. This time we tried a few shelf shots. Some items pictured on the shelf are also in the group set-ups. I hope identifying the shelf pieces will help item identification problems.

You can collect a set of Diane in crystal, but collecting a set in any color will be nearly impossible unless you get lucky enough to find a set in one place. Many collectors of crystal accent their sets with an occasional colored piece. The gold decorated Crown Tuscan pieces shown at the bottom of page 88 are sought both by Diane collectors and by connoisseurs of the Crown Tuscan color. A few pieces of dark Emerald green, blue, and Heatherbloom have surfaced; but I have been unable to find a saucer in Heatherbloom for my lonely cup or a bottom for my dark Emerald green candy lid.

Note the martini pitcher or cocktail beverage mixer in the top photo on page 89. The decanter set in the Faberware holders on the tray is an unusual find! You normally find these in color, but not in an etched Cambridge line.

Row 1: bitters bottle, oil bottle, Regency stems (ftd. juice, wine, tall sherbet, and water goblet).
Row 2: #3122: juice tumbler, water tumbler, cordial, pousse cafe, cocktail, tall sherbet, wine, water goblet.
Row 3: #1066 cordial, #3106 cordial, #3130 wine, cigarette urn, #3779 comport, marmalade, 5" globe vase.
Row 4: #3122 finger bowl w/liner; #3400 sugar, butter, and creamer, cocktail icer.
Row 5: #3400 plate, 4 ftd. oval bowl, #498 10 oz. tumbler, #3400 80 oz. pitcher.

| | Crystal | | Crystal |
|---|---|---|---|
| Basket, 6", 2 hdld., ftd. | 16.00 | Comport, 5½" | 25.00 |
| Bottle, bitters | 125.00 | Comport, 5⅜", blown | 35.00 |
| Bowl, #3106, finger, w/liner | 30.00 | Creamer | 14.00 |
| Bowl, #3122 | 25.00 | Creamer, indiv. #3500 (pie crust edge) | 15.00 |
| Bowl, #3400, cream soup, w/liner | 27.50 | Creamer, indiv. #3900, scalloped edge | 15.00 |
| Bowl, 5", berry | 20.00 | Creamer, scroll handle, #3400 | 15.00 |
| Bowl, 5¼" 2 hdld., bonbon | 18.00 | Cup | 20.00 |
| Bowl, 6", 2 hdld., ftd., bonbon | 17.00 | Decanter, ball | 185.00 |
| Bowl, 6", 2 pt., relish | 18.00 | Decanter, lg. ftd. | 165.00 |
| Bowl, 6", cereal | 25.00 | Decanter, short ft., cordial | 195.00 |
| Bowl, 6½", 3 pt. relish | 20.00 | Hurricane lamp, candlestick base | 115.00 |
| Bowl, 7", 2 hdld., ftd., bonbon | 22.00 | Hurricane lamp, keyhole base w/prisms | 195.00 |
| Bowl, 7", 2 pt., relish | 20.00 | Ice bucket, w/chrome hand | 65.00 |
| Bowl, 7", relish or pickle | 22.00 | Mayonnaise, div., w/liner & ladles | 40.00 |
| Bowl, 9", 3 pt., celery or relish | 30.00 | Mayonnaise (sherbet type w/ladle) | 32.50 |
| Bowl, 9½", pickle (like corn) | 22.00 | Mayonnaise, w/liner, ladle | 35.00 |
| Bowl, 10", 4 ft., flared | 40.00 | Oil, 6 oz., w/stopper | 115.00 |
| Bowl, 10", baker | 40.00 | Pitcher, ball | 145.00 |
| Bowl, 11", 2 hdld. | 35.00 | Pitcher, Doulton | 300.00 |
| Bowl, 11", 4 ftd. | 40.00 | Pitcher, martini | 600.00 |
| Bowl, 11½" tab hdld., ftd. | 40.00 | Pitcher, upright | 165.00 |
| Bowl, 12", 3 pt., celery & relish | 32.50 | Plate, 6", 2 hdld., plate. | 7.00 |
| Bowl, 12", 4 ft. | 40.00 | Plate, 6", sq., bread/butter | 5.00 |
| Bowl, 12", 4 ft., flared | 40.00 | Plate, 6½", bread/butter | 5.00 |
| Bowl, 12", 4 ft., oval | 42.00 | Plate, 8", 2 hdld., ftd., bonbon | 11.00 |
| Bowl, 12", 4 ft., oval, w/"ears" hdld. | 50.00 | Plate, 8", salad | 10.00 |
| Bowl, 12", 5 pt., celery & relish | 32.50 | Plate, 8½" | 11.00 |
| Butter, rnd. | 120.00 | Plate, 10½", dinner | 65.00 |
| Cabinet flask | 225.00 | Plate, 12", 4 ft., service | 35.00 |
| Candelabrum, 2-lite, keyhole | 22.50 | Plate, 13", 4 ft., torte | 35.00 |
| Candelabrum, 3-lite, keyhole | 32.50 | Plate, 13½", 2 hdld. | 30.00 |
| Candlestick, 1-lite, keyhole | 17.50 | Plate, 14", torte | 40.00 |
| Candlestick, 5" | 17.50 | Platter, 13½" | 70.00 |
| Candlestick, 6", 2-lite, "fleur-de-lis" | 30.00 | Salt & pepper, ftd., w/glass tops, pr. | 32.00 |
| Candlestick, 6", 3-lite | 35.00 | Salt & pepper, pr., flat | 28.00 |
| Candy box, w/cover, rnd. | 77.50 | Saucer | 5.00 |
| Cigarette urn | 42.50 | Stem, #1066, 1 oz., cordial | 55.00 |
| Cocktail shaker, glass top | 135.00 | Stem, #1066, 3 oz., cocktail | 16.00 |
| Cocktail shaker, metal top | 90.00 | Stem, #1066, 3 oz., wine | 25.00 |
| Cocktail icer, 2 pc. | 60.00 | Stem, #1066, 3½ oz., tall cocktail | 17.50 |

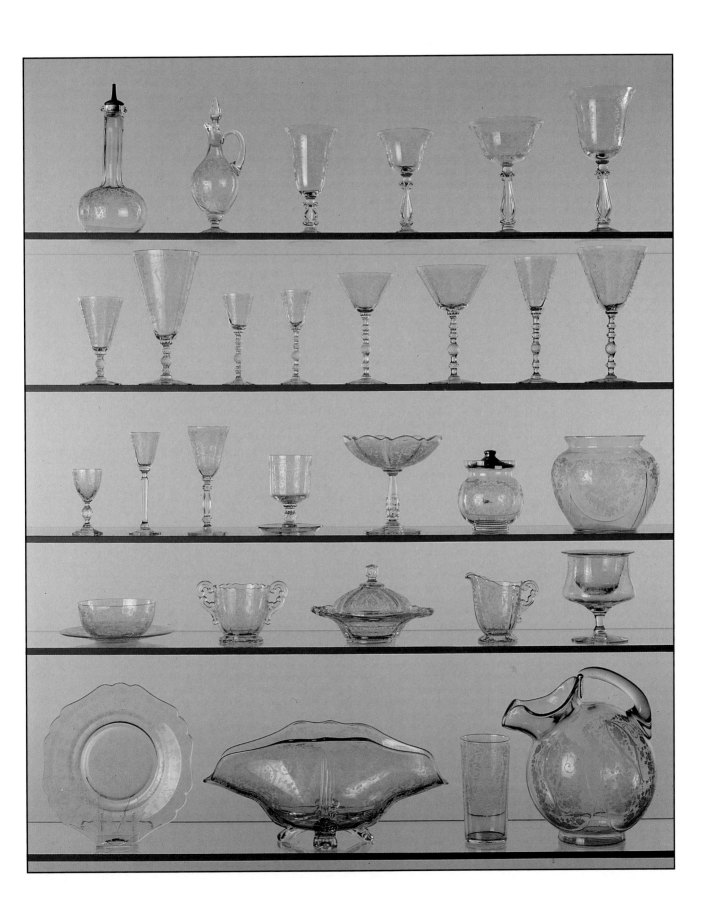

## DIANE, Cambridge Glass Company, 1934 – Early 1950's (continued)

| | Crystal |
|---|---|
| Stem, #1066, 4½ oz., claret | 35.00 |
| Stem, #1066, 5 oz., oyster/cocktail | 12.00 |
| Stem, #1066, 7 oz., low sherbet | 11.50 |
| Stem, #1066, 7 oz., tall sherbet | 13.50 |
| Stem, #1066, 11 oz., water | 20.00 |
| Stem, #3122, 1 oz., cordial | 55.00 |
| Stem, #3122, 2½ oz., wine | 25.00 |
| Stem, #3122, 3 oz., cocktail | 14.00 |
| Stem, #3122, 4½ oz., claret | 35.00 |
| Stem, #3122, 4½ oz., oyster/cocktail | 15.00 |
| Stem, #3122, 7 oz., low sherbet | 11.00 |
| Stem, #3122, 7 oz., tall sherbet | 15.00 |
| Stem, #3122, 9 oz., water goblet | 20.00 |
| Sugar, indiv., #3500 (pie crust edge) | 13.00 |
| Sugar, indiv., #3900, scalloped edge | 13.00 |
| Sugar, scroll handle, #3400 | 14.00 |
| Tumbler, 2½ oz., sham bottom | 40.00 |
| Tumbler, 5 oz., ft., juice | 27.00 |
| Tumbler, 5 oz., sham bottom | 30.00 |
| Tumbler, 7 oz., old-fashioned, w/sham bottom | 40.00 |
| Tumbler, 8 oz., ft. | 22.00 |
| Tumbler, 10 oz., sham bottom | 30.00 |
| Tumbler, 12 oz., sham bottom | 32.00 |
| Tumbler, 13 oz. | 30.00 |

| | Crystal |
|---|---|
| Tumbler, 14 oz., sham bottom | 37.50 |
| Tumbler, #1066, 3 oz. | 20.00 |
| Tumbler, #1066, 5 oz., juice | 12.50 |
| Tumbler, #1066, 9 oz., water | 12.00 |
| Tumbler, #1066, 12 oz., tea | 20.00 |
| Tumbler, #3106, 3 oz., ftd. | 17.50 |
| Tumbler, #3106, 5 oz., ftd., juice | 13.00 |
| Tumbler, #3106, 9 oz., ftd., water | 11.00 |
| Tumbler, #3106, 12 oz., ftd., tea | 20.00 |
| Tumbler, #3122, 2½ oz. | 27.50 |
| Tumbler, #3122, 5 oz., juice | 13.00 |
| Tumbler, #3122, 9 oz., water | 15.00 |
| Tumbler, #3122, 12 oz., tea | 17.00 |
| Tumbler, #3135, 2½ oz., ftd., bar | 30.00 |
| Tumbler, #3135, 10 oz., ftd., tumbler | 14.00 |
| Tumbler, #3135, 12 oz., ftd., tea | 25.00 |
| Vase, 5", globe | 30.00 |
| Vase, 6", high ft., flower | 35.00 |
| Vase, 8", high ft., flower | 50.00 |
| Vase, 9", keyhole base | 55.00 |
| Vase, 10", bud | 45.00 |
| Vase, 11", flower | 60.00 |
| Vase, 11", ped. ft., flower | 65.00 |
| Vase, 12", keyhole base | 75.00 |
| Vase, 13", flower | 95.00 |

Note: See Page 228-229 for stem identification.

# ELAINE, Cambridge Glass Company, 1934 – 1950's

Colors: crystal

New collectors often confuse this with Chantilly; look closely at these patterns so you can tell them apart. (Chantilly has a thick scroll, whereas Elaine's is thin and angled.) This is an elegant pattern and easily started, since there is little competition for it at the moment.

| | Crystal |
|---|---|
| Basket, 6", 2 hdld. (upturned sides) | 15.00 |
| Bowl, #3104, finger, w/liner | 27.50 |
| Bowl, 5¼", 2 hdld., bonbon | 13.00 |
| Bowl, 6", 2 hdld., ftd., bonbon | 16.00 |
| Bowl, 6", 2 pt., relish | 16.00 |
| Bowl, 6½", 3 pt., relish | 15.00 |
| Bowl, 7", 2 pt., pickle or relish | 16.00 |
| Bowl, 7", ftd., tab hdld. bonbon | 27.00 |
| Bowl, 7", pickle or relish | 20.00 |
| Bowl, 9", 3 pt., celery & relish | 25.00 |
| Bowl, 9½", pickle (like corn dish) | 22.00 |
| Bowl, 10", 3 ftd., flared | 30.00 |
| Bowl, 11", tab hdld. | 30.00 |
| Bowl, 11½", ftd., tab hdld. | 30.00 |
| Bowl, 12", 3 pt., celery & relish | 30.00 |
| Bowl, 12", 4 ftd., flared | 35.00 |
| Bowl, 12", 4 ftd., oval, "ear" hdld. | 40.00 |
| Bowl, 12", 5 pt. celery & relish | 37.50 |
| Candlestick, 5" | 17.50 |
| Candlestick, 6", 2-lite | 27.50 |
| Candlestick, 6", 3-lite | 35.00 |
| Candy box, w/cover, rnd. | 75.00 |
| Cocktail icer, 2 pc. | 55.00 |
| Comport, 5½" | 30.00 |
| Comport, 5⅜", #3500 stem | 39.00 |
| Comport, 5⅜", blown | 40.00 |
| Creamer (several styles) | 11.00 |
| Creamer, indiv. | 12.00 |
| Cup | 20.00 |
| Decanter, lg., ftd. | 175.00 |
| Hat, 9" | 275.00 |
| Hurricane lamp, candlestick base | 115.00 |
| Hurricane lamp, keyhole ft., w/prisms | 185.00 |
| Ice bucket, w/chrome handle | 60.00 |
| Mayonnaise (cupped "sherbet" w/ladle) | 25.00 |
| Mayonnaise (div. bowl, liner, 2 ladles) | 37.50 |
| Mayonnaise, w/liner & ladle | 30.00 |
| Oil, 6 oz., hdld., w/stopper | 65.00 |
| Pitcher, ball | 135.00 |
| Pitcher, Doulton | 295.00 |
| Pitcher, upright | 185.00 |
| Plate, 6", 2 hdld. | 10.00 |
| Plate, 6½", bread/butter | 7.00 |
| Plate, 8", 2 hdld., ftd. | 15.00 |
| Plate, 8", salad | 15.00 |
| Plate, 8", tab hdld., bonbon | 15.00 |
| Plate, 10½", dinner | 65.00 |
| Plate, 11½" 2 hdld., ringed "Tally Ho" sand. | 25.00 |
| Plate, 12", 4 ftd., service | 25.00 |
| Plate, 13", 4 ftd., torte | 30.00 |
| Plate, 13½", tab hdld., cake | 30.00 |
| Plate, 14", torte | 30.00 |
| Salt & pepper, flat, pr. | 27.50 |

| | Crystal |
|---|---|
| Salt & pepper, ftd., pr | 30.00 |
| Salt & pepper, hdld., pr | 35.00 |
| Saucer | 3.00 |
| Stem, #1402, 1 oz., cordial | 57.50 |
| Stem, #1402, 3 oz., wine | 25.00 |
| Stem, #1402, 3½ oz., cocktail | 20.00 |
| Stem, #1402, 5 oz., claret | 27.50 |
| Stem, #1402, low sherbet | 14.00 |
| Stem, #1402, tall sherbet | 15.00 |
| Stem, #1402, goblet | 20.00 |
| Stem, #3104, (very tall stems), ¾ oz., brandy | 135.00 |
| Stem, #3104, 1 oz., cordial | 135.00 |
| Stem, #3104, 1 oz., pousse-cafe | 135.00 |
| Stem, #3104, 2 oz., sherry | 100.00 |
| Stem, #3104, 2½ oz., creme de menthe | 100.00 |
| Stem, #3104, 3 oz., wine | 90.00 |
| Stem, #3104, 3½ oz., cocktail | 60.00 |
| Stem, #3104, 4½ oz., claret | 75.00 |
| Stem, #3104, 5 oz., roemer | 75.00 |
| Stem, #3104, 5 oz., tall hock | 70.00 |
| Stem, #3104, 7 oz., tall sherbet | 60.00 |
| Stem, #3104, 9 oz., goblet | 95.00 |
| Stem, #3121, 1 oz., cordial | 57.50 |
| Stem, #3121, 3 oz., cocktail | 22.00 |
| Stem, #3121, 3½ oz., wine | 30.00 |
| Stem, #3121, 4½ oz., claret | 30.00 |
| Stem, #3121, 4½ oz., oyster cocktail | 15.00 |
| Stem, #3121, 5 oz., parfait, low stem | 25.00 |
| Stem, #3121, 6 oz., low sherbet | 15.00 |
| Stem, #3121, 6 oz., tall sherbet | 17.50 |
| Stem, #3121, 10 oz., water | 21.00 |
| Stem, #3500, 1 oz., cordial | 57.50 |
| Stem, #3500, 2½ oz., wine | 27.50 |
| Stem, #3500, 3 oz., cocktail | 20.00 |
| Stem, #3500, 4½ oz., claret | 30.00 |
| Stem, #3500, 4½ oz., oyster cocktail | 14.00 |
| Stem, #3500, 5 oz., parfait, low stem | 23.00 |
| Stem, #3500, 7 oz., low sherbet | 13.00 |
| Stem, #3500, 7 oz., tall sherbet | 15.00 |
| Stem, #3500, 10 oz., water | 20.00 |
| Sugar (several styles) | 10.00 |
| Sugar, indiv. | 12.00 |
| Tumbler, #1402, 9 oz., ftd., water | 17.00 |
| Tumbler, #1402, 12 oz., tea | 27.50 |
| Tumbler, #1402, 12 oz., tall ftd., tea | 27.50 |
| Tumbler, #3121, 5 oz., ftd., juice | 19.00 |
| Tumbler, #3121, 10 oz., ftd., water | 20.00 |
| Tumbler, #3121, 12 oz., ftd., tea | 25.00 |
| Tumbler, #3500, 5 oz., ftd., juice | 17.00 |
| Tumbler, #3500, 10 oz., ftd., water | 18.00 |
| Tumbler, #3500, 12 oz., ftd., tea | 27.50 |
| Vase, 6", ftd. | 35.00 |
| Vase, 8", ftd. | 45.00 |
| Vase, 9", keyhole, ftd. | 55.00 |

Note: see Pages 228-229 for stem identification.

# EMPRESS, Blank #1401, A.H. Heisey & Co.

Colors: "Flamingo" pink, "Sahara" yellow, "Moongleam" green, cobalt and "Alexandrite"; some Tangerine

I have included a shelf shot of Empress in Alexandrite. Notice that crystal is no longer priced here. You will find crystal prices listed under the name Queen Ann. When the colors were made, this pattern was called Empress; but when crystal was added later, the name was changed to Queen Ann.

Row 1: 9" vase, 7" candlestick, 6" square plate, 8" square plate
Row 2: Nut dish, 6" mint, 11" floral bowl, cup and saucer
Row 3: Ash tray, sugar, creamer, mayonnaise w/ladle
Row 4: 7" round plate, shaker, 10" celery tray, shaker, 7" 3-part relish

| | Flam. | Sahara | Moon. | Cobalt | Alexan. |
|---|---|---|---|---|---|
| Ash tray. | 85.00 | 60.00 | 200.00 | 250.00 | 210.00 |
| Bonbon, 6" | 20.00 | 25.00 | 30.00 | | |
| Bowl, cream soup | 26.00 | 27.00 | 35.00 | | 65.00 |
| Bowl, cream soup, w/sq. liner | 25.00 | 30.00 | 45.00 | | 165.00 |
| Bowl, frappe, w/center | 45.00 | 60.00 | 75.00 | | |
| Bowl, nut, dolphin ftd., indiv. | 22.00 | 26.00 | 32.00 | | 125.00 |
| Bowl, 4½", nappy | 8.00 | 10.00 | 12.50 | | |
| Bowl, 5", preserve, 2 hdld. | 18.00 | 22.00 | 27.50 | | |
| Bowl, 6", ftd., jelly, 2 hdld. | 17.00 | 23.00 | 27.50 | | |
| Bowl, 6", dolp. ftd., mint | 20.00 | 25.00 | 30.00 | | 165.00 |
| Bowl, 6", grapefruit, sq. top, grnd. bottom | 12.50 | 15.00 | 22.50 | | |
| Bowl, 6½", oval, lemon, w/cover | 65.00 | 75.00 | 90.00 | | |
| Bowl, 7", 3 pt., relish, triplex | 40.00 | 30.00 | 45.00 | | 225.00 |
| Bowl, 7", 3 pt., relish, ctr. hand. | 45.00 | 50.00 | 75.00 | | |
| Bowl, 7½", dolp. ftd., nappy | 60.00 | 65.00 | 75.00 | 275.00 | 325.00 |
| Bowl, 7½", dolp. ftd., nasturtium | 120.00 | 120.00 | 130.00 | 325.00 | 400.00 |
| Bowl, 8", nappy | 30.00 | 35.00 | 40.00 | | |
| Bowl, 8½", ftd., floral, 2 hdld | 40.00 | 50.00 | 65.00 | | |
| Bowl, 9", floral, rolled edge | 32.00 | 38.00 | 42.00 | | |
| Bowl, 9", floral, flared | 70.00 | 75.00 | 90.00 | | |
| Bowl, 10", 2 hdld., oval dessert | 45.00 | 60.00 | 65.00 | | |
| Bowl, 10", lion head, floral | 550.00 | 550.00 | 700.00 | | |
| Bowl, 10", oval, veg. | 35.00 | 45.00 | 55.00 | | |
| Bowl, 10", square, salad, 2 hdld. | 40.00 | 55.00 | 65.00 | | |
| Bowl, 10", triplex, relish | 45.00 | 55.00 | 65.00 | | |
| Bowl, 11", dolphin ftd., floral | 60.00 | 60.00 | 90.00 | 400.00 | 500.00 |
| Bowl, 13", pickle/olive, 2 pt. | 18.00 | 30.00 | 32.00 | | |
| Bowl, 15", dolp. ftd., punch | 800.00 | 850.00 | 1,000.00 | | |
| Candlestick, low, 4 ftd., w/2 hdld. | 35.00 | 40.00 | 45.00 | | |
| Candlestick, 6", dolphin ftd. | 115.00 | 100.00 | 120.00 | 260.00 | 265.00 |
| Candy, w/cover, 6", dolphin ftd. | 120.00 | 150.00 | 200.00 | 360.00 | |
| Comport, 6", ftd. | 50.00 | 55.00 | 65.00 | | |
| Comport, 6", square | 70.00 | 75.00 | 85.00 | | |
| Comport, 7", oval | 60.00 | 66.00 | 75.00 | | |
| Compotier, 6", dolphin ftd. | 250.00 | 200.00 | 250.00 | | |
| Creamer, dolphin ftd. | 35.00 | 30.00 | 42.50 | | 215.00 |
| Creamer, indiv. | 30.00 | 35.00 | 40.00 | | 210.00 |
| Cup | 27.00 | 31.00 | 36.00 | | 100.00 |
| Cup, after dinner | 50.00 | 50.00 | 60.00 | | |
| Cup, bouillon, 2 hdld. | 25.00 | 25.00 | 30.00 | | |
| Cup, 4 oz., custard or punch | 25.00 | 28.00 | 30.00 | | |
| Cup, #1401½, has rim as demi-cup | 28.00 | 32.00 | 40.00 | | |
| Grapefruit, w/square liner | 25.00 | 30.00 | 35.00 | | |
| Ice tub, w/metal handles | 95.00 | 100.00 | 135.00 | | |
| Jug, 3 pint, ftd. | 175.00 | 200.00 | 225.00 | | |

| | Flam. | Sahara | Moon. | Cobalt | Alexan. |
|---|---|---|---|---|---|
| Jug, flat ............................................................ | | | 165.00 | | |
| Marmalade, w/cover, dolphin ftd. ................. | 70.00 | 80.00 | 95.00 | | |
| Mayonnaise, 5½", ftd. with ladle.................... | 50.00 | 55.00 | 65.00 | | 350.00 |
| Mustard, w/cover.......................................... | 75.00 | 70.00 | 85.00 | | |
| Oil bottle, 4 oz............................................... | 100.00 | 120.00 | 130.00 | | |
| Plate............................................................... | 7.00 | 10.00 | 12.00 | | |
| Plate, bouillon liner...................................... | 9.00 | 13.00 | 15.00 | | 20.00 |
| Plate, 4½"...................................................... | 6.00 | 6.00 | 8.00 | | |
| Plate, 6"......................................................... | 11.00 | 14.00 | 16.00 | | 35.00 |
| Plate, 6", square........................................... | 10.00 | 13.00 | 15.00 | | 30.00 |
| Plate, 7"......................................................... | 12.00 | 15.00 | 17.00 | | 40.00 |
| Plate, 7", square........................................... | 12.00 | 15.00 | 17.00 | 55.00 | 45.00 |
| Plate, 8", square........................................... | 18.00 | 22.00 | 35.00 | 70.00 | 65.00 |
| Plate, 8"......................................................... | 16.00 | 20.00 | 24.00 | 70.00 | 65.00 |
| Plate, 9"......................................................... | 25.00 | 35.00 | 40.00 | | |
| Plate, 10½"..................................................... | 100.00 | 100.00 | 125.00 | | |
| Plate, 10½", square....................................... | 100.00 | 100.00 | 125.00 | | 175.00 |
| Plate, 12"....................................................... | 45.00 | 55.00 | 65.00 | | |
| Plate, 12", muffin, sides upturned................. | 50.00 | 60.00 | 70.00 | | |
| Plate, 12", sandwich, 2 hdld......................... | 35.00 | 40.00 | 50.00 | | 165.00 |
| Plate, 13", hors d'oeuvre, 2 hdld. ................. | 40.00 | 45.00 | 55.00 | | |
| Plate, 13", square, 2 hdld............................. | 40.00 | 45.00 | 55.00 | | |
| Platter, 14"..................................................... | 35.00 | 40.00 | 47.50 | | |
| Salt & pepper, pr. ......................................... | 100.00 | 110.00 | 135.00 | | 400.00 |
| Saucer, square.............................................. | 8.00 | 14.00 | 16.00 | | 25.00 |
| Saucer, after dinner...................................... | 7.00 | 10.00 | 10.00 | | |
| Saucer........................................................... | 8.00 | 14.00 | 16.00 | | 25.00 |
| Stem, 2½ oz., oyster cocktail ........................ | 20.00 | 25.00 | 30.00 | | |
| Stem, 4 oz., saucer champagne ..................... | 35.00 | 40.00 | 60.00 | | |
| Stem, 4 oz., sherbet....................................... | 22.00 | 28.00 | 35.00 | | |
| Stem, 9 oz., Empress stemware, unusual........ | 55.00 | 65.00 | 75.00 | | |
| Sugar, indiv. .................................................. | 30.00 | 35.00 | 40.00 | | 210.00 |
| Sugar, dolphin ftd., 3 hdld. .......................... | 35.00 | 30.00 | 27.00 | | 210.00 |
| Tray, condiment & liner for indiv. sugar/creamer........................................ | 40.00 | 30.00 | 45.00 | | |
| Tray, 10", 3 pt., relish................................... | 25.00 | 30.00 | 35.00 | | |
| Tray, 10", 7 pt., hors d'oeuvre....................... | 160.00 | 150.00 | 200.00 | | |
| Tray, 10", celery............................................ | 16.00 | 22.00 | 26.00 | | 150.00 |
| Tray, 12", ctr. hdld., sand. ........................... | 48.00 | 57.00 | 65.00 | | |
| Tray, 12", sq. ctr. hdld., sand. ...................... | 52.00 | 60.00 | 67.50 | | |
| Tray, 13", celery............................................ | 20.00 | 24.00 | 30.00 | | |
| Tray, 16", 4 pt., buffet relish ......................... | 75.00 | 75.00 | 86.00 | | |
| Tumbler, 8 oz., dolphin ftd., unusual ............ | 125.00 | 150.00 | 195.00 | | |
| Tumbler, 8 oz., grnd. bottom ......................... | 40.00 | 35.00 | 39.50 | | |
| Tumbler, 12 oz., tea, grnd. bottom.................. | 45.00 | 40.00 | 50.00 | | |
| Vase, 8", flared............................................. | 80.00 | 90.00 | 105.00 | | |
| Vase, 9", ftd................................................... | 110.00 | 110.00 | 160.00 | | 725.00 |

# FAIRFAX NO. 2375, Fostoria Glass Company, 1927 – 1944

Colors: blue, Azure blue, Orchid, amber, Rose, green, Topaz; some Ruby, black, and Wisteria

Fairfax is the Fostoria blank on which many of the most popular Fostoria etchings are found, notably June, Versailles, and Trojan. Most collectors do not get as excited about this #2375 line without an etching. Azure blue (shown on page 97) and Orchid (illustrated on top of page 98) are the most collected colors. While I am referring to page 98, I should point out that I have placed a pink vase and two Wisteria cordials in the photo to show the difference between those colors and Orchid.

Fairfax collectors have a choice of stems. In the photo at the top of page 97 are stem and tumbler line #5299; this is more commonly found in yellow with the Trojan etch. The other stem line, #5298, is shown in the bottom photo and it is generally used for Versailles and June etchings. Some collectors are mixing the stem lines; but tumblers are more difficult to mix because they have different shapes. The #5299 tumblers are more cone-shaped than the #5298, which are rounded.

You might notice the amber covered candy on page 98, located behind the butter dish in the bottom photograph. There is a cutting on this piece that technically makes it not Fairfax. I point that out to save a few letters over the next two years from readers with magnifiers looking for errors. (I kid you not!)

Due to confusion among collectors and dealers alike, I have shown the various Fostoria stems on page 99 so that differences in shapes can be seen. The claret and high sherbets are major concerns. Each is 6" high. Notice that the claret is shaped like the wine. Note, too, the parfait is taller than the juice!

| | Rose, Blue, Orchid | Amber | Green, Topaz |
|---|---|---|---|
| Ash tray, 2½" | 15.00 | 7.50 | 10.00 |
| Ash tray, 4" | 17.50 | 10.00 | 12.50 |
| Ash tray, 5½" | 20.00 | 13.00 | 17.50 |
| Baker, 9", oval | 25.00 | 15.00 | 20.00 |
| Baker, 10½", oval | 35.00 | 20.00 | 22.50 |
| Bonbon | 12.50 | 9.00 | 10.00 |
| Bottle, salad dressing | 155.00 | 65.00 | 75.00 |
| Bouillon, ftd. | 11.00 | 7.00 | 8.00 |
| Bowl, 9", lemon, 2 hdld. | 12.00 | 6.00 | 7.00 |
| Bowl, sweetmeat | 15.00 | 10.00 | 12.00 |
| Bowl, 5", fruit | 12.00 | 5.00 | 6.00 |
| Bowl, 6", cereal | 20.00 | 9.00 | 11.00 |
| Bowl, 7", soup | 25.00 | 12.00 | 14.00 |
| Bowl, 8", rnd., nappy | 27.50 | 13.00 | 14.00 |
| Bowl, lg., hdld., dessert | 25.00 | 12.00 | 14.00 |
| Bowl, 12" | 25.00 | 15.00 | 18.00 |
| Bowl, 12", centerpiece | 25.00 | 17.50 | 20.00 |
| Bowl, 13", oval, centerpiece | 30.00 | 20.00 | 22.50 |
| Bowl, 15", centerpiece | 35.00 | 20.00 | 24.00 |
| Butter dish, w/cover | 135.00 | 80.00 | 90.00 |
| Candlestick, flattened top | 15.00 | 10.00 | 10.00 |
| Candlestick, 3" | 12.50 | 9.00 | 10.00 |
| Celery, 11½" | 20.00 | 12.00 | 14.00 |
| Cheese & cracker set (2 styles) | 35.00 | 20.00 | 22.50 |
| Cigarette box | 25.00 | 18.00 | 22.00 |
| Comport, 5" | 15.00 | 15.00 | 17.00 |
| Comport, 7" | 25.00 | 10.00 | 12.00 |
| Cream soup, ftd. | 20.00 | 9.00 | 8.00 |
| Creamer, flat | | 10.00 | 12.00 |
| Creamer, ftd. | 11.00 | 7.00 | 9.00 |
| Creamer, tea | 17.50 | 7.00 | 9.00 |
| Cup, after dinner | 22.00 | 10.00 | 12.50 |
| Cup, flat | | 4.00 | 6.00 |
| Cup, ftd. | 8.00 | 6.00 | 7.00 |
| Flower holder, oval, window box | 60.00 | 22.00 | 30.00 |
| Grapefruit | 30.00 | 15.00 | 20.00 |
| Grapefruit liner | 25.00 | 12.00 | 15.00 |
| Ice bucket | 50.00 | 30.00 | 35.00 |
| Ice bowl | 15.00 | 12.00 | 10.00 |
| Ice bowl liner | 20.00 | 12.00 | * 10.00 |
| Mayonnaise | 15.00 | 9.00 | 10.00 |
| Mayonnaise ladle | 35.00 | 20.00 | 25.00 |
| Mayonnaise liner, 7" | 5.00 | 3.00 | 3.50 |
| Nut cup, blown | 25.00 | 15.00 | 20.00 |
| Oil, ftd. | 135.00 | 80.00 | 90.00 |

| | Rose, Blue, Orchid | Amber | Green, Topaz |
|---|---|---|---|
| Pickle, 8½" | 18.00 | 7.00 | 9.00 |
| Pitcher, #5000 | 200.00 | 110.00 | 130.00 |
| Plate, canape | 15.00 | 10.00 | 10.00 |
| Plate, whipped cream | 11.00 | 8.00 | 9.00 |
| Plate, 6", bread/butter | 3.00 | 2.00 | 2.50 |
| Plate, 7½", salad | 5.00 | 3.00 | 3.50 |
| Plate, 7½", cream soup or mayonnaise liner | 6.00 | 4.00 | 4.50 |
| Plate, 8¾", salad | 10.00 | 4.50 | 5.00 |
| Plate, 9½", luncheon | 15.00 | 6.00 | 7.00 |
| Plate, 10¼", dinner | 40.00 | 17.00 | 25.00 |
| Plate, 10¼", grill | 32.00 | 15.00 | 22.00 |
| Plate, 10", cake | 17.50 | 13.00 | 15.00 |
| Plate, 12", bread, oval | 40.00 | 25.00 | 27.50 |
| Plate, 13", chop | 20.00 | 14.00 | 16.00 |
| Platter, 10½", oval | 32.00 | 17.00 | 20.00 |
| Platter, 12", oval | 37.50 | 20.00 | 25.00 |
| Platter, 15", oval | 65.00 | 27.00 | 35.00 |
| Relish, 3 part, 8½" | 15.00 | 10.00 | 12.00 |
| Relish, 11½" | 18.00 | 11.00 | 13.00 |
| Sauce boat | 40.00 | 20.00 | 25.00 |
| Sauce boat liner | 15.00 | 9.00 | 10.00 |
| Saucer, after dinner | 6.00 | 4.00 | 5.00 |
| Saucer | 4.00 | 2.50 | 3.00 |
| Shaker, ftd., pr | 55.00 | 30.00 | 35.00 |
| Shaker, indiv., ftd., pr | | 20.00 | 25.00 |
| Stem, 4", ¾ oz., cordial | 60.00 | 25.00 | 35.00 |
| Stem, 4¼", 6 oz., low sherbet | 18.00 | 9.00 | 11.00 |
| Stem, 5¼", 3 oz., cocktail | 24.00 | 12.00 | 18.00 |
| Stem, 5½", 3 oz., wine | 30.00 | 18.00 | 22.50 |
| Stem, 6", 4 oz., claret | 37.50 | 25.00 | 27.50 |
| Stem, 6", 6 oz., high sherbet | 20.00 | 10.00 | 12.50 |
| Stem, 8¼", 10 oz., water | 30.00 | 16.00 | 20.00 |
| Sugar, flat | 27.50 | 10.00 | 12.00 |
| Sugar, ftd. | 10.00 | 6.00 | 8.00 |
| Sugar cover | 30.00 | 20.00 | 22.50 |
| Sugar pail | 45.00 | 25.00 | 30.00 |
| Sugar, tea | 17.50 | 6.00 | 8.00 |
| Tray, 11", ctr. hdld. | 20.00 | 12.00 | 15.00 |
| Tumbler, 2½ oz., ftd. | 22.00 | 10.00 | 12.00 |
| Tumbler, 4½", 5 oz., ftd. | 18.00 | 10.00 | 11.00 |
| Tumbler, 5¼", 9 oz., ftd. | 20.00 | 12.00 | 13.00 |
| Tumbler, 6", 12 oz., ftd. | 25.00 | 13.50 | 18.00 |
| Vase, 8" (2 styles) | 60.00 | 35.00 | 45.00 |
| Whipped cream pail | 45.00 | 25.00 | 30.00 |

* Green $20.00

See page 99 for stem identification

# FOSTORIA STEMS AND SHAPES

**Top Row: Left to Right**
1. Water, 10 oz., 8¼"
2. Claret, 4 oz., 6"
3. Wine, 3 oz., 5½"
4. Cordial, ¾ oz., 4"
5. Sherbet, low, 6 oz., 4¼"
6. Cocktail, 3 oz., 5¼"
7. Sherbet, high, 6 oz., 6"

**Bottom Row: Left to Right**
1. Grapefruit and liner
2. Ice tea tumbler, 12 oz., 6"
3. Water tumbler, 9 oz., 5¼"
4. Parfait, 6 oz., 5¼"
5. Juice tumbler, 5 oz., 4½"
6. Oyster cocktail, 5½ oz.
7. Bar tumbler, 2½ oz.

# FIRST LOVE, Duncan & Miller Glass Company, 1937

Color: crystal

First Love by Duncan & Miller is their best known etching! There were several mould lines incorporated into making this extensive pattern. They include #30 (Pall Mall), #111 (Terrace), #115 (Canterbury), #117 (Three Feathers), #126 (Venetian), #5111½ (Terrace blown stemware). I have included four catalogue pages (104-107) that should show you examples of each of these mould lines as well as one page showing the different stemware.

Thanks again to the First Love collectors and dealers in Duncan glass who helped me compile and price this list. Any additional pieces or pricing contributions that you have, please let me know!

| | Crystal | | Crystal |
|---|---|---|---|
| Ash tray, 3½" sq., #111 | 17.50 | Candy, 6½", w/5" lid, #115 | 65.00 |
| Ash tray, 3½" x 2½", #30 | 16.50 | Carafe, w/stopper, water, #5200 | 120.00 |
| Ash tray, 5" x 3", #12, club | 35.00 | Cheese stand, 3" x 5¼", #111 | 25.00 |
| Ash tray, 5" x 3¼", #30 | 24.00 | Cheese stand, 5¾" x 3½", #115 | 25.00 |
| Ash tray, 6½" x 4¼", #30 | 35.00 | Cigarette box w/lid, 4" x 4¼" | 32.00 |
| Basket, 9¼" x 10" x 7¼", #115 | 135.00 | Cigarette box w/lid, 4½" x 3½", #30 | 35.00 |
| Basket,10" x 4¼" x 7", oval hdld., #115 | 145.00 | Cigarette box w/lid, 4¾" x 3¾" | 35.00 |
| Bottle, oil w/stopper, 8", #5200 | 60.00 | Cocktail shaker, 14 oz., #5200 | 110.00 |
| Bowl, 3" x 5", rose, #115 | 40.00 | Cocktail shaker, 16 oz., #5200 | 110.00 |
| Bowl, 4" x 1½" finger, #30 | 32.00 | Cocktail shaker, 32 oz., #5200 | 135.00 |
| Bowl, 4¼", finger, #5111½ | 35.00 | Comport w/lid, 8¾" x 5½", #111 | 110.00 |
| Bowl, 6" x 2½", oval, olive, #115 | 25.00 | Comport, 3½"x 4¾"W, #111 | 30.00 |
| Bowl, 6¾" x 4¼", ftd., flared rim, #111 | 30.00 | Comport, 5" x 5½", flared rim, #115 | 32.00 |
| Bowl, 7½" x 3", 3 pt., ftd., #117 | 35.00 | Comport, 5¼" x 6¾", flat top, #115 | 32.00 |
| Bowl, 8" sq. x 2½", hdld., #111 | 55.00 | Comport, 6" x 4¾", low #115 | 37.50 |
| Bowl, 8½" x 4", #115 | 37.50 | Creamer, 2½", individual, #115 | 18.00 |
| Bowl, 9" x 4½", ftd., #111 | 42.00 | Creamer, 3", 10 oz., #111 | 18.00 |
| Bowl, 9½" x 2½", hdld., #111 | 45.00 | Creamer, 3¾", 7 oz., #115 | 15.00 |
| Bowl, 10" x 3¾", ftd., flared rim, #111 | 55.00 | Creamer, sugar w/butter pat lid, | |
| Bowl, 10" x 4½", #115 | 45.00 | breakfast set, #28 | 60.00 |
| Bowl, 10½" x 5", crimped, #115 | 44.00 | Cruet, #25 | 90.00 |
| Bowl, 10½" x 7" x 7", #126 | 60.00 | Cruet, #30 | 90.00 |
| Bowl, 10¾" x 4¾" #115 | 42.50 | Cup, #115 | 18.00 |
| Bowl, 11" x 1 ¾", #30 | 55.00 | Decanter w/stopper, 16 oz., #5200 | 115.00 |
| Bowl, 11" x 3¼", flared rim, #111 | 62.50 | Decanter w/stopper, 32 oz., #30 | 135.00 |
| Bowl, 11" x 5¼", flared rim, #6 | 67.50 | Decanter w/stopper, 32 oz., #5200 | 135.00 |
| Bowl, 11½" x 8¼", oval, #115 | 45.00 | Hat, 4½", #30 | 300.00 |
| Bowl, 12" x 3½", #6 | 65.00 | Hat, 5½" x 8½" x 6¼", #30 | 300.00 |
| Bowl, 12" x 3¼", flared, #115 | 60.00 | Honey dish, 5" x 3", #91 | 25.00 |
| Bowl, 12" x 4" x 7½", oval, #117 | 65.00 | Ice bucket, 6", #30 | 85.00 |
| Bowl, 12½", flat, ftd., #126 | 70.00 | Lamp, hurricane, w/prisms, 15", #115 | 135.00 |
| Bowl, 13" x 3¼" x 8¾", oval, flared, | | Lamp shade only, #115 | 100.00 |
| #115 | 55.00 | Lid for candy urn, #111 | 35.00 |
| Bowl, 13" x 7" x 9¼", #126 | 67.50 | Mayonnaise, 4¾" x 4½", div. w/7½" | |
| Bowl, 13" x 7", #117 | 62.50 | underplate | 35.00 |
| Bowl, 14" x 7½" x 6", oval, #126 | 65.00 | Mayonnaise, 5¼" x 3", div. w/6½" plate, | |
| Box, candy w/lid, 4¾" x 6¼" | 55.00 | #115 | 35.00 |
| Butter or cheese, 7" sq. x 1¼", #111 | 115.00 | Mayonnaise, 5½" x 2½", ftd., hdld., | |
| Candelabra, 2-lite, #41 | 35.00 | #111 | 35.00 |
| Candelabrum, 6", 2-lite w/prisms, #30 | 55.00 | Mayonnaise, 5½" x 2¾", #115 | 35.00 |
| Candle, 3", 1-lite, #111 | 25.00 | Mayonnaise, 5½" x 3½", crimped, #11 | 32.00 |
| Candle, 3", low, #115 | 25.00 | Mayonnaise, 5¾" x 3", w/dish hdld. | |
| Candle, 3½", #115 | 25.00 | tray, #111 | 35.00 |
| Candle, 4", cornucopia, #117 | 25.00 | Mayonnaise, w/7" tray hdld. #111 | 35.00 |
| Candle, 4", low, #111 | 25.00 | Mustard w/lid & underplate | 57.50 |
| Candle, 5¼", 2-lite, globe, #30 | 30.00 | Nappy, 5" x 1", w/bottom star, #25 | 20.00 |
| Candle, 6", 2-lite, #30 | 30.00 | Nappy, 5" x 1¾", one hdld., #115 | 18.00 |
| Candy box, 6" x 3½", 3 hdld., 3 pt., | | Nappy, 5½" x 2", div., hdld., #111 | 18.00 |
| w/lid, #115 | 60.00 | Nappy, 5½" x 2", one hdld., heart, #115 | 28.00 |
| Candy box, 6" x 3½", 3 pt., w/lid, | | Nappy, 6" x 1¾", hdld., #111 | 22.00 |
| crown finial, #106 | 67.50 | Perfume tray, 8" x 5", #5200 | 25.00 |
| Candy jar, 5" x 7¼", w/lid, ftd., #25 | 67.50 | Perfume, 5", #5200 | 67.50 |

A PAIR OF

# Duncan

HURRICANES

. . . *a gift that looks like*
*a million dollars*

HURRICANE CANDELABRA with hand-cut
and polished imported prisms are breath-
taking . . . but with the lacy First Love
etching on the hurricane shade they
are irresistible.

These Hurricane Candelabra are made
by the makers of "the loveliest glassware in America." Many pieces of
Duncan glass are now collector's items
and are in antique shows.

If your department store or jewelry
or gift shops do not have the Duncan
First Love Hurricane Candelabra, they
will be glad to order them for you.
There is also a full line of stemware
and flatware and decorative pieces with
the same etching. Write for the First
Love folder.

*The loveliest glassware in America*

THE DUNCAN & MILLER GLASS COMPANY

WASHINGTON, PA.

# FIRST LOVE, Duncan & Miller Glass Company, 1937 (continued)

| | Crystal |
|---|---|
| Pitcher, #5200 | 135.00 |
| Pitcher, 9", 80 oz., ice lip, #5202 | 145.00 |
| Plate, 6", #111 | 12.00 |
| Plate, 6", #115 | 12.00 |
| Plate, 6", hdld. lemon, #111 | 14.00 |
| Plate, 6", sq., #111 | 14.00 |
| Plate, 7", #111 | 17.50 |
| Plate, 7½", #111 | 18.00 |
| Plate, 7½", #115 | 18.00 |
| Plate, 7½", mayonnaise liner, hdld. #115 | 15.00 |
| Plate, 7½", sq., #111 | 19.00 |
| Plate, 7½", 2 hdld., #115 | 19.00 |
| Plate, 8½", #30 | 20.00 |
| Plate, 8½", #111 | 20.00 |
| Plate, 8½", #115 | 20.00 |
| Plate, 11", #111 | 47.50 |
| Plate, 11", 2 hdld., sandwich #115 | 30.00 |
| Plate, 11", hdld., #111 | 40.00 |
| Plate, 11", hdld., cracker w/ring #115 | 40.00 |
| Plate, 11", hdld., cracker w/ring, #111 | 40.00 |
| Plate, 11", hdld., sandwich, #111 | 40.00 |
| Plate, 11¼", dinner, #115 | 55.00 |
| Plate, 12", egg, #30 | 115.00 |
| Plate, 12", torte, rolled edge, #111 | 40.00 |
| Plate, 13", torte, flat edge, #111 | 50.00 |
| Plate, 13", torte, rolled edge, #111 | 57.50 |
| Plate, 13¼", torte, #111 | 57.50 |
| Plate, 13½", cake, hdld., #115 | 50.00 |
| Plate, 14", #115 | 50.00 |
| Plate, 14", cake, #115 | 50.00 |
| Plate, 14½", cake, lg. base, #30 | 50.00 |
| Plate, 14½", cake, sm. base, #30 | 50.00 |
| Relish, 6" x 1¾", hdld., 2 pt., #111 | 20.00 |
| Relish, 6" x 1¾", hdld., 2 pt., #115 | 20.00 |
| Relish, 8" x 4½", pickle, 2 pt., #115 | 25.00 |
| Relish, 8", 3 pt., hdld., #115 | 25.00 |
| Relish, 9" x 1½", 2 pt. pickle, #115 | 25.00 |
| Relish, 9" x 1½", 3 hdld, 3 pt., #115 | 32.50 |
| Relish, 9" x 1½", 3 hdld., flared, #115 | 32.50 |
| Relish, 10", 5 pt. tray, #30 | 60.00 |
| Relish, 10½" x 1½", hdld., 5 pt., #111 | 70.00 |
| Relish, 10½" x 1¼", 2 hdld, 3 pt., #115 | 57.50 |
| Relish, 10½" x 7", #115 | 37.50 |
| Relish, 11¾", tray, #115 | 45.00 |
| Relish, 12", 4 pt., hdld., #111 | 40.00 |
| Relish, 12", 5 pt., hdld., #111 | 50.00 |
| Salt and pepper pr., #30 | 30.00 |
| Salt and pepper pr., #115 | 40.00 |
| Sandwich tray, 12" x 5¼", ctr. handle, #115 | 80.00 |
| Saucer, #115 | 8.50 |
| Stem, 3¾", 1 oz., cordial, #5111½ | 60.00 |
| Stem, 3¾", 4½ oz., oyster cocktail, #5111½ | 22.50 |
| Stem, 4", 5 oz., ice cream, #5111½ | 14.00 |
| Stem, 4¼", 3 oz., cocktail, #115 | 22.50 |
| Stem, 4½", 3½ oz., cocktail, #5111½ | 22.50 |
| Stem, 5", 5 oz., saucer champagne, #5111½ | 18.00 |

| | Crystal |
|---|---|
| Stem, 5¼", 3 oz., wine, #5111½ | 32.50 |
| Stem, 5¼", 5 oz., ftd. juice, #5111½ | 24.00 |
| Stem, 5¾", 10 oz., low luncheon goblet #5111½ | 17.50 |
| Stem, 6", 4½ oz., claret, #5111½ | 45.00 |
| Stem, 6½", 12 oz., ftd. ice tea, #5111½ | 32.50 |
| Stem, 6¾", 10 oz., tall water goblet, #5111½ | 24.00 |
| Stem, 6¾", 14 oz., ftd. ice tea, #5111½ | 35.00 |
| Stem, cordial, #111 | 17.50 |
| Sugar, 2½", individual, #115 | 14.00 |
| Sugar, 3", 7 oz., #115 | 14.00 |
| Sugar, 3", 10 oz., #111 | 15.00 |
| Tray, 8" x 2", hdld. celery, #111 | 17.50 |
| Tray, 8" x 4¾", individual sug/cr. #115 | 17.50 |
| Tray, 8¾", celery, #91 | 30.00 |
| Tray, 11", celery, #91 | 40.00 |
| Tumbler, 2", 1½ oz., whiskey, #5200 | 52.50 |
| Tumbler, 2½" x 3⅜", sham, Teardrop, ftd. | 57.50 |
| Tumbler, 3", sham, #5200 | 32.50 |
| Tumbler, 4¾", 10 oz., sham, #5200 | 37.50 |
| Tumbler, 5½", 12 oz., sham, #5200 | 37.50 |
| Tumbler, 6", 14 oz., sham, #5200 | 37.50 |
| Tumbler, 8 oz., flat, #115 | 30.00 |
| Urn, 4½" x 4½", #111 | 27.50 |
| Urn, 4½" x 4½", #115 | 27.50 |
| Urn, 4¾", rnd ft. | 27.50 |
| Urn, 5", #525 | 35.00 |
| Urn, 5½", ring hdld, sq. ft. | 57.50 |
| Urn, 5½", sq. ft. | 35.00 |
| Urn, 6½", sq. hdld. | 67.50 |
| Urn, 7", #529 | 37.50 |
| Vase, 4", flared rim, #115 | 25.00 |
| Vase, 4½" x 4¾", #115 | 25.00 |
| Vase, 5" x 5", crimped, #115 | 30.00 |
| Vase, 6", #507 | 55.00 |
| Vase, 8" x 4¾", cornucopia, #117 | 65.00 |
| Vase, 8", ftd., #506 | 90.00 |
| Vase, 8", ftd., #507 | 90.00 |
| Vase, 8½" x 2¾", #505 | 95.00 |
| Vase, 8½" x 6", #115 | 90.00 |
| Vase, 9" x 4½", #505 | 95.00 |
| Vase, 9", #509 | 90.00 |
| Vase, 9", bud, #506 | 80.00 |
| Vase, 9½" x 3½", #506 | 100.00 |
| Vase, 10" x 4¾", #5200 | 90.00 |
| Vase, 10", #507 | 95.00 |
| Vase, 10, ftd., #111 | 110.00 |
| Vase, 10", ftd., #505 | 110.00 |
| Vase, 10", ftd., #506 | 110.00 |
| Vase, 10½" x 12 x 9½", #126 | 135.00 |
| Vase, 10½", #126 | 125.00 |
| Vase, 11" x 5¼", #505 | 135.00 |
| Vase, 11½ x 4½", #506 | 135.00 |
| Vase, 12", flared #115 | 135.00 |
| Vase, 12", ftd., #506 | 135.00 |
| Vase, 12", ftd., #507 | 135.00 |

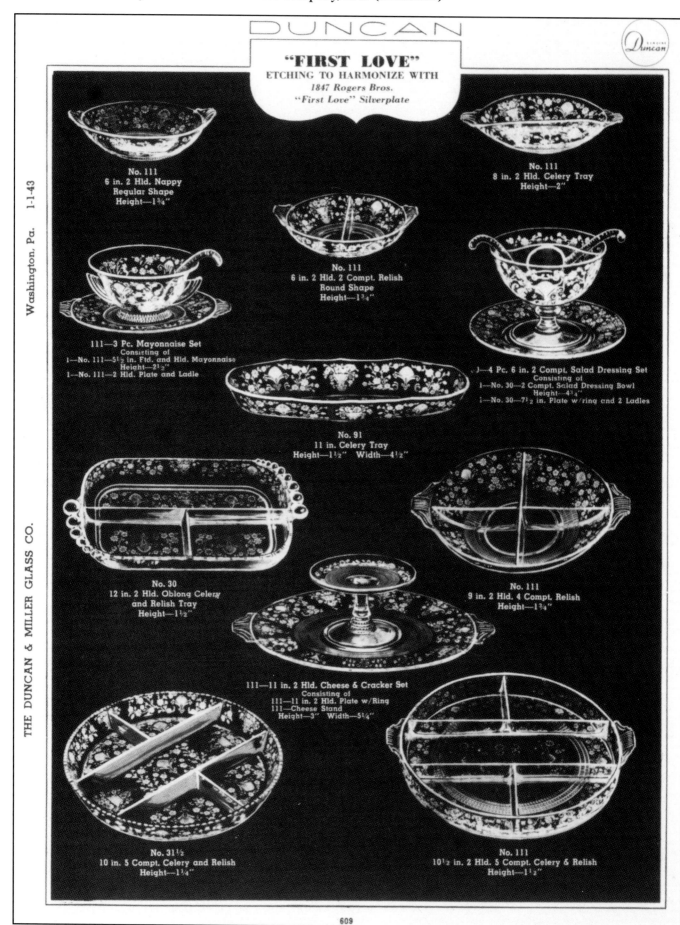

DUNCAN

**"FIRST LOVE"**
ETCHING TO HARMONIZE WITH
*1847 Rogers Bros.*
*"First Love" Silverplate*

No. 111
6 in. 2 Hld. Nappy
Regular Shape
Height—1¾"

No. 111
8 in. 2 Hld. Celery Tray
Height—2"

No. 111
6 in. 2 Hld. 2 Compt. Relish
Round Shape
Height—1¾"

111—3 Pc. Mayonnaise Set
Consisting of
1—No. 111—5½ in. Ftd. and Hld. Mayonnaise
Height—2½"
1—No. 111—2 Hld. Plate and Ladle

—4 Pc. 6 in. 2 Compt. Salad Dressing Set
Consisting of
1—No. 30—2 Compt. Salad Dressing Bowl
Height—4½"
1—No. 30—7½ in. Plate w/ring and 2 Ladles

No. 91
11 in. Celery Tray
Height—1½"  Width—4½"

No. 30
12 in. 2 Hld. Oblong Celery
and Relish Tray
Height—1½"

No. 111
9 in. 2 Hld. 4 Compt. Relish
Height—1¾"

111—11 in. 2 Hld. Cheese & Cracker Set
Consisting of
111—11 in. 2 Hld. Plate w/Ring
111—Cheese Stand
Height—3"  Width—5¼"

No. 31½
10 in. 5 Compt. Celery and Relish
Height—1¼"

No. 111
10½ in. 2 Hld. 5 Compt. Celery & Relish
Height—1½"

Washington, Pa.  1-1-43

THE DUNCAN & MILLER GLASS CO.

609

104

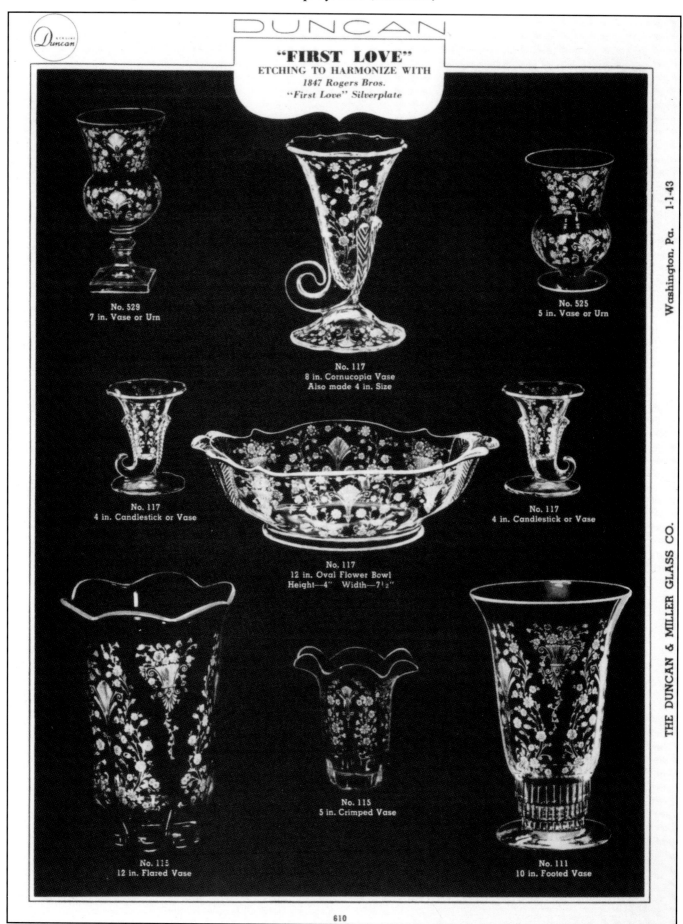

DUNCAN

Genuine *Duncan*

**"FIRST LOVE"**
ETCHING TO HARMONIZE WITH
1847 Rogers Bros.
*"First Love" Silverplate*

No. 529
7 in. Vase or Urn

No. 117
8 in. Cornucopia Vase
Also made 4 in. Size

No. 525
5 in. Vase or Urn

No. 117
4 in. Candlestick or Vase

No. 117
12 in. Oval Flower Bowl
Height—4"   Width—7½"

No. 117
4 in. Candlestick or Vase

No. 115
12 in. Flared Vase

No. 115
5 in. Crimped Vase

No. 111
10 in. Footed Vase

Washington, Pa.   1-1-43

THE DUNCAN & MILLER GLASS CO.

610

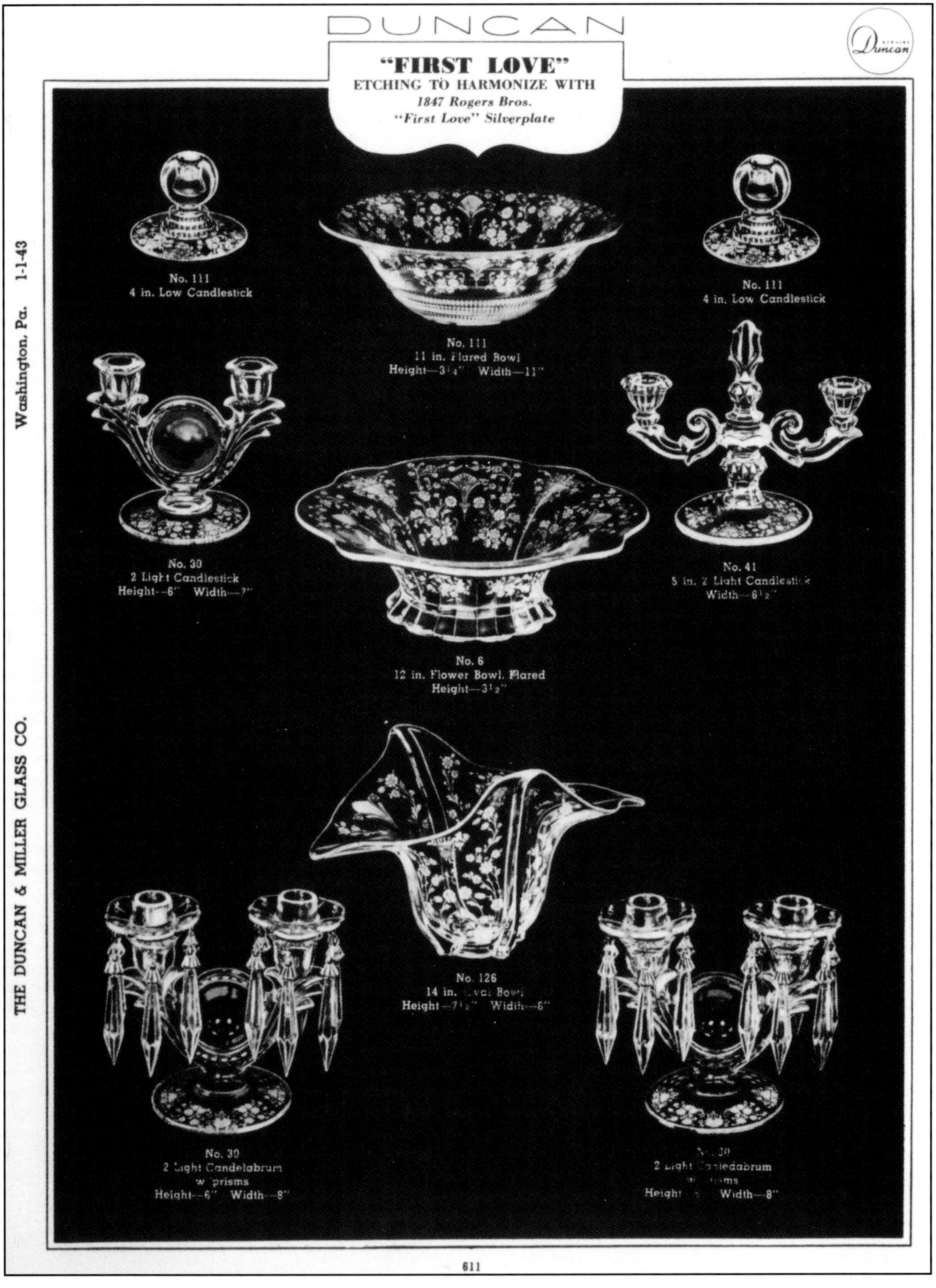

DUNCAN

**"FIRST LOVE"**
ETCHING TO HARMONIZE WITH
1847 Rogers Bros.
"First Love" Silverplate

Duncan

No. 111
4 in. Low Candlestick

No. 111
11 in. Flared Bowl
Height—3¼"  Width—11"

No. 111
4 in. Low Candlestick

No. 30
2 Light Candlestick
Height—6"  Width—7"

No. 6
12 in. Flower Bowl, Flared
Height—3½"

No. 41
5 in. 2 Light Candlestick
Width—8½"

No. 126
14 in. Oval Bowl
Height—7½"  Width—6"

No. 30
2 Light Candelabrum
w prisms
Height—6"  Width—8"

No. 30
2 Light Candelabrum
w prisms
Height—  Width—8"

Washington, Pa.  1-1-43

THE DUNCAN & MILLER GLASS CO.

611

# FLANDERS, Tiffin Glass Company, Mid 1910's – Mid 1930's

Colors: crystal, pink, yellow

Tiffin's Flanders is often confused with Cambridge's Gloria by collectors, and even some dealers. My mom was always confusing them in my shop. She called me in Florida last year to tell me about the pink Gloria pitcher that she had bought for me to photograph. When I got back to Kentucky, it turned out to be Flanders! Refer to Gloria to see the differences.

Stemware is normally found on Tiffin's #17024 blank. This line usually has a crystal foot and stem with tops of crystal, pink, or yellow. Other color combinations include green foot with pink stems, and pink tumblers as well as pitchers with crystal handle and foot. I have not seen many pieces with green stems. Round plates are line #8800 and each size plate has a different number. Scalloped plates are line #5831. Pitchers were sold both with and without a top. If you try to put a top on one of the pitchers sold without a top, you may be in for a surprise since many of the topless pitchers were curved in so much that a top will not fit. Remember that the pitcher cover is plain with no pattern etched on it.

Note the octagon shaped sandwich server in the bottom photograph. Several of these have surfaced in the last year. Shakers have been found in crystal and yellow, but none have been seen in pink. A pink, two handled bouillon has turned up and a crystal, Chinese type, hurricane lamp has been found. (See Fuchsia on page 111 for example.) Also, a 7¾" footed bowl, standing only 4¼" tall, has just been discovered in Texas.

| | Crystal | Pink | Yellow | | Crystal | Pink | Yellow |
|---|---|---|---|---|---|---|---|
| Bowl, 2 hdld., bouillon .... | 35.00 | 50.00 | 45.00 | Plate, 8" ........................... | 9.00 | 15.00 | 12.50 |
| Bowl, finger, w/liner........ | 20.00 | 50.00 | 35.00 | Plate, 10¼", dinner .......... | 30.00 | 70.00 | 50.00 |
| Bowl, 2 hdld., bonbon...... | 15.00 | 30.00 | 20.00 | Relish, 3 pt. ...................... | 25.00 | 50.00 | 40.00 |
| Bowl, 12", flanged rim, | | | | Salt & pepper, pr. ............. | 80.00 | | 135.00 |
| console ...................... | 30.00 | 65.00 | 40.00 | Saucer .............................. | 8.00 | 15.00 | 10.00 |
| Candlestick, 2 styles......... | 30.00 | 60.00 | 40.00 | Stem, claret ...................... | 40.00 | 110.00 | 70.00 |
| Candy jar, w/cover, flat .... | 100.00 | 300.00 | 200.00 | Stem, cordial..................... | 50.00 | 90.00 | 75.00 |
| Candy jar, w/cover, ftd. .... | 75.00 | 195.00 | 145.00 | Stem, cocktail ................... | 15.00 | 35.00 | 30.00 |
| Celery, 11" ........................ | 20.00 | 50.00 | 40.00 | Stem, oyster cocktail ........ | 12.00 | 30.00 | 20.00 |
| Cheese & cracker.............. | 35.00 | 95.00 | 75.00 | Stem, parfait..................... | 30.00 | 75.00 | 60.00 |
| Comport, 3½" .................... | 25.00 | 50.00 | 35.00 | Stem, saucer champagne.. | 15.00 | 30.00 | 20.00 |
| Comport, 6" ...................... | 50.00 | 110.00 | 80.00 | Stem, sherbet ................... | 10.00 | 25.00 | 17.50 |
| Creamer, flat..................... | 40.00 | 125.00 | 80.00 | Stem, water ...................... | 15.00 | 42.00 | 27.50 |
| Creamer, ftd. .................... | 35.00 | 110.00 | 65.00 | Stem, wine ....................... | 25.00 | 65.00 | 37.50 |
| Cup, 2 styles..................... | 35.00 | 65.00 | 50.00 | Sugar, flat ........................ | 40.00 | 120.00 | 75.00 |
| Decanter ........................... | 150.00 | 295.00 | 225.00 | Sugar, ftd.......................... | 35.00 | 105.00 | 60.00 |
| Grapefruit, w/liner............ | 30.00 | 80.00 | 50.00 | Tumbler, 2½ oz., ftd. ........ | 35.00 | 75.00 | 45.00 |
| Hurricane lamp, Chinese | | | | Tumbler, 9 oz., ftd., water.. | 12.00 | 35.00 | 20.00 |
| style.............................. | 135.00 | | | Tumbler, 10 oz., ftd........... | 15.00 | 40.00 | 25.00 |
| Mayonnaise, w/liner........ | 30.00 | 75.00 | 50.00 | Tumbler, 12 oz., ftd., tea... | 20.00 | 45.00 | 27.50 |
| Nut cup, ftd., blown ........ | 30.00 | 60.00 | 50.00 | Vase, bud ......................... | 30.00 | 75.00 | 45.00 |
| Oil bottle & stopper .......... | 125.00 | 275.00 | 200.00 | Vase, ftd........................... | 75.00 | 200.00 | 125.00 |
| Parfait, hdld. ..................... | 60.00 | 135.00 | 85.00 | Vase, Dahlia style.............. | 100.00 | 235.00 | 175.00 |
| Pitcher & cover ................. | 200.00 | 350.00 | 275.00 | Vase, fan .......................... | 75.00 | 185.00 | 110.00 |
| Plate, 6" ........................... | 4.00 | 12.00 | 9.00 | | | | |

# FUCHSIA, Tiffin Glass Company, Late 1937 – 1940

Colors: crystal

New items continue to surface in Fuchsia. It takes several serious collectors vying for the best set available to ensure that dealers will search every nook and cranny to keep their collections going. That is one of the reasons that new pieces are being discovered in Fuchsia.

There are now three stemware lines for Fuchsia. The normally found stem is #15083, unfortunately not shown in my photographs. If you have a stem that is not one of the types shown, it most likely will be #15083.

The other stemware lines are shown in the top photo. The cordial next to the water goblet has an "S" like stem #17457. Other stems found in this line are listed below. Another stemware line is represented by the goblet. This rounded top stem is part of line #17453. Unfortunately, my #17453 cocktail and saucer champagne did not arrive at our photography session intact. They couldn't be salvaged with glue. It's bad enough to break pieces during or after photography, but I do get upset if they get broken before we get them recorded for posterity! I found one small group of these in Atlanta several years ago. I do not know how readily they can be found. The footed finger bowl and a flat finger bowl are both shown in the foreground of the top picture. The three footed bowl with a ladle was called a whipped cream bowl by Tiffin. The cup and saucer are pictured in the bottom photo. As with all Tiffin patterns, cup and saucers are hard to find. I traded with a collector to obtain this set. Sometimes money can't buy what you want, but trades for items can oft times be worked out if you can find something that is needed by the other collector!

You can see the rarely seen cocktail shaker in *The Very Rare Glassware of the Depression Years* – 3rd Series.

You may find items not listed, so let me know what...with photographs and measurements, please!

| | Crystal | | Crystal |
|---|---|---|---|
| Ash tray, 2¼" x 3¾" w/cigarette rest | 20.00 | Plate, 10½", 2 hdld., cake, #5831 | 50.00 |
| Bell, 5", #15083 | 75.00 | Plate, 10½", muffin tray, pearl edge | 50.00 |
| Bowl, 4", finger, ftd., #041 | 45.00 | Plate, 13", lily roled and crimped edge | 60.00 |
| Bowl, 4½" finger, w/#8814 liner | 60.00 | Plate, 14¼", sandwich, #8833 | 40.00 |
| Bowl, 5³⁄₁₆", 2 hdld., #5831 | 25.00 | Relish, 6⅜", 3 pt., #5902 | 25.00 |
| Bowl, 6¼", cream soup, ftd., #5831 | 50.00 | Relish, 9¼", square, 3 pt. | 35.00 |
| Bowl, 7¼", salad, #5902 | 35.00 | Relish, 10½" x 12½", hdld., 3 pt., #5902 | 60.00 |
| Bowl, 8⅜", 2 hdld., #5831 | 50.00 | Relish, 10½" x 12½", hdld., 5 pt. | 70.00 |
| Bowl, 9¾", deep salad | 60.00 | Salt and pepper, pr., #2 | 95.00 |
| Bowl, 10", salad | 55.00 | Saucer, #5831 | 15.00 |
| Bowl, 10½", console, fan shaped sides, #319 | 60.00 | Stem, 4¹⁄₁₆", cordial, #15083 | 32.50 |
| Bowl, 11⅞", console, flared, 5902 | 75.00 | Stem, 4⅛", sherbet, #15083 | 12.00 |
| Bowl, 12", flanged rim, console #5831 | 55.00 | Stem, 4¼", cocktail, #15083 | 18.00 |
| Bowl, 12⅝", console, flared, #5902 | 85.00 | Stem, 4⅝", 3½ oz., cocktail, #17453 | 37.50 |
| Bowl, 13", crimped #5902 | 75.00 | Stem, 4⅞", saucer champagne, hollow stem | 65.00 |
| Candlestick, 2-lite, w/pointed center, #5831 | 60.00 | Stem, 5¹⁄₁₆", wine, #15083 | 30.00 |
| Candlestick, 2-lite, tapered center, #15306 | 60.00 | Stem, 5¼", claret, #15083 | 20.00 |
| Candlestick, 5", 2-lite, ball center | 60.00 | Stem, 5⅜", cocktail, "S" stem, #17457 | 45.00 |
| Candlestick, 5⅝, 2-lite, w/fan center, #5902 | 60.00 | Stem, 5⅜", cordial, "S" stem, #17457 | 95.00 |
| Candlestick, single, #348 | 35.00 | Stem, 5⅜", 7 oz., saucer champagne, #17453 | 30.00 |
| Celery, 10", oval, #5831 | 32.50 | Stem, 5⅜", saucer champagne, #15083 | 15.00 |
| Celery, 10½", rectangular, #5902 | 35.00 | Stem, 5⅜", saucer champagne, "S" stem, #17457 | 35.00 |
| Cigarette box, w/lid, 4" x 2¾", #9305 | 90.00 | Stem, 5¹⁵⁄₁₆", parfait, #15083 | 25.00 |
| Cocktail shaker, 8", w/metal top | 195.00 | Stem, 6¼", low water, #15083 | 25.00 |
| Comport, 6¼", #5831 | 30.00 | Stem, 7⅜", 9 oz., water, #17453 | 40.00 |
| Comport, 6½", w/beaded stem, #15082 | 35.00 | Stem, 7½", water, high, #15083 | 25.00 |
| Creamer, 2⅞", individual, #5831 | 40.00 | Stem, 7⅝", water, "S" stem, #17457 | 50.00 |
| Creamer, 3⅜", flat w/beaded handle, #5902 | 27.50 | Sugar, 2⅞", individual, #5831 | 40.00 |
| Creamer, 4½", ftd., #5831 | 22.50 | Sugar, 3⅜", flat, w/beaded handle, #5902 | 27.50 |
| Cup, #5831 | 60.00 | Sugar, 4½", ftd., #5831 | 22.50 |
| Hurricane, 12", Chinese style | 125.00 | Tray, sugar/creamer | 40.00 |
| Icer, with insert | 125.00 | Tray, 9½", 2 hdld. for cream/sugar | 40.00 |
| Mayonnaise, flat, w/6¼" liner #5902 w/ladle | 45.00 | Tumbler, 2⁷⁄₁₆", 2 oz., bar, flat, #506 | 55.00 |
| Mayonnaise, ftd., w/ladle, #5831 | 45.00 | Tumbler, 3⁵⁄₁₆", oyster cocktail, #14196 | 14.00 |
| Nut dish, 6¼" | 30.00 | Tumbler, 3⅜", old-fashioned, flat, #580 | 35.00 |
| Pickle, 7⅜", #5831 | 40.00 | Tumbler, 4¹³⁄₁₆", flat, juice | 20.00 |
| Pitcher & cover, #194 | 350.00 | Tumbler, 4⁵⁄₁₆", 5 oz., ftd., juice, #15083 | 18.00 |
| Plate, 6¼", bread and butter, #5902 | 8.00 | Tumbler, 5⅛", water, flat, #517 | 25.00 |
| Plate, 6¼", sherbet, #8814 | 10.00 | Tumbler, 5⁵⁄₁₆", 9 oz., ftd., water, #15083 | 15.00 |
| Plate, 6⅜", 2 hdld., #5831 | 12.50 | Tumbler, 6⁵⁄₁₆", 12 oz., ftd., tea, #15083 | 30.00 |
| Plate, 7", marmalade, 3-ftd., #310½ | 22.50 | Vase, 6½", bud, #14185 | 30.00 |
| Plate, 7⅞", clam soup or mayo liner, #5831 | 12.50 | Vase, 8³⁄₁₆", flared, crimped | 75.00 |
| Plate, 7⅞", salad, #8814 | 15.00 | Vase, 8¼", bud, #14185 | 35.00 |
| Plate, 7½", salad, #5831 | 15.00 | Vase, 10½", bud, #14185 | 45.00 |
| Plate, 8¼", luncheon, #5902 | 17.50 | Vase, 10¾", bulbous bottom, #5872 | 150.00 |
| Plate, 8⅛", luncheon, #8833 | 22.50 | Vase, 10⅞", beaded stem, #15082 | 75.00 |
| Plate, 8⅜", bonbon, pearl edge | 25.00 | Vase, 11¾", urn, 2 hdld., trophy | 100.00 |
| Plate, 9½", dinner, #5902 | 55.00 | Whipped cream, 3-ftd., #310 | 32.50 |

# GLORIA, (etching 1746), Cambridge Glass 3400 Line Dinnerware, Introduced 1930

Colors: crystal, yellow, Peach-Blo, green, Emerald green, amber, blue, Heatherbloom

Gloria is most often confused with Tiffin's Flanders. Look closely at these two patterns and notice that the flower on Gloria bends the stem. They are easily distinguished once you see them side by side.

Yellow or crystal sets can be completed with work and patience, but any other color will take more than patience. Note the amber footed stem in the top picture. There is a little of this combination available, but not much. Personally, I like that combination better than all yellow or all amber. Oh, for those who are wondering, Peach-Blo is a Cambridge term for pink!

The bottom photograph shows a few pieces of Heatherbloom and blue. These will cost up to 60% more than the prices listed for other colors. I have not been able to find a saucer for my blue or Heatherbloom cups pictured. Additionally, I have shown the Heatherbloom creamer as a pattern shot on page 115. The single shot may show that color better than in a grouping. Color separations at the printers sometimes mask the color to some degree.

I am very fond of the dark Emerald green in this pattern, and it sells as fast as I can find a piece or two. If I could only find a cordial in that color!

The pitchers shown atop page 115 are all rarely seen. The amber one is a Doulton style that is usually found in color without an etching!

| | Crystal | Green, Pink/ Yellow | | Crystal | Green, Pink/ Yellow |
|---|---|---|---|---|---|
| Basket, 6", 2 hdld. (sides up) | 16.00 | 30.00 | Comport, 5", 4 ftd. | 17.00 | 37.50 |
| Bowl, 3", indiv. nut, 4 ftd. | 45.00 | 65.00 | Comport, 6", 4 ftd. | 19.00 | 37.50 |
| Bowl, 3½", cranberry, 4 ftd. | 25.00 | 50.00 | Comport, 7", low | 30.00 | 50.00 |
| Bowl, 5", ftd., crimped edge, bonbon | 14.00 | 22.00 | Comport, 7", tall | 35.00 | 75.00 |
| Bowl, 5", sq. fruit, "saucer" | 7.00 | 16.00 | Comport, 9½", tall, 2 hdld., ftd. bowl | 65.00 | 140.00 |
| Bowl, 5½", bonbon, 2 hdld. | 14.00 | 21.00 | Creamer, ftd. | 11.00 | 17.50 |
| Bowl, 5½", bonbon, ftd. | 12.00 | 19.00 | Creamer, tall, ftd. | 11.00 | 20.00 |
| Bowl, 5½", flattened, ftd., bonbon | 12.00 | 18.00 | Cup, rnd. or sq. | 15.00 | 25.00 |
| Bowl, 5½", fruit, "saucer" | 7.50 | 15.00 | Cup, 4 ftd., sq. | 25.00 | 65.00 |
| Bowl, 6", rnd., cereal | 12.00 | 25.00 | Cup, after dinner (demitasse), rnd. | | |
| Bowl, 6", sq., cereal | 12.00 | 22.00 | or sq. | 60.00 | 100.00 |
| Bowl, 8", 2 pt., 2 hdld., relish | 15.00 | 23.00 | Fruit cocktail, 6 oz., ftd. (3 styles) | 9.00 | 17.50 |
| Bowl, 8", 3 pt., 3 hdld., relish | 22.50 | 34.00 | Ice pail, metal handle w/tongs | 45.00 | 85.00 |
| Bowl, 8¾", 2 hdld., figure, "8" pickle | 17.50 | 30.00 | Icer, w/insert | 60.00 | 85.00 |
| Bowl, 8¾", 2 pt., 2 hdld., figure "8" | | | Mayonnaise, w/liner & ladle, | | |
| relish | 20.00 | 32.00 | (4 ftd. bowl) | 35.00 | 65.00 |
| Bowl, 9", salad, tab hdld. | 20.00 | 55.00 | Oil, w/stopper; tall, ftd., hdld. | 90.00 | 175.00 |
| Bowl, 9½", 2 hdld., veg. | 55.00 | 90.00 | Oyster cocktail, #3035, 4½ oz. | 10.00 | 17.50 |
| Bowl, 10", oblong, tab hdld., "baker" | 37.50 | 70.00 | Oyster cocktail, 4½ oz., low stem | 10.00 | 17.50 |
| Bowl, 10", 2 hdld. | 32.00 | 70.00 | Pitcher, 67 oz., middle indent | 150.00 | 275.00 |
| Bowl, 11", 2 hdld., fruit | 30.00 | 55.00 | Pitcher, 80 oz., ball | 160.00 | 260.00 |
| Bowl, 12", 4 ftd., console | 25.00 | 55.00 | Pitcher, w/cover, 64 oz. | 175.00 | 310.00 |
| Bowl, 12", 4 ftd., flared rim | 22.00 | 55.00 | Plate, 6", 2 hdld. | 8.00 | 13.50 |
| Bowl, 12", 4 ftd., oval | 30.00 | 65.00 | Plate, 6", bread/butter | 6.00 | 9.00 |
| Bowl, 12", 5 pt., celery & relish | 25.00 | 45.00 | Plate, 7½", tea | 8.00 | 12.00 |
| Bowl, 13", flared rim | 25.00 | 55.00 | Plate, 8½" | 9.00 | 14.00 |
| Bowl, cream soup, w/rnd. liner | 18.00 | 35.00 | Plate, 9½", dinner | 55.00 | 75.00 |
| Bowl, cream soup, w/sq. saucer | 18.00 | 35.00 | Plate, 10", tab hdld. salad | 15.00 | 32.00 |
| Bowl, finger, flared edge, w/rnd. plate | 14.00 | 26.00 | Plate, 11", 2 hdld. | 15.00 | 30.00 |
| Bowl, finger, ftd. | 15.00 | 30.00 | Plate, 11", sq., ftd. cake | 60.00 | 115.00 |
| Bowl, finger, w/rnd. plate | 20.00 | 35.00 | Plate, 11½", tab hdld., sandwich | 17.50 | 40.00 |
| Butter, w/cover, 2 hdld. | 115.00 | 285.00 | Plate, 14", chop or salad | 40.00 | 75.00 |
| Candlestick, 6", ea. | 17.50 | 32.50 | Plate, sq., bread/butter | 6.00 | 9.00 |
| Candy box, w/cover, 4 ftd. w/tab hdld. | 65.00 | 115.00 | Plate, sq., dinner | 55.00 | 75.00 |
| Cheese compote w/11½" cracker plate, | | | Plate, sq., salad | 7.00 | 12.00 |
| tab hdld. | 30.00 | 60.00 | Plate, sq., service | 22.00 | 45.00 |
| Cocktail shaker, grnd. stopper, spout | | | Platter, 11½" | 55.00 | 115.00 |
| (like pitcher) | 95.00 | 200.00 | Salt & pepper, pr., short | 30.00 | 55.00 |
| Comport, 4", fruit cocktail | 10.00 | 20.00 | Salt & pepper, pr., w/glass top, tall | 32.50 | 70.00 |

# GLORIA, (etching #1746), Cambridge Glass 3400 Line Dinnerware, Introduced 1930 (continued)

| | Crystal | Green Pink/ Yellow | | Crystal | Green Pink/ Yellow |
|---|---|---|---|---|---|
| Salt & pepper, ftd., metal tops.............. | 35.00 | 62.50 | Tray, 4 pt., ctr. hdld., relish................. | 30.00 | 45.00 |
| Saucer, rnd........................................... | 2.00 | 4.00 | Tray, 9", pickle, tab hdld. ..................... | 15.00 | 25.00 |
| Saucer, rnd. after dinner ...................... | 8.00 | 15.00 | Tumbler, #3035, 5 oz., high ftd. ............ | 11.00 | 20.00 |
| Saucer, sq., after dinner (demitasse).... | 10.00 | 17.00 | Tumbler, #3035, 10 oz., high ftd. ......... | 12.00 | 22.00 |
| Saucer, sq............................................. | 2.00 | 3.00 | Tumbler, #3035, 12 oz., high ftd. ......... | 17.00 | 30.00 |
| Stem, #3035, 2½ oz., wine ................... | 20.00 | 40.00 | Tumbler, #3115, 5 oz., ftd., juice ......... | 12.00 | 20.00 |
| Stem, #3035, 3 oz., cocktail ................ | 17.50 | 28.00 | Tumbler, #3115, 8 oz., ftd. .................. | 12.00 | 20.00 |
| Stem, #3035, 3½ oz., cocktail.............. | 17.00 | 27.00 | Tumbler, #3115, 10 oz., ftd. ................. | 13.00 | 21.00 |
| Stem, #3035, 4½ oz., claret ................ | 30.00 | 50.00 | Tumbler, #3115, 12 oz., ftd. ................. | 17.00 | 30.00 |
| Stem, #3035, 6 oz., low sherbet .......... | 11.00 | 16.00 | Tumbler, #3120, 2½ oz., ftd. (used | | |
| Stem, #3035, 6 oz., tall sherbet ........... | 12.50 | 18.00 | w/cocktail shaker) ........................... | 22.00 | 40.00 |
| Stem, #3035, 9 oz., water ................... | 15.00 | 30.00 | Tumbler, #3120, 5 oz., ftd. .................. | 12.00 | 20.00 |
| Stem, #3035, 3½ oz., cocktail.............. | 17.00 | 30.00 | Tumbler, #3120, 10 oz., ftd. ................. | 12.00 | 20.00 |
| Stem, #3115, 9 oz., goblet ................... | 15.00 | 30.00 | Tumbler, #3120, 12 oz., ftd. ................. | 17.00 | 30.00 |
| Stem, #3120, 1 oz., cordial.................. | 55.00 | 125.00 | Tumbler, #3120, 2½ oz., ftd. (used | | |
| Stem, #3120, 4½ oz., claret ................ | 30.00 | 50.00 | w/shaker) ......................................... | 22.00 | 40.00 |
| Stem, #3120, 6 oz., low sherbet .......... | 10.00 | 15.00 | Tumbler, #3130, 5 oz., ftd. .................. | 12.00 | 20.00 |
| Stem, #3120, 6 oz., tall sherbet............ | 11.00 | 16.00 | Tumbler, #3130, 10 oz., ftd. ................. | 13.00 | 20.00 |
| Stem, #3120, 9 oz., water ................... | 15.00 | 25.00 | Tumbler, #3130, 12 oz., ftd. ................. | 15.00 | 25.00 |
| Stem, #3130, 2½ oz., wine ................... | 20.00 | 42.50 | Tumbler, #3135, 5 oz., juice ................ | 12.00 | 20.00 |
| Stem, #3130, 6 oz., low sherbet .......... | 10.00 | 15.00 | Tumbler, #3135, 10 oz., water.............. | 12.00 | 20.00 |
| Stem, #3130, 6 oz., tall sherbet............ | 11.00 | 16.00 | Tumbler, #3135, 12 oz., tea ................. | 17.00 | 30.00 |
| Stem, #3130, 8 oz., water ................... | 18.00 | 30.00 | Tumbler, 12 oz., flat, (2 styles), one | | |
| Stem, #3135, 1 oz., cordial.................. | 60.00 | 135.00 | indent side to match 67 oz. pitcher . | 18.00 | 35.00 |
| Stem, #3135, 6 oz., low sherbet .......... | 11.00 | 15.00 | Vase, 9", oval, 4 indent........................ | 75.00 | 150.00 |
| Stem, #3135, 6 oz., tall sherbet............ | 12.00 | 16.00 | Vase, 10", keyhole base ........................ | 50.00 | 120.00 |
| Stem, #3135, 8 oz., water ................... | 18.00 | 30.00 | Vase, 10", squarish top ........................ | 65.00 | 150.00 |
| Sugar, ftd.............................................. | 11.00 | 18.00 | Vase, 11"............................................... | 45.00 | 95.00 |
| Sugar, tall, ftd. ..................................... | 11.00 | 19.00 | Vase, 11", neck indent .......................... | 65.00 | 125.00 |
| Sugar shaker, w/glass top..................... | 150.00 | 275.00 | Vase, 12", keyhole base, flared rim ...... | 50.00 | 110.00 |
| Syrup, tall, ftd....................................... | 50.00 | 95.00 | Vase, 12", squarish top ........................ | 50.00 | 100.00 |
| Tray, 11", ctr. hdld., sandwich ............. | 20.00 | 37.50 | Vase, 14", keyhole base, flared rim ...... | 70.00 | 150.00 |
| Tray, 2 pt., ctr. hdld., relish................. | 25.00 | 37.50 | | | |

Note: See Pages 228-229 for stem identification.

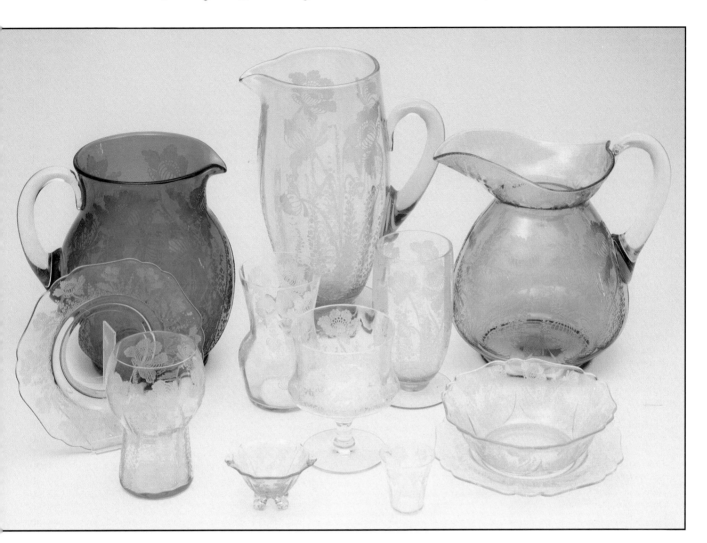

# GREEK KEY, A.H. Heisey & Co.

Colors: crystal; "Flamingo" pink punch bowl and cups only

Prices are steadily increasing in Greek Key due to heavy collector demand!

| | Crystal | | Crystal |
|---|---|---|---|
| Bowl, finger | 20.00 | Pitcher, 1 pint | 90.00 |
| Bowl, jelly, w/cover, 2 hdld. ftd | 145.00 | Pitcher, 1 quart | 150.00 |
| Bowl, indiv., ftd., almond | 25.00 | Pitcher, 3 pint | 165.00 |
| Bowl, 4", nappy | 20.00 | Pitcher, ½ gal. | 200.00 |
| Bowl, 4", shallow, low ft., jelly | 25.00 | Oil bottle, 2 oz., squat, w/#8 stopper | 100.00 |
| Bowl, 4½", nappy | 20.00 | Oil bottle, 2 oz., w/#6 stopper | 110.00 |
| Bowl, 4½", scalloped, nappy | 17.50 | Oil bottle, 4 oz., squat, w/#8 stopper | 80.00 |
| Bowl, 4½", shallow, low ft., jelly | 16.00 | Oil bottle, 4 oz., w/#6 stopper | 80.00 |
| Bowl, 5", ftd., almond | 35.00 | Oil bottle, 6 oz., w/#6 stopper | 100.00 |
| Bowl, 5", ftd., almond, w/cover | 90.00 | Oil bottle, 6 oz., squat, w/#8 stopper | 100.00 |
| Bowl, 5", hdld., jelly | 75.00 | Plate, 4½" | 12.00 |
| Bowl, 5", low ft., jelly, w/cover | 80.00 | Plate, 5" | 14.00 |
| Bowl, 5", nappy | 22.50 | Plate, 5½" | 14.00 |
| Bowl, 5½", nappy | 25.00 | Plate, 6" | 20.00 |
| Bowl, 5½", shallow nappy, ftd. | 55.00 | Plate, 6½" | 20.00 |
| Bowl, 6", nappy | 25.00 | Plate, 7" | 35.00 |
| Bowl, 6", shallow nappy | 27.50 | Plate, 8" | 40.00 |
| Bowl, 6½", nappy | 30.00 | Plate, 9" | 50.00 |
| Bowl, 7", low ft., straight side | 50.00 | Plate, 10" | 85.00 |
| Bowl, 7", nappy | 40.00 | Plate, 16", orange bowl liner | 100.00 |
| Bowl, 8", low ft., straight side | 60.00 | Puff box, #1, w/cover | 85.00 |
| Bowl, 8", nappy | 60.00 | Puff box, #3, w/cover | 95.00 |
| Bowl, 8", scalloped nappy | 65.00 | Salt & pepper, pr. | 75.00 |
| Bowl, 8", shallow, low ft. | 75.00 | Sherbet, 4½ oz., ftd., straight rim | 15.00 |
| Bowl, 8½", shallow nappy | 75.00 | Sherbet, 4½ oz., ftd., flared rim | 15.00 |
| Bowl, 9", flat banana split | 30.00 | Sherbet, 4½ oz., high ft., shallow | 15.00 |
| Bowl, 9", ftd. banana split | 27.50 | Sherbet, 4½ oz., ftd., shallow | 15.00 |
| Bowl, 9", low ft., straight side | 50.00 | Sherbet, 4½ oz., ftd., cupped rim | 15.00 |
| Bowl, 9", nappy | 45.00 | Sherbet, 6 oz., low ft. | 13.00 |
| Bowl, 9", shallow, low ft. | 55.00 | Spooner, lg. | 75.00 |
| Bowl, 9½", shallow nappy | 55.00 | Spooner, 4½", (or straw jar) | 75.00 |
| Bowl, 10", shallow, low ft. | 85.00 | Stem, ¾ oz., cordial | 250.00 |
| Bowl, 11", shallow nappy | 60.00 | Stem, 2 oz., wine | 175.00 |
| Bowl, 12", orange bowl | 150.00 | Stem, 2 oz., sherry | 200.00 |
| Bowl, 12", punch, ftd. | 200.00 | Stem, 3 oz., cocktail | 45.00 |
| (Flamingo) | 750.00 | Stem, 3½ oz., burgundy | 125.00 |
| Bowl, 12", orange, flared rim | 115.00 | Stem, 4½ oz., saucer champagne | 40.00 |
| Bowl, 14½", orange, flared rim | 175.00 | Stem, 4½ oz., claret | 150.00 |
| Bowl, 15", punch, ftd. | 225.00 | Stem, 7 oz. | 95.00 |
| Bowl, 18", punch, shallow | 225.00 | Stem, 9 oz. | 125.00 |
| Butter, indiv. (plate) | 35.00 | Stem, 9 oz., low ft. | 100.00 |
| Butter/jelly, 2 hdld., w/cover | 180.00 | Straw jar, w/cover | 300.00 |
| Candy, w/cover, ½ lb. | 135.00 | Sugar | 35.00 |
| Candy, w/cover, 1 lb. | 140.00 | Sugar, oval, hotel | 40.00 |
| Candy, w/cover, 2 lb. | 195.00 | Sugar, rnd., hotel | 30.00 |
| Cheese & cracker set, 10" | 80.00 | Sugar & creamer, oval, individual | 75.00 |
| Compote, 5" | 60.00 | Tray, 9", oval celery | 40.00 |
| Compote, 5", w/cover | 85.00 | Tray, 12", oval celery | 45.00 |
| Creamer | 35.00 | Tray, 12½", French roll | 100.00 |
| Creamer, oval, hotel | 40.00 | Tray, 13", oblong | 110.00 |
| Creamer, rnd., hotel | 30.00 | Tray, 15", oblong | 120.00 |
| Cup, 4½ oz., punch | 20.00 | Tumbler, 2½ oz., (or toothpick) | 300.00 |
| Cup, punch, (Flamingo) | 40.00 | Tumbler, 5 oz., flared rim | 20.00 |
| Coaster | 12.00 | Tumbler, 5 oz., straight side | 20.00 |
| Egg cup, 5 oz. | 60.00 | Tumbler, 5½ oz., water | 20.00 |
| Hair receiver | 80.00 | Tumbler, 7 oz., flared rim | 22.00 |
| Ice tub, lg., tab hdld. | 110.00 | Tumbler, 7 oz., straight side | 25.00 |
| Ice tub, sm., tab hdld. | 100.00 | Tumbler, 8 oz., w/straight, flared, cupped, | |
| Ice tub, w/cover, hotel | 175.00 | shallow | 35.00 |
| Ice tub, w/cover, 5", individual w/5" plate | 95.00 | Tumbler, 10 oz., flared rim | 37.00 |
| Jar, 1 qt., crushed fruit, w/cover | 300.00 | Tumbler, 10 oz., straight wide | 37.00 |
| Jar, 2 qt., crushed fruit, w/cover | 325.00 | Tumbler, 12 oz., flared rim | 40.00 |
| Jar, lg. cover, horseradish | 75.00 | Tumbler, 12 oz., straight side | 40.00 |
| Jar, sm. cover, horseradish | 65.00 | Tumbler, 13 oz., straight side | 42.00 |
| Jar, tall celery | 70.00 | Tumbler, 13 oz., flared rim | 42.00 |
| Jar, w/knob cover, pickle | 125.00 | Water bottle | 185.00 |

# HEATHER, Etching #343, Fostoria Glass Company

Colors: crystal

Heather is another Fostoria pattern that is being divided among family, and now second and third generation family members are seeking replacements for pieces missing or long since broken.

The large plate standing up in the back is really the 12¼" salver. You may think of it as a cake stand, but it was listed by Fostoria as a salver. The pattern shows on the piece even if it loses its rightful shape at that angle.

I have tried to give as complete a listing for this pattern as possible from old catalogues, but I'm sure there are additional pieces. Supply me with your information please. (Be sure to send a picture with all measurements.)

| | Crystal | | Crystal |
|---|---|---|---|
| Basket, 10¼" x 6½", wicker hdld. | 65.00 | Plate, 9½", small dinner | 20.00 |
| Bowl, 4½", hdld. | 12.00 | Plate, 10½", snack tray | 20.00 |
| Bowl, 5", fruit | 14.00 | Plate, 10", hdld., cake | 20.00 |
| Bowl, 6¼", snack, ftd. | 12.50 | Plate, 14", torte | 30.00 |
| Bowl, 6", cereal | 22.00 | Platter, 12" | 47.50 |
| Bowl, 7¼", bonbon, 3 ftd. | 15.00 | Preserve, w/cover, 6" | 30.00 |
| Bowl, 7⅛", 3 ftd., triangular | 14.00 | Relish, 7⅜", 2 part | 15.00 |
| Bowl, 8", flared | 22.50 | Relish, 11⅛", 3 part | 21.50 |
| Bowl, 9½", hdld., serving bowl | 25.00 | Salt and pepper, 3⅛", pr. | 17.50 |
| Bowl, 9½", oval, serving bowl | 30.00 | Salver, 12¼", ftd. (like cake stand) | 47.50 |
| Bowl, 10½", salad | 30.00 | Saucer | 3.50 |
| Bowl, 10¾", ftd., flared | 32.50 | Stem, #6037, 1 oz., cordial, 4" | 35.00 |
| Bowl, 10", oval, hdld. | 30.00 | Stem, #6037, 4 oz., claret-wine, 6" | 27.50 |
| Bowl, 11¼", lily pond | 32.50 | Stem, #6037, 4 oz., cocktail, 5" | 18.00 |
| Bowl, 11, ftd., rolled edge | 37.50 | Stem, #6037, 4½ oz., oyster cocktail, 4" | 19.00 |
| Bowl, 12", flared | 35.00 | Stem, #6037, 6 oz., parfait, 6⅛" | 18.00 |
| Butter, w/cover, ¼ lb. | 30.00 | Stem, #6037, 7 oz., low sherbet, 4¾" | 11.00 |
| Candlestick, 4½" | 15.00 | Stem, #6037, 7 oz., saucer champagne, 6" | 13.00 |
| Candlestick, 7¾", triple | 35.00 | Stem, #6037, 9oz., goblet, 7⅞" | 22.00 |
| Candlestick, 7", double | 27.50 | Stem, #6037, 9oz., low goblet, 6⅜" | 22.00 |
| Candy, w/cover, 7" | 32.50 | Sugar, 4", ftd. | 8.00 |
| Comport, 2¾", cheese | 15.00 | Sugar, individual | |
| Comport, 4⅜" | 17.50 | Tid bit, 8⅛", 3 ftd., upturned edge | 17.50 |
| Cracker plate, 10¾" | 30.00 | Tid bit, 10¼", 2 tier, metal hdld. | 25.00 |
| Creamer, 4¼" | 8.00 | Tray, 7⅛", for ind. sug/cr | 12.00 |
| Creamer, individual | 8.00 | Tray, 9½", hdld., muffin | 25.00 |
| Cup, 6 oz., ftd. | 15.00 | Tray, 9⅛", hdld., utility | 25.00 |
| Ice Bucket | 65.00 | Tray, 11½", center hdld. | 27.50 |
| Mayonnaise, 3 pc. | 27.50 | Tumbler, #6037, 5 oz., ftd., juice, 4⅞" | 20.00 |
| Mayonnaise, 4 pc., div. w/2 ladles | 32.50 | Tumbler, #6037, 12 oz., ftd., tea, 6⅛" | 25.00 |
| Mustard, w/spoon, cover | 27.50 | Vase, 5", #4121 | 35.00 |
| Oil, w/stopper, 5 oz. | 40.00 | Vase, 6", bud | 17.50 |
| Pickle, 8¾" | 15.00 | Vase, 6", ftd. bud, #6021 | 35.00 |
| Pitcher, 6⅛", 16 oz. | 50.00 | Vase, 6", ftd., #4143 | 45.00 |
| Pitcher, 7⅛", 48 oz. | 95.00 | Vase, 7½", hdld. | 65.00 |
| Plate, 6", bread/butter | 5.00 | Vase, 8½", oval | 62.00 |
| Plate, 7½", crescent salad | 32.50 | Vase, 8", flip, #2660 | 85.00 |
| Plate, 7½", salad | 7.50 | Vase, 8", ftd., bub, #5092 | 85.00 |
| Plate, 8½", luncheon | 12.50 | Vase, 10", ftd., #2470 | 85.00 |
| Plate, 8", party, w/indent for cup | 20.00 | | |

119

# HERMITAGE, #2449, Fostoria Glass Company, 1932 – 1945

Colors: Amber, Azure (blue), crystal, Ebony, green, Topaz, Wisteria

My listings are from a Fostoria catalogue that had January 1, 1933, entered on the front page in pencil. If you find a piece not listed or in a color not listed, please let me know. Not all pieces were made in all colors according to this catalogue. For example the 5" fruit, 6" cereal, and 7" soup were not supposed to be made in green or Wisteria.

| | Crystal | amber/green/Topaz | Azure/Wisteria |
|---|---|---|---|
| Ash tray holder, #2449 | 5.00 | 8.00 | 12.00 |
| *Ash tray, #2449 | 3.00 | 5.00 | 8.00 |
| Bottle, 3 oz., oil, #2449 | 17.50 | 35.00 | |
| Bottle, 27 oz., bar w/stopper, #2449 | 45.00 | | |
| Bowl, 4½", finger, #2449½ | 4.00 | 6.00 | 10.00 |
| Bowl, 5", fruit, #2449½ | 5.00 | 8.00 | 12.00 |
| Bowl, 6", cereal, #2449½ | 6.00 | 9.00 | 14.00 |
| Bowl, 6½", salad, #2449½ | 6.00 | 9.00 | 14.00 |
| Bowl, 7", soup, #2449½ | 8.00 | 12.00 | 20.00 |
| Bowl, 7½", salad, #2449½ | 8.00 | 12.00 | 20.00 |
| Bowl, 8", deep, ped., ft., #2449 | 17.50 | 32.00 | 50.00 |
| Bowl, 10", ftd., #2449 | 20.00 | 35.00 | |
| Bowl, grapefruit w/crystal liner #2449 | 20.00 | 35.00 | |
| Candle, 6", #2449 | 12.50 | 22.00 | 35.00 |
| Coaster, 5⅝", #2449 | 5.00 | 7.50 | 11.00 |
| Comport, 6", #2449 | 12.00 | 17.50 | 27.50 |
| Creamer, ftd., #2449 | 4.00 | 6.00 | 10.00 |
| Cup, ftd.,#2449 | 6.00 | 10.00 | 15.00 |
| Decanter, 28 oz., w/stopper, #2449 | 35.00 | 50.00 | 75.00 |
| Fruit cocktail, 2⅜", 5 oz., ftd., #2449 | 5.00 | 7.50 | 12.00 |
| Ice tub, 6", #2449 | 17.50 | 35.00 | 50.00 |
| Icer, #2449 | 10.00 | 18.00 | 30.00 |
| Mayonnaise, 5⅝" w/7" plate, #2449 | 20.00 | 35.00 | |
| Mug, 9 oz., ftd., #2449 | 12.50 | | |
| Mug, 12 oz., ftd., #2449 | 15.00 | | |
| Mustard w/cover & spoon, #2449 | 17.50 | 27.50 | |
| Pitcher, pint, #2449 | 22.50 | 35.00 | 50.00 |
| Pitcher, 3 pint, #2449 | 30.00 | 55.00 | 100.00 |
| Plate, 6", #2449½ | 3.00 | 5.00 | 8.00 |
| Plate, 7" ice dish liner | 4.00 | 6.00 | 10.00 |
| Plate, 7", #2449½ | 4.00 | 6.00 | 10.00 |
| Plate, 7⅜", crescent salad, #2449 | 10.00 | 17.50 | 30.00 |
| Plate, 8", #2449½ | 6.00 | 10.00 | 15.00 |
| Plate, 9", #2449½ | 12.50 | 20.00 | 30.00 |
| Plate, 12", sandwich, #2449 | | 12.50 | 20.00 |
| Relish, 6", 2 pt., #2449 | 6.00 | 10.00 | 15.00 |
| Relish, 7¼", 3 pt., #2449 | 8.00 | 11.00 | 17.50 |
| Relish, 8", pickle, #2449 | 8.00 | 11.00 | 17.50 |
| Relish, 11", celery, #2449 | 10.00 | 15.00 | 25.00 |
| Salt & pepper, 3⅜", #2449 | 20.00 | 35.00 | 55.00 |
| Salt, indiv., #2449 | 4.00 | 6.00 | 10.00 |
| Saucer, #2449 | 2.00 | 3.50 | 5.00 |
| Sherbet, 3", 7 oz., low, ftd., #2449 | 6.00 | 8.00 | 12.50 |
| Stem, 3¼", 5½ oz., high sherbet, #2449 | 8.00 | 11.00 | 17.50 |
| Stem, 4⅝", 4 oz., claret, #2449 | 10.00 | 15.00 | |
| Stem, 5¼", 9 oz., water goblet, #2449 | 10.00 | 15.00 | 25.00 |
| Sugar, ftd., #2449 | 4.00 | 6.00 | 10.00 |
| Tray, 6½", condiment, #2449 | 6.00 | 10.00 | 15.00 |
| Tumbler, 2½", 2 oz., #2449½ | 4.00 | 6.00 | 10.00 |
| Tumbler, 2½", 2 oz., ftd., #2449 | 5.00 | 8.00 | |
| Tumbler, 3", 4 oz., cocktail, ftd., #2449 | 5.00 | 7.50 | 12.00 |
| Tumbler, 3¼", 6 oz. old-fashioned, #2449½ | 6.00 | 9.00 | 15.00 |
| Tumbler, 3⅞", 5 oz., #2449½ | 5.00 | 8.00 | 12.00 |
| Tumbler, 4", 5 oz., ftd., #2449 | 5.00 | 8.00 | 12.00 |
| Tumbler, 4⅛", 9 oz., ftd., #2449 | 6.00 | 10.00 | 15.00 |
| Tumbler, 4¾", 9 oz., #2449½ | 6.00 | 10.00 | 15.00 |
| Tumbler, 5¼", 12 oz., ftd., iced tea, #2449 | 10.00 | 15.00 | 25.00 |
| Tumbler, 5⅞", 13 oz., #2449½ | 10.00 | 15.00 | 25.00 |
| Vase, 6", ftd. | 22.00 | 32.50 | |

* Ebony - $10.00

# IMPERIAL HUNT SCENE, #718, Cambridge Glass Company, Late 1920's – 1930's

Colors: amber, black, crystal, Emerald green, green, pink, Willow blue

Imperial Hunt scene reminds me of Tiffin patterns because all you see are stems. Serving pieces are few and far between. If your desire is to collect a pattern with an array of stems and tumblers — this is the one!

I just saw a two color combination cordial that I would like to own. It is pink with a green stem. Unfortunately, the owner appreciates it more than I do — by his price! I set limits on what I will pay for cordials for my collection.

I have asked for years if anyone has ever seen an Imperial Hunt Scene cup and have always received the answer that they are pictured in the catalogue; so they must exist. Finally, cups in crystal #1402 Tally-Ho turned up; now, has anyone seen some crystal Tally-Ho saucers with Imperial Hunt Scene etching?

Black and dark Emerald green will fetch 25% to 40% higher prices than those listed.

| | Crystal | Colors |
|---|---|---|
| Bowl, 6", cereal. | 15.00 | 26.50 |
| Bowl, 8". | 35.00 | 65.00 |
| Bowl, 8½", 3 pt. | 25.00 | 50.00 |
| Candlestick, 2-lite, keyhole. | 17.50 | 35.00 |
| Candlestick, 3-lite, keyhole. | 27.50 | 55.00 |
| Comport, 5½", #3085 | | 35.00 |
| Creamer, ftd. | 15.00 | 30.00 |
| Cup | 45.00 | |
| Decanter | | 235.00 |
| Finger bowl, w/plate, #3085 | | 35.00 |
| Humidor, tobacco | | 365.00 |
| Ice bucket. | 40.00 | 75.00 |
| Ice tub. | 35.00 | 70.00 |
| Mayonnaise, w/liner. | 30.00 | 50.00 |
| Pitcher, w/cover, 63 oz., #3085. | | 275.00 |
| Pitcher, w/cover, 76 oz., #711. | 150.00 | 250.00 |
| Plate, 8". | 12.00 | 22.00 |
| Saucer. | 10.00 | |
| Stem, 1 oz., cordial, #1402. | 55.00 | |
| Stem, 2½ oz., wine, #1402. | 45.00 | |
| Stem, 3 oz., cocktail, #1402. | 40.00 | |
| Stem, 6 oz., tomato, #1402. | 40.00 | |
| Stem, 6½ oz., sherbet, #1402. | 35.00 | |
| Stem, 7½ oz., sherbet, #1402. | 40.00 | |
| Stem, 10 oz., water, #1402. | 40.00 | |
| Stem, 14 oz., #1402. | 50.00 | |
| Stem, 18 oz., #1402. | 60.00 | |
| Stem, 1 oz., cordial, #3085. | | 165.00 |
| Stem, 2½ oz., cocktail, #3085. | | 40.00 |
| Stem, 2½ oz., wine, #3085. | | 55.00 |
| Stem, 4½ oz., claret, #3085. | | 67.50 |
| Stem, 5½ oz., parfait, #3085. | | 60.00 |
| Stem, 6 oz., low sherbet, #3085. | | 22.50 |
| Stem, 6 oz., high sherbet, #3085. | | 27.50 |
| Stem, 9 oz., water, #3085. | | 45.00 |
| Sugar, ftd. | 15.00 | 30.00 |
| Tumbler, 2½ oz., flat, #1402. | 25.00 | |
| Tumbler, 5 oz., flat, #1402. | 20.00 | |
| Tumbler, 7 oz., flat, #1402. | 20.00 | |
| Tumbler, 10 oz., flat, #1402. | 23.00 | |
| Tumbler, 10 oz., flat, tall, #1402. | 25.00 | |
| Tumbler, 15 oz., flat, #1402. | 35.00 | |
| Tumbler, 2½ oz., ftd., #3085. | | 35.00 |
| Tumbler, 5 oz., ftd., #3085. | | 25.00 |
| Tumbler, 8 oz., ftd., #3085. | | 25.00 |
| Tumbler, 10 oz., ftd., #3085. | | 30.00 |
| Tumbler, 12 oz., ftd., #3085. | | 35.00 |

# IPSWICH, Blank #1405, A.H. Heisey & Co.

Colors: crystal, "Flamingo" pink, "Sahara" yellow, "Moongleam" green, cobalt and "Alexandrite"

With the following three sentences in the last book, I saved answering about fifty letters I receive each year about this pattern. "If you find any colored piece of Ipswich, other than those listed below, it was made at Imperial and not Heisey. Even if it is marked Heisey, it was still manufactured at Imperial. Mostly, I get letters on (Alexandrite) candy jars that are actually Imperial's Heather color."

The only piece of Ipswich made in Alexandrite is the goblet. If you have any problems in determining whether a piece you have is Alexandrite or not, look in the back of this book on page 230. We have been able to show this color more consistently than any other book ever has. You can also take an Alexandrite piece outside in natural light where it will look pinkish and then near a fluorescent bulb where it will change to a blue hue.

Note the candle vase in green (between the creamer and sugar) that goes atop the candlestick centerpiece. The bottom arrived after we had photographed the large set-up; so we included it as a pattern shot. No matter how many times you photograph glassware for books, some item you can not leave out shows up when it is nearly impossible to include it — but we try!

| | Crystal | Pink | Sahara | Green | Cobalt | Alexan |
|---|---|---|---|---|---|---|
| Bowl, finger w/underplate | 20.00 | 55.00 | 60.00 | 70.00 | | |
| Bowl, 11", ftd., floral | 50.00 | | | | 250.00 | |
| Candlestick, 6", 1-lite | 75.00 | 205.00 | 150.00 | 200.00 | 350.00 | |
| Candlestick centerpiece, ftd., vase, "A" prisms | 95.00 | 275.00 | 300.00 | 450.00 | 500.00 | |
| Candy jar, ¼ lb., w/cover | 150.00 | | | | | |
| Candy jar, ½ lb., w/cover | 150.00 | 225.00 | 250.00 | 300.00 | | |
| Cocktail shaker, 1 quart, strainer #86 stopper | 225.00 | 600.00 | 700.00 | 800.00 | | |
| Creamer | 25.00 | 50.00 | 40.00 | 90.00 | | |
| Stem, 4 oz., oyster cocktail, ftd | 22.00 | 37.50 | 35.00 | 40.00 | | |
| Stem, 5 oz., saucer champagne, (knob in stem) | 22.00 | 37.50 | 35.00 | 40.00 | | |
| Stem, 10 oz., goblet, (knob in stem) | 30.00 | 50.00 | 45.00 | 55.00 | | 750.00 |
| Stem, 12 oz., schoppen, flat bottom | 30.00 | | | | | |
| Pitcher, ½ gal. | 150.00 | 250.00 | 350.00 | 750.00 | | |
| Oil bottle, 2 oz., ftd., #86 stopper | 80.00 | 185.00 | 175.00 | 200.00 | | |
| Plate, 7", square | 20.00 | 40.00 | 25.00 | 40.00 | | |
| Plate, 8", square | 20.00 | 45.00 | 30.00 | 45.00 | | |
| Sherbet, 4 oz., ftd., (knob in stem) | 10.00 | 30.00 | 25.00 | 35.00 | | |
| Sugar | 25.00 | 50.00 | 40.00 | 90.00 | | |
| Tumbler, 5 oz., ftd., (soda) | 30.00 | 40.00 | 40.00 | 50.00 | | |
| Tumbler, 8 oz., ftd., (soda) | 30.00 | 40.00 | 40.00 | 60.00 | | |
| Tumbler, 10 oz., cupped rim, flat bottom | 40.00 | 60.00 | 50.00 | 60.00 | | |
| Tumbler, 10 oz., straight rim, flat bottom | 40.00 | 60.00 | 50.00 | 60.00 | | |
| Tumbler, 12 oz., ftd., (soda) | 35.00 | 65.00 | 55.00 | 65.00 | | |

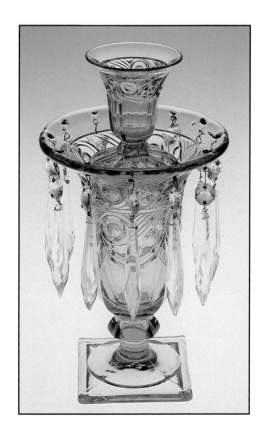

# JUNE, Fostoria Glass Company, 1928 – 1944

Colors: crystal, "Azure" blue, "Topaz" yellow, "Rose" pink

June continues to be **the** Fostoria pattern to own. Both pink and blue are selling as fast as dealers can find it for their customers. Even crystal is being collected! Yellow has lost some of its luster for now. A large set of pink turned up at an estate sale in the Atlanta area last year. Every piece sold, but the last piece to sell was the only known pink June decanter! I often wonder who would buy a set but leave the best piece. It had to be someone who was going to use it and had no reason to want a decanter. Surely, no dealer would have left a decanter!

There is not enough room in this book to list all the line numbers for the items in June! If you will refer to Versailles, I have listed all the Fostoria line numbers for each piece. Since these are virtually the same listings, you can use the item number listings from Versailles if you need such information. There is other Fostoria information under Versailles you need to read if you collect June!

| | Crystal | Rose, Blue | Topaz | | Crystal | Rose, Blue | Topaz |
|---|---|---|---|---|---|---|---|
| Ash tray | 23.00 | 45.00 | 32.00 | Ice dish liner (tomato, crab, fruit) | 5.00 | 20.00 | 10.00 |
| Bottle, salad dressing, #2083 or #2375 | 165.00 | 500.00 | 295.00 | Mayonnaise, w/liner | 25.00 | 65.00 | 40.00 |
| Bowl, baker, 9", oval | 35.00 | 90.00 | 65.00 | Oil, ftd | 200.00 | 550.00 | 325.00 |
| Bowl, baker, 10", oval | 40.00 | 105.00 | 75.00 | Oyster cocktail, 5½ oz. | 16.00 | 35.00 | 25.00 |
| Bowl, bonbon | 12.50 | 27.50 | 20.00 | Parfait, 5¼" | 30.00 | 95.00 | 55.00 |
| Bowl, bouillon, ftd. | 12.00 | 35.00 | 20.00 | Pitcher | 225.00 | 525.00 | 300.00 |
| Bowl, finger, w/liner | 32.50 | 55.00 | 25.00 | Plate, canape | 10.00 | 25.00 | 15.00 |
| Bowl, mint, 3-ftd., 4½" | 10.00 | 35.00 | 20.00 | Plate, lemon | 14.00 | 25.00 | 18.00 |
| Bowl, 5", mint | 11.00 | 22.00 | 18.00 | Plate, 6", bread/butter | 4.50 | 12.00 | 6.00 |
| Bowl, 6", cereal | 15.00 | 37.50 | 25.00 | Plate, 6", finger bowl liner | 4.50 | 10.00 | 6.00 |
| Bowl, 6", nappy, 3-ftd., jelly | 10.00 | 30.00 | 18.00 | Plate, 7½", salad | 5.00 | 9.00 | 8.00 |
| Bowl, 7", soup | 40.00 | 110.00 | 110.00 | Plate, 7½, cream soup | 4.00 | 12.00 | 7.50 |
| Bowl, lg., dessert, hdld. | 25.00 | 100.00 | 60.00 | Plate, 8¾", luncheon | 6.00 | 15.00 | 10.00 |
| Bowl, 10" | 30.00 | 100.00 | 60.00 | Plate, 9½", sm. dinner | 10.00 | 35.00 | 22.00 |
| Bowl, 10", Grecian | 35.00 | 90.00 | 55.00 | Plate, 10", grill | 30.00 | 80.00 | 65.00 |
| Bowl, 11", centerpiece | 25.00 | 65.00 | 40.00 | Plate, 10", cake, hdld (no indent) | 20.00 | 60.00 | 40.00 |
| Bowl, 12", centerpiece, several types | 25.00 | 90.00 | 45.00 | Plate, 10", cheese with indent, hdld | 20.00 | 60.00 | 40.00 |
| Bowl, 13", oval centerpiece, w/flower frog | 50.00 | 140.00 | 70.00 | Plate, 10¼", dinner | 35.00 | 90.00 | 60.00 |
| Candlestick, 2" | 10.00 | 25.00 | 20.00 | Plate, 13", chop | 22.00 | 65.00 | 45.00 |
| Candlestick, 3" | 12.00 | 25.00 | 18.00 | Plate, 14", torte | | | 60.00 |
| Candlestick, 3", Grecian | 20.00 | 45.00 | 30.00 | Platter, 12" | 25.00 | 105.00 | 60.00 |
| Candlestick, 5" | 20.00 | 45.00 | 30.00 | Platter, 15" | 45.00 | 185.00 | 105.00 |
| Candy, w/cover, 3 pt. | | 265.00 | | Relish, 8½", 3-part | 15.00 | 40.00 | 25.00 |
| Candy, w/cover, ½ lb., ¼ lb. | | | 165.00 | Sauce boat | 40.00 | 275.00 | 95.00 |
| Celery, 11½" | 25.00 | 75.00 | 35.00 | Sauce boat liner | 15.00 | 75.00 | 30.00 |
| Cheese & cracker set, #2368 or #2375 | 25.00 | 100.00 | 45.00 | Saucer, after dinner | 6.00 | 15.00 | 10.00 |
| Comport, 5", #2400 | 18.00 | 55.00 | 27.50 | Saucer | 4.00 | 7.50 | 5.00 |
| Comport, 6", #5298 or #5299 | 20.00 | 80.00 | 40.00 | Shaker, ftd., pr | 60.00 | 165.00 | 110.00 |
| Comport, 7", #2375 | 22.00 | 90.00 | 45.00 | Sherbet, high, 6", 6 oz. | 17.50 | 35.00 | 25.00 |
| Comport, 8", #2400 | 40.00 | 125.00 | 55.00 | Sherbet, low, 4¼", 6 oz. | 15.00 | 30.00 | 20.00 |
| Cream soup, ftd. | 15.00 | 45.00 | 32.50 | Sugar, ftd., straight or scalloped top | 12.00 | 25.00 | 20.00 |
| Creamer, ftd. | 12.00 | 25.00 | 17.50 | Sugar cover | 50.00 | 200.00 | 125.00 |
| Creamer, tea | 20.00 | 55.00 | 40.00 | Sugar pail | 65.00 | 210.00 | 130.00 |
| Cup, after dinner | 20.00 | 75.00 | 40.00 | Sugar, tea | 20.00 | 55.00 | 40.00 |
| Cup, ftd. | 15.00 | 30.00 | 22.00 | Sweetmeat | 15.00 | 35.00 | 20.00 |
| Decanter | 400.00 | 1500.00 | 525.00 | Tray, service and lemon | | 325.00 | 275.00 |
| Goblet, claret, 6", 4 oz. | 35.00 | 115.00 | 70.00 | Tray, 11", ctr. hdld. | 20.00 | 45.00 | 35.00 |
| Goblet, cocktail, 5¼", 3 oz. | 20.00 | 45.00 | 32.50 | Tumbler, 2½ oz., ftd. | 20.00 | 60.00 | 35.00 |
| Goblet, cordial, 4", ¾ oz. | 50.00 | 120.00 | 70.00 | Tumbler, 5 oz., 4½", ftd. | 15.00 | 40.00 | 25.00 |
| Goblet, water, 8¼", 10 oz. | 25.00 | 55.00 | 35.00 | Tumbler, 9 oz., 5¼", ftd. | 15.00 | 40.00 | 22.50 |
| Goblet, wine, 5½", 3 oz. | 25.00 | 95.00 | 50.00 | Tumbler, 12 oz., 6", ftd. | 20.00 | 55.00 | 30.00 |
| Grapefruit | 30.00 | 100.00 | 60.00 | Vase, 8", 2 styles | 75.00 | 235.00 | 155.00 |
| Grapefruit liner | 25.00 | 75.00 | 40.00 | Vase, 8½", fan, ftd. | 75.00 | 195.00 | 125.00 |
| Ice bucket | 47.50 | 115.00 | 75.00 | Whipped cream bowl | 10.00 | 20.00 | 14.00 |
| Ice dish | 22.50 | 55.00 | 40.00 | Whipped cream pail | 75.00 | 200.00 | 125.00 |

Note: See stemware identification on page 99.

# KASHMIR, Fostoria Glass Company, 1930 – 1934

Colors: "Topaz" yellow, green; some blue

I am seeing more Kashmir in my travels, but it is not rapidly disappearing as some of the other Fostoria patterns do. This would be a great set to collect in blue. Everyone else is buying June and Versailles and you could sneak up on a beautiful blue set without much competition. I see a lot of yellow for sale, but, as yet, there are few buyers! You could put a set of yellow Kashmir together cheaper than any other yellow Fostoria pattern other than Fairfax.

The stemware and tumbler line is #5099 which is the same line on which Trojan is found.

Both styles of after dinner cups are shown in the picture of blue. The square shaped saucer set is more difficult to find than the round saucer set. Notice that I have found very little green in my travels. Those cup and saucer sets are all I have ever been able to buy!

| | Yellow, Green | Blue | | Yellow, Green | Blue |
|---|---|---|---|---|---|
| Ash tray | 25.00 | 30.00 | Plate, 10", dinner | 40.00 | 55.00 |
| Bowl, cream soup | 22.00 | 25.00 | Plate, 10", grill | 35.00 | 50.00 |
| Bowl, finger | 15.00 | 20.00 | Plate, cake, 10" | 35.00 | |
| Bowl, 5", fruit | 13.00 | 15.00 | Salt & pepper, pr. | 100.00 | 150.00 |
| Bowl, 6", cereal | 25.00 | 30.00 | Sandwich, center hdld. | 35.00 | 40.00 |
| Bowl, 7", soup | 25.00 | 35.00 | Sauce boat, w/liner | 75.00 | 115.00 |
| Bowl, 8½", pickle | 20.00 | 30.00 | Saucer, rnd. | 5.00 | 10.00 |
| Bowl, 9", baker | 37.50 | 45.00 | Saucer, after dinner, sq. | 7.50 | |
| Bowl, 10" | 40.00 | 45.00 | Saucer, after dinner, rnd. | 7.50 | 10.00 |
| Bowl, 12", centerpiece | 40.00 | 50.00 | Stem, ¾ oz., cordial | 85.00 | 110.00 |
| Candlestick, 2" | 15.00 | 17.50 | Stem, 2½ oz., ftd. | 25.00 | 40.00 |
| Candlestick, 3" | 20.00 | 25.00 | Stem, 2 oz., ftd., whiskey | 25.00 | 30.00 |
| Candlestick, 5" | 22.50 | 27.50 | Stem, 2½ oz., wine | 32.00 | 40.00 |
| Candlestick, 9½" | 40.00 | 60.00 | Stem, 3 oz., cocktail | 22.00 | 25.00 |
| Candy, w/cover | 75.00 | 95.00 | Stem, 3½ oz., ftd., cocktail | 22.00 | 25.00 |
| Cheese and cracker set | 65.00 | 85.00 | Stem, 4 oz., claret | 35.00 | 50.00 |
| Comport, 6" | 35.00 | 45.00 | Stem, 4½ oz., oyster cocktail | 16.00 | 18.00 |
| Creamer, ftd. | 17.50 | 20.00 | Stem, 5½ oz., parfait | 30.00 | 40.00 |
| Cup | 15.00 | 20.00 | Stem, 5 oz., ftd., juice | 15.00 | 25.00 |
| Cup, after dinner, flat | 35.00 | | Stem, 5 oz., low sherbet | 13.00 | 20.00 |
| Cup, after dinner, ftd. | 35.00 | 50.00 | Stem, 6 oz., high sherbet | 17.50 | 22.50 |
| Grapefruit | 50.00 | | Stem, 9 oz., water | 20.00 | 35.00 |
| Grapefruit liner | 40.00 | | Stem, 10 oz., ftd., water | 22.00 | 30.00 |
| Ice bucket | 65.00 | 90.00 | Stem, 11 oz. | 22.50 | |
| Oil, ftd. | 275.00 | 425.00 | Stem, 12 oz., ftd. | 25.00 | 35.00 |
| Pitcher, ftd. | 275.00 | 375.00 | Stem, 13 oz., ftd., tea | 25.00 | |
| Plate, 6", bread & butter | 5.00 | 6.00 | Stem, 16 oz., ftd., tea | 35.00 | |
| Plate, 7", salad, rnd. | 6.00 | 7.00 | Sugar, ftd. | 15.00 | 20.00 |
| Plate, 7", salad, sq. | 6.00 | 7.00 | Sugar lid | 45.00 | 75.00 |
| Plate, 8", salad | 8.00 | 10.00 | Vase, 8" | 85.00 | 110.00 |
| Plate, 9" luncheon | 9.00 | 12.00 | | | |

Note: See stemware identification on page 99.

# LARIAT, Blank #1540, A.H. Heisey & Co.

Colors: crystal; rare in black and amber

The cutting most often found on Lariat is Moonglo. This is shown on the stems on the right in the top picture. Both styles of cordials are shown with the Moonglo cutting in that top photo. One cordial has a single loop of Lariat while the other has a double loop. The double loop one is harder to find! A shaker is shown in both photos, but it is a difficult piece to "round-up"; so be on the trail for it.

The ad shown on page 132 is from an October 1948 issue of *Better Homes and Gardens*.

| | Crystal |
|---|---|
| Ash tray, 4" | 15.00 |
| Basket, 7½", bonbon | 100.00 |
| Basket, 8½", ftd. | 165.00 |
| Basket, 10", ftd. | 195.00 |
| Bowl, 2-hdld., cream soup | 40.00 |
| Bowl, 7 quart, punch | 110.00 |
| Bowl, 4", nut, individual | 20.00 |
| Bowl, 7", 2 pt., mayo | 20.00 |
| Bowl, 7", nappy | 15.00 |
| Bowl, 8", flat, nougat | 15.00 |
| Bowl, 9½", camellia | 22.00 |
| Bowl, 10", hdld., celery | 35.00 |
| Bowl, 10½", 2 hdld., salad | 32.00 |
| Bowl, 10½", salad | 32.00 |
| Bowl, 11", 2 hdld., oblong, relish | 25.00 |
| Bowl, 12", floral or fruit | 20.00 |
| Bowl, 13", celery | 22.00 |
| Bowl, 13", gardenia | 25.00 |
| Bowl, 13", oval, floral | 27.00 |
| Candlestick, 1-lite | 15.00 |
| Candlestick, 2-lite | 25.00 |
| Candlestick, 3-lite | 35.00 |
| Candy box, w/cover, caramel | 55.00 |
| Candy, w/cover, 7" | 60.00 |
| Candy, w/cover, 8", w/horsehead finial (rare) | 1,500.00 |
| Cheese, 5", ftd., w/cover | 40.00 |
| Cheese dish, w/cover, 8" | 50.00 |
| Cigarette box | 45.00 |
| Coaster, 4" | 8.00 |
| Compote, 10", w/cover | 100.00 |
| Creamer | 15.00 |
| Creamer & sugar, w/tray, indiv. | 37.50 |
| Cup | 15.00 |
| Cup, punch | 6.00 |
| Ice tub | 75.00 |
| Jar, w/cover, 12", urn | 175.00 |
| Lamp & globe, 7", black-out | 100.00 |
| Lamp & globe, 8", candle, handled | 95.00 |
| Mayonnaise, 5" bowl, 7" plate w/ladle set | 55.00 |

| | Crystal |
|---|---|
| Oil bottle, 4 oz., hdld., w/#133 stopper | 120.00 |
| Oil bottle, 6 oz., oval | 75.00 |
| Plate, 6", finger bowl liner | 7.00 |
| Plate, 7", salad | 10.00 |
| Plate, 8", salad | 12.00 |
| Plate, 11", cookie | 25.00 |
| Plate, 12", demi-torte, rolled edge | 27.00 |
| Plate, 13", deviled egg, round | 150.00 |
| Plate, 14", 2 hdld., sandwich | 50.00 |
| Plate, 15", deviled egg, oval | 185.00 |
| Plate, 21", buffet | 60.00 |
| Platter, 15", oval | 50.00 |
| Salt & pepper, pr. | 200.00 |
| Saucer | 5.00 |
| Stem, 1 oz., cordial, double loop | 250.00 |
| Stem, 1 oz., cordial blown, single loop | 150.00 |
| Stem, 2½ oz., wine, blown | 25.00 |
| Stem, 3½ oz., cocktail, pressed | 15.00 |
| Stem, 3½ oz., cocktail, blown | 15.00 |
| Stem, 3½ oz., wine, pressed | 20.00 |
| Stem, 4 oz., claret, blown | 25.00 |
| Stem, 4¼ oz., oyster cocktail or fruit | 15.00 |
| Stem, 4½ oz., oyster cocktail, blown | 15.00 |
| Stem, 5½ oz., sherbet/saucer champagne blown | 15.00 |
| Stem, 6 oz., low sherbet | 10.00 |
| Stem, 6 oz., sherbet/saucer champagne, pressed | 12.50 |
| Stem, 9 oz., pressed | 20.00 |
| Stem, 10 oz., blown | 20.00 |
| Sugar | 15.00 |
| Tray, rnd., center hdld., w/ball finial | 165.00 |
| Tray for sugar & creamer, 8" 2-handled | 20.00 |
| Tumbler, 5 oz., ftd., juice | 15.00 |
| Tumbler, 5 oz., ftd., juice, blown | 15.00 |
| Tumbler, 12 oz., ftd., ice tea | 18.00 |
| Tumbler, 12 oz., ftd., ice tea, blown | 18.00 |
| Vase, 7", ftd., fan | 25.00 |
| Vase, swung | 125.00 |

CORDIAL, YET CAREFREE··· *that's Heisey Lariat*

*Lariat* carries an air of matchless charm, expressed in its lighthearted loop design. Cordial, yet carefree, it will be esteemed by you as highly as any of your treasures. Rare as the western air, this hand-cast crystal gaily blends your own good taste with the trend that is today. Your Heisey dealer will be pleased to show you the complete selection of LARIAT stemware and table accessories.

*Lariat is one of several patterns pictured in "CHOOSING YOUR CRYSTAL PATTERN," an informal, streamlined guide to proper crystal, china and silver. Send 10c to Department HB, A. H. HEISEY & CO., NEWARK, OHIO*

THE FINEST IN GLASSWARE, MADE IN AMERICA BY HANL

# LODESTAR, Pattern #1632, A.H. Heisey & Co.

Color: Dawn

Only this Heisey pattern **in the Dawn color** is **named Lodestar.** Crystal pieces in the pattern become Satellite and the prices drop dramatically! Note the star-like shape on each base design.

| | Dawn |
|---|---|
| Ash tray | 80.00 |
| Bowl, 4½", sauce dish, #1626 | 35.00 |
| Bowl, 5", mayonnaise | 55.00 |
| Bowl, 6¾", #1565 | 45.00 |
| Bowl, 8" | 55.00 |
| Bowl, 11", crimped | 95.00 |
| Bowl, 12", deep floral | 75.00 |
| Candleblock, 2¾" tall, 1-lite star, #1543, pr., (Satellite) | 275.00 |
| Candlestick, 2" tall, 1-lite centerpiece, pr. | 100.00 |
| Candlestick, 5¾" tall, 2-lite, pr. | 600.00 |
| Candy jar, w/cover, 5" | 135.00 |
| Celery, 10" | 60.00 |
| Creamer | 50.00 |
| Creamer, w/handle | 85.00 |
| Jar, w/cover, 8", #1626 | 140.00 |
| Pitcher, 1 qt., #1626 | 150.00 |
| Plate, 8½" | 65.00 |
| Plate, 14" | 85.00 |
| Relish, 7½", 3 pt. | 55.00 |
| Salt and pepper, pr., #1485 | 250.00 |
| Sugar | 50.00 |
| Sugar, w/handles | 85.00 |
| Tumbler, 6 oz., juice | 40.00 |
| Vase, 8", #1626 | 140.00 |
| Vase, 8", crimped, #1626 | 175.00 |

# MINUET, Etching #1530, QUEEN ANN Blank, #1509; TOUJOURS Blank, #1511; SYMPHONE Blank, #5010, et. al.; 1939 – 1950's

Colors: crystal

Minuet is one of the Heisey patterns that everyone seems to recognize. I have seen one piece in the middle of a junque shop and the owner still knew it was Minuet. The price was not unreasonable, but I already had a creamer for my photograph.

The finger bowl shown in the foreground of the bottom photograph was bought on a Queen Ann plate.

Stemware is rather abundant, but serving pieces are difficult to find. The last cocktail icer I had sat on our table about fifteen minutes when we put it out for sale.

| | Crystal | | Crystal |
|---|---|---|---|
| Bell, dinner, #3408 | 75.00 | Plate, 7", salad | 10.00 |
| Bowl, finger, #3309 | 50.00 | Plate, 7", salad, #1511 TOUJOURS | 12.00 |
| Bowl, 6", ftd., mint | 17.50 | Plate, 8", luncheon | 15.00 |
| Bowl, 6", ftd., 2 hdld., jelly | 20.00 | Plate, 8", luncheon, #1511 TOUJOURS | 22.50 |
| Bowl, 6½", salad dressings | 25.00 | Plate, 10½", service | 55.00 |
| Bowl, 7", salad dressings | 30.00 | Plate, 12", rnd., 2 hdld., sandwich | 50.00 |
| Bowl, 7", triplex, relish | 35.00 | Plate, 13", floral, salver, #1511 TOUJOURS | 50.00 |
| Bowl, 7½", sauce, ftd. | 30.00 | Plate, 14", torte, #1511 TOUJOURS | 50.00 |
| Bowl, 9½", 3 pt., "5 o'clock" relish | 60.00 | Plate, 15", sand., #1511 TOUJOURS | 55.00 |
| Bowl, 10", salad, #1511 TOUJOURS | 60.00 | Plate, 16", snack rack, w/#1477 center | 80.00 |
| Bowl, 11", 3 pt., "5 o'clock" relish | 65.00 | Salt & pepper, pr. (#10) | 65.00 |
| Bowl, 11", ftd., floral | 60.00 | Saucer | 10.00 |
| Bowl, 12", oval, floral, #1511 TOUJOURS | 60.00 | Stem, #5010, SYMPHONE, 1 oz., cordial | 135.00 |
| Bowl, 12", oval, #1514 | 60.00 | Stem, #5010, 2½ oz., wine | 70.00 |
| Bowl, 13", floral, #1511 TOUJOURS | 55.00 | Stem, #5010, 3½ oz., cocktail | 35.00 |
| Bowl, 13", pickle & olive | 35.00 | Stem, #5010, 4 oz., claret | 37.50 |
| Bowl, 13½", shallow salad | 75.00 | Stem, #5010, 4½ oz., oyster cocktail | 20.00 |
| Candelabrum, 1-lite w/prisms | 95.00 | Stem, #5010, 6 oz., saucer champagne | 17.50 |
| Candelabrum, 2-lite, bobeche & prisms | 165.00 | Stem, #5010, 6 oz., sherbet | 15.00 |
| Candlestick, 1-lite, #112 | 30.00 | Stem, #5010, 9 oz., water | 30.00 |
| Candlestick, 2-lite, #1511 TOUJOURS | 145.00 | Sugar, indiv., #1511 TOUJOURS | 37.50 |
| Candlestick, 3-lite, #142 CASCADE | 65.00 | Sugar, indiv., #1509 QUEEN ANN | 37.50 |
| Candlestick, 5", 2-lite, #134 TRIDENT | 42.50 | Sugar dolphin ft., #1509 QUEEN ANN | 40.00 |
| Centerpiece vase & prisms #1511 TOUJOURS | 185.00 | Sugar, #1511 TOUJOURS | 50.00 |
| Cocktail icer, w/liner #3304 UNIVERSAL | 195.00 | Tray, 12", celery, #1511 TOUJOURS | 32.50 |
| Comport, 5½", #5010 | 35.00 | Tray, 15", social hour | 65.00 |
| Comport, 7½", #1511 TOUJOURS | 50.00 | Tray for indiv. sugar & creamer | 25.00 |
| Creamer, #1511 TOUJOURS | 50.00 | Tumbler, #5010, 5 oz., fruit juice | 32.50 |
| Creamer, dolphin ft. | 42.50 | Tumbler, #5010, 9 oz., low ftd., water | 35.00 |
| Creamer, indiv., #1509 QUEEN ANN | 37.50 | Tumbler, #5010, 12 oz., tea | 45.00 |
| Creamer, indiv., #1511 TOUJOURS | 37.50 | Tumbler, #2351, 12 oz., tea | 40.00 |
| Cup | 37.50 | Vase, 5", #5013 | 45.00 |
| Ice bucket, dolphin ft. | 150.00 | Vase, 5½", ftd., #1511 TOUJOURS | 55.00 |
| Marmalade, w/cover, #1511 TOUJOURS (apple shape) | 95.00 | Vase, 6", urn, #5012 | 70.00 |
| Mayonnaise, 5½", dolphin ft. | 45.00 | Vase, 7½", urn, #5012 | 85.00 |
| Mayonnaise, ftd., #1511 TOUJOURS | 45.00 | Vase, 8", #4196 | 85.00 |
| Pitcher, 73 oz., #4164 | 285.00 | Vase, 9", urn, #5012 | 95.00 |
| Plate, 7", mayonnaise liner | 10.00 | Vase, 10", #4192 | 95.00 |
| | | Vase, 10", #4192, SATURN optic | 110.00 |

# MT. VERNON, Cambridge Glass Company, late 1920's – 1940's

Colors: amber, crystal, Carmen, Royal Blue, Heatherbloom, Emerald green (light and dark); rare in Violet

The range of colors in Mt. Vernon gives collectors a wide choice. Large sets can be accumulated in only amber and crystal. Red, cobalt blue, and Heatherbloom are found, but not in the large quantities that collectors would like to see. Prices for those three colors will run as high as double the prices listed for amber and crystal. These latter colors are impossible to acquire in anything except luncheon sets.

| Item | Amber/Crystal | Item | Amber/Crystal |
|---|---|---|---|
| Ash tray, 3½", #63 | 8.00 | Honey jar, w/cover (marmalade), #74 | 30.00 |
| Ash tray, 4", #68 | 12.00 | Ice bucket, w/tongs, #92 | 35.00 |
| Ash tray, 6" x 4½", oval, #71 | 12.00 | Lamp, 9" hurricane, #1607 | 70.00 |
| Bonbon, 7", ftd., #10 | 12.50 | Mayonnaise, divided, 2 spoons, #107 | 25.00 |
| Bottle, bitters, 2½ oz., #62 | 55.00 | Mug, 14 oz., stein, #84 | 27.50 |
| Bottle, 7 oz., sq., toilet, #18 | 65.00 | Mustard, w/cover, 2½ oz., #28 | 22.00 |
| Bowl, finger, #23 | 10.00 | Pickle, 6", 1 hdld., #78 | 12.00 |
| Bowl, 4½", ivy ball or rose, ftd., #12 | 27.50 | Pitcher, 50 oz., #90 | 80.00 |
| Bowl, 5¼", fruit, #6 | 10.00 | Pitcher, 66 oz., #13 | 85.00 |
| Bowl, 6", cereal, #32 | 12.50 | Pitcher, 80 oz., ball, #95 | 95.00 |
| Bowl, 6", preserve, #76 | 12.00 | Pitcher, 86 oz., #91 | 115.00 |
| Bowl, 6½", rose, #106 | 18.00 | Plate, finger bowl liner, #23 | 4.00 |
| Bowl, 8", pickle, #65 | 17.50 | Plate, 6", bread & butter, #4 | 3.00 |
| Bowl, 8½", 4 pt., 2 hdld., sweetmeat, #105 | 32.00 | Plate, 6⅜", bread & butter, #19 | 4.00 |
| Bowl, 10", 2 hdld., #39 | 20.00 | Plate, 8½", salad, #5 | 7.00 |
| Bowl, 10½", deep, #43 | 30.00 | Plate, 10½", dinner, #40 | 30.00 |
| Bowl, 10½", salad, #120 | 25.00 | Plate, 11½", hdld., #37 | 20.00 |
| Bowl, 11", oval, 4 ftd., #136 | 27.50 | Relish, 6", 2 pt., 2 hdld., #106 | 12.00 |
| Bowl, 11", oval, #135 | 25.00 | Relish, 8", 2 pt., hdld., #101 | 17.50 |
| Bowl, 11½", belled, #128 | 30.00 | Relish, 8", 3 pt., 3 hdld., #103 | 20.00 |
| Bowl, 11½", shallow, #126 | 30.00 | Relish, 11", 3 part, #200 | 25.00 |
| Bowl, 11½", shallow cupped, #61 | 30.00 | Relish, 12", 2 part, #80 | 30.00 |
| Bowl, 12", flanged, rolled edge, #129 | 32.50 | Relish, 12", 5 part, #104 | 30.00 |
| Bowl, 12", oblong, crimped, #118 | 32.50 | Salt, indiv., #24 | 7.00 |
| Bowl, 12", rolled edge, crimped, #117 | 32.50 | Salt, oval, 2 hdld., #102 | 12.00 |
| Bowl, 12½", flanged, rolled edge, #45 | 35.00 | Salt & pepper, pr., #28 | 22.50 |
| Bowl, 12½", flared, #121 | 35.00 | Salt & pepper, pr., short, #88 | 20.00 |
| Bowl, 12½", flared, #44 | 35.00 | Salt & pepper, tall, #89 | 25.00 |
| Bowl, 13", shallow, crimped, #116 | 35.00 | Salt dip, #24 | 9.00 |
| Box, 3", w/cover, round, #16 | 27.50 | Sauce boat & ladle, tab hdld., #30-445 | 60.00 |
| Box, 4", w/cover, sq., #17 | 30.00 | Saucer, #7 | 7.50 |
| Box, 4½", w/cover, ftd., round, #15 | 37.50 | Stem, 3 oz., wine, #27 | 13.50 |
| Butter tub, w/cover, #73 | 65.00 | Stem, 3½ oz., cocktail, #26 | 9.00 |
| Cake stand, 10½" ftd., #150 | 35.00 | Stem, 4 oz., oyster cocktail, #41 | 9.00 |
| Candelabrum, 13½", #38 | 50.00 | Stem, 4½ oz., claret, #25 | 13.50 |
| Candlestick, 4", #130 | 10.00 | Stem, 4½ oz., low sherbet, #42 | 7.50 |
| Candlestick, 5", 2-lite, #110 | 20.00 | Stem, 6½ oz., tall sherbet, #2 | 10.00 |
| Candlestick, 8", #35 | 25.00 | Stem, 10 oz., water, #1 | 15.00 |
| Candy, w/cover, 1 lb., ftd., #9 | 65.00 | Sugar, ftd., #8 | 10.00 |
| Celery, 10½", #79 | 15.00 | Sugar, indiv., #4 | 12.00 |
| Celery, 11", #98 | 17.50 | Sugar, #86 | 10.00 |
| Celery, 12", #79 | 20.00 | Tray, for indiv., sugar & creamer, #4 | 10.00 |
| Cigarette box, 6", w/cover, oval, #69 | 27.50 | Tumbler, 1 oz., ftd., cordial, #87 | 22.00 |
| Cigarette holder, #66 | 15.00 | Tumbler, 2 oz., whiskey, #55 | 10.00 |
| Coaster, 3", plain, #60 | 5.00 | Tumbler, 3 oz., ftd., juice, #22 | 9.00 |
| Coaster, 3", ribbed, #70 | 5.00 | Tumbler, 5 oz., #56 | 12.00 |
| Cocktail icer, 2 pc., #85 | 22.50 | Tumbler, 5 oz., ftd., #21 | 12.00 |
| Cologne, 2½ oz., w/stopper, #1340 | 35.00 | Tumbler, 7 oz., old-fashioned, #57 | 15.00 |
| Comport, 4½", #33 | 12.00 | Tumbler, 10 oz., ftd., water, #3 | 15.00 |
| Comport, 5½", 2 hdld., #77 | 15.00 | Tumbler, 10 oz., table, #51 | 12.00 |
| Comport, 6", #34 | 15.00 | Tumbler, 10 oz., tall, #58 | 12.00 |
| Comport, 6½", #97 | 17.50 | Tumbler, 12 oz., barrel shape, #13 | 15.00 |
| Comport, 6½", belled, #96 | 22.50 | Tumbler, 12 oz., ftd., tea, #20 | 17.00 |
| Comport, 7½" #11 | 25.00 | Tumbler, 14 oz., barrel shape, #14 | 20.00 |
| Comport, 8", #81 | 25.00 | Tumbler, 14 oz., tall, #59 | 22.00 |
| Comport, 9", oval, 2 hdld., #100 | 27.50 | Urn, w/cover (same as candy), #9 | 65.00 |
| Comport, 9½", #99 | 27.50 | Vase, 5", #42 | 15.00 |
| Creamer, ftd., #8 | 10.00 | Vase, 6", crimped, #119 | 20.00 |
| Creamer, indiv., #4 | 10.00 | Vase, 6", ftd., #50 | 25.00 |
| Creamer, #86 | 10.00 | Vase, 6½", squat, #107 | 27.50 |
| Cup, #7 | 6.50 | Vase, 7", #58 | 30.00 |
| Decanter, 11 oz., #47 | 50.00 | Vase, 7", ftd., #54 | 35.00 |
| Decanter, 40 oz., w/stopper, #52 | 70.00 | Vase, 10", ftd., #46 | 50.00 |

# NAVARRE, (Plate Etching #327) Fostoria Glass Company, 1937 – 1980

Colors: crystal; all other colors found made very late

Navarre's popularity continues to grow; so does the cost. That is the price you pay for collecting a much sought pattern. By the same token, a highly collected pattern is easier to sell when the time comes. Harder to find pieces increase in price the fastest. It is better to buy them when you see them or take the chance it will cost even more if and when you see it again.

As of now, I am going to stick to pricing the older crystal pieces of Navarre. Colors of pink, blue, and green were all made in the 1970's as were additional crystal pieces not originally made in the late 1930's and the 1940's. The later pieces included carafes, roemer wines, continental champagnes and brandies. You can find all of these later pieces in my new *Collectible Glassware from the 40's, 50's & 60's....*

Most of these later pieces were signed "Fostoria" although some carried only a sticker. I am telling you this to make you aware of the colors made in Navarre. A few of the Depression era glass shows do not allow this glass to be sold since it was so recently manufactured.

| | Crystal | | Crystal |
|---|---|---|---|
| Bell, dinner | 45.00 | Plate, #2440, 7½", salad | 15.00 |
| Bowl, #2496, 4", square, hdld. | 12.00 | Plate, #2440, 8½", luncheon | 20.00 |
| Bowl, #2496, 4⅜", hdld. | 12.00 | Plate, #2440, 9½", dinner | 42.50 |
| Bowl, #869, 4½", finger | 42.50 | Plate, #2496, 10", hdld., cake | 47.50 |
| Bowl, #2496, 4⅝", tri-cornered | 15.00 | Plate, #2440, 10½" oval cake | 47.50 |
| Bowl, #2496, 5", hdld., ftd. | 18.50 | Plate, #2496, 14", torte | 57.50 |
| Bowl, #2496, 6", square, sweetmeat | 17.50 | Plate, #2464, 16", torte | 85.00 |
| Bowl, #2496, 6¼", 3 ftd., nut | 18.50 | Relish, #2496, 6", 2 part, square | 32.50 |
| Bowl, #2496, 7⅜", ftd., bonbon | 27.50 | Relish, #2496, 10" x 7½", 3 part | 47.50 |
| Bowl, #2496, 10", oval, floating garden | 55.00 | Relish, #2496, 10", 4 part | 52.50 |
| Bowl, #2496, 10½", hdld., ftd. | 65.00 | Relish, #2419, 13¼", 5 part | 87.50 |
| Bowl, #2470½, 10½", ftd. | 57.50 | Salt & pepper, #2364, 3¼", flat, pr. | 57.50 |
| Bowl, #2496, 12", flared | 62.50 | Salt & pepper, #2375, 3½", ftd., pr. | 100.00 |
| Bowl, #2545, 12½", oval, "Flame" | 57.50 | Salad dressing bottle, #2083, 6½" | 325.00 |
| Candlestick, #2496, 4" | 20.00 | Sauce dish, #2496, div. mayo., 6½" | 37.50 |
| Candlestick, #2496, 4½", double | 35.00 | Sauce dish, #2496, 6½" x 5¼" | 125.00 |
| Candlestick, #2472, 5", double | 42.50 | Sauce dish liner, #2496, 8" oval | 27.50 |
| Candlestick, #2496, 5½" | 30.00 | Saucer, #2440 | 6.00 |
| Candlestick, #2496, 6", triple | 45.00 | Stem, #6106, 1 oz., cordial, 3⅞" | 47.50 |
| Candlestick, #2545, 6¾", double, "Flame" | 50.00 | Stem, #6106, 3¼ oz., wine, 5½" | 35.00 |
| Candlestick, #2482, 6¾", triple | 50.00 | Stem, #6106, 3½ oz., cocktail, 6" | 25.00 |
| Candy, w/cover, #2496, 3 part | 115.00 | Stem, #6106, 4 oz., oyster cocktail, 3⅝" | 27.50 |
| Celery, #2440, 9" | 30.00 | Stem, #6106, 4½ oz., claret, 6½" | 40.00 |
| Celery, #2496, 11" | 40.00 | Stem, #6106, 6 oz., low sherbet, 4⅜" | 24.00 |
| Comport, #2496, 3¼", cheese | 27.50 | Stem, #6106, 6 oz., saucer champagne, 5⅝" | 24.00 |
| Comport, #2400, 4½" | 30.00 | | |
| Comport, #2496, 4¾" | 30.00 | Stem, #6106, 10 oz., water, 7⅝" | 30.00 |
| Cracker, #2496, 11" plate | 42.50 | Sugar, #2440, 3⅝", ftd. | 18.00 |
| Creamer, #2440, 4¼", ftd. | 20.00 | Sugar, #2496, individual | 16.00 |
| Creamer, #2496, individual | 17.50 | Syrup, #2586, metal cut-off top, 5½" | 325.00 |
| Cup, #2440 | 18.00 | Tid bit, #2496, 8¼", 3 ftd., turned up edge | 22.00 |
| Ice bucket, #2496, 4⅜" high | 110.00 | Tray, #2496½", for ind. sugar/creamer | 22.00 |
| Ice bucket, #2375, 6" high | 145.00 | Tumbler, #6106, 5 oz., ftd., juice, 4⅝" | 25.00 |
| Mayonnaise, #2375, 3 piece | 67.50 | Tumbler, #6106, 10 oz., ftd., water, 5⅜" | 25.00 |
| Mayonnaise, #2496½", 3 piece | 67.50 | Tumbler, #6106, 13 oz., ftd., tea, 5⅞" | 31.50 |
| Pickle, #2496, 8" | 27.50 | Vase, #4108, 5" | 85.00 |
| Pickle, #2440, 8½" | 30.00 | Vase, #4121, 5" | 85.00 |
| Pitcher, #5000, 48 oz., ftd. | 325.00 | Vase, #4128, 5" | 85.00 |
| Plate, #2440, 6", bread/butter | 11.00 | Vase, #2470, 10", ftd. | 150.00 |

# NEW ERA, #4044, A.H. Heisey Co., 1934 – 1941; 1944 – 1957 (stems, celery tray, and candlesticks)

Colors: crystal, frosted crystal, some cobalt with crystal stem and foot.

New Era is being sought by "Art Deco" collectors. Many pieces in this pattern were monogrammed. Today, those pieces are very difficult to sell at any price unless you can find someone with the same three initials. Plates without scratches and after dinner cups and saucers will probably keep you searching for a long time!

The double branched candelabra with the New Era bobeches is a prize. These are not so hard to find as very desirable to own!

The cordial shown below is cut with "Venus" pattern!

| | Crystal | | Crystal |
|---|---|---|---|
| Ash tray or indiv. nut | 30.00 | Stem, 1 oz. cordial | 45.00 |
| Bottle, rye w/stopper | 120.00 | Stem, 3 oz. wine | 35.00 |
| Bowl, 11" floral | 35.00 | Stem, 3½ oz., high, cocktail | 10.00 |
| Candelabra, 2-lite w/2 #4044 bobeche | | Stem, 3½ oz. oyster cocktail | 10.00 |
| & prisms | 70.00 | Stem, 4 oz. claret | 15.00 |
| Creamer | 35.00 | Stem, 6 oz. champagne | 12.50 |
| Cup | 10.00 | Stem, 10 oz. goblet | 15.00 |
| Cup, after dinner | 60.00 | Stem, low, 6 oz. sherbet | 10.00 |
| Pilsner, 8 oz. | 25.00 | Sugar | 35.00 |
| Pilsner, 12 oz. | 30.00 | Tray, 13" celery | 30.00 |
| Plate, 5½" x 4½" bread & butter | 15.00 | Tumbler, 5 oz. ftd. soda | 7.00 |
| Plate, 9"x 7" | 25.00 | Tumbler, 8 oz. ftd. soda | 10.00 |
| Plate, 10" x 8" | 40.00 | Tumbler, 12 oz. ftd. soda | 12.50 |
| Relish, 13" 3-part | 25.00 | Tumbler, 14 oz. ftd. soda | 15.00 |
| Saucer | 5.00 | Tumbler, low, footed 10 oz. | 10.00 |
| Saucer, after dinner | 10.00 | | |

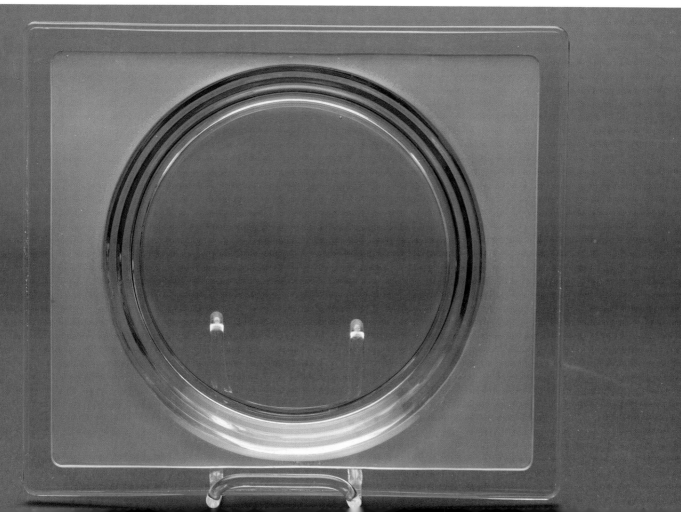

# OCTAGON, Blank #1231 – Ribbed; also Blank #500 and Blank #1229, A.H. Heisey & Co.

Colors: crystal, "Flamingo" pink, "Sahara" yellow, "Moongleam" green, "Hawthorne" orchid, "Marigold," a deep, amber/yellow, and "Dawn"

Two items of Marigold Octagon are pictured here. It is the only place that Heisey color is shown in this book. Be careful in buying Marigold since the color peels and cracks very easily. Then, it becomes wanted by no one!

Octagon is one of those Heisey patterns that everyone recognizes, since it is usually marked; yet few collectors buy it. True, it is one of the plainer patterns, but it does come in a multitude of colors! The piece in the prices below that jumps out at you is the 12", 4-part, tray. Otherwise, Octagon is reasonably priced and is frequently just sitting around waiting for a new home.

|  | Crystal | Flam. | Sahara | Moon. | Hawth. | Marigold |
|---|---|---|---|---|---|---|
| Basket, 5", #500. | 85.00 | 250.00 | 260.00 | 300.00 | 450.00 | |
| Bonbon, 6", sides up, #1229 | 5.00 | 15.00 | 15.00 | 20.00 | 33.00 | |
| Bowl, cream soup, 2 hdld. | 10.00 | 20.00 | 25.00 | 30.00 | 40.00 | |
| Bowl, 2-hdld, ind. nut bowl | 10.00 | 17.50 | 25.00 | 20.00 | 60.00 | 65.00 |
| Bowl, 5½", jelly, #1229 | 10.00 | 15.00 | 15.00 | 17.00 | 25.00 | |
| Bowl, 6", mint, #1229 | 10.00 | 15.00 | 15.00 | 17.00 | 25.00 | 30.00 |
| Bowl, 6", #500 | 14.00 | 20.00 | 22.00 | 25.00 | 35.00 | |
| Bowl, 6½", grapefruit | 10.00 | 20.00 | 22.00 | 25.00 | 35.00 | |
| Bowl, 8", ftd., #1229 comport | 15.00 | 25.00 | 35.00 | 45.00 | 55.00 | |
| Bowl, 9", flat soup | 10.00 | 15.00 | 20.00 | 27.50 | 30.00 | |
| Bowl, 9", vegetable | 15.00 | 20.00 | 25.00 | 30.00 | 50.00 | |
| Candlestick, 3", 1-lite | 10.00 | 25.00 | 27.00 | 30.00 | 40.00 | |
| Cheese dish, 6", 2 hdld., #1229 | 7.00 | 10.00 | 10.00 | 12.00 | 15.00 | |
| Creamer #500 | 7.00 | 20.00 | 30.00 | 35.00 | 40.00 | |
| Creamer, hotel | 10.00 | 15.00 | 15.00 | 20.00 | 30.00 | |
| Cup, after dinner | 5.00 | 15.00 | 15.00 | 20.00 | 42.00 | |
| Cup #1231 | 5.00 | 15.00 | 20.00 | 20.00 | 35.00 | |
| Dish, frozen dessert, #500 | 10.00 | 20.00 | 20.00 | 20.00 | 35.00 | 50.00 |
| Ice tub, #500 | 30.00 | 70.00 | 75.00 | 80.00 | 115.00 | 150.00 |
| Mayonnaise, 5½", ftd., #1229 | 10.00 | 25.00 | 30.00 | 35.00 | 45.00 | |
| Nut, two hndld. | 10.00 | 18.00 | 18.00 | 20.00 | 60.00 | 70.00 |
| Plate, cream soup liner | 3.00 | 5.00 | 7.00 | 9.00 | 12.00 | |
| Plate, 6" | 4.00 | 8.00 | 8.00 | 10.00 | 15.00 | |
| Plate, 7", bread | 5.00 | 10.00 | 10.00 | 15.00 | 20.00 | |
| Plate, 8", luncheon | 7.00 | 10.00 | 10.00 | 15.00 | 25.00 | |
| Plate, 10", sand., #1229 | 15.00 | 20.00 | 25.00 | 30.00 | 35.00 | |
| Plate, 10", muffin, #1229 sides up | 15.00 | 25.00 | 30.00 | 35.00 | 40.00 | |
| Plate, 10½" | 17.00 | 25.00 | 30.00 | 35.00 | 45.00 | |
| Plate, 10½", ctr. hdld., sandwich | 25.00 | 40.00 | 40.00 | 45.00 | 70.00 | |
| Plate, 12", muffin, #1229 sides up | 20.00 | 27.00 | 30.00 | 35.00 | 45.00 | |
| Plate, 13", hors d'oeuvre, #1229 | 20.00 | 30.00 | 30.00 | 40.00 | 55.00 | |
| Plate, 14" | 22.00 | 25.00 | 30.00 | 35.00 | 50.00 | |
| Platter, 12¾" oval | 20.00 | 25.00 | 30.00 | 40.00 | 50.00 | |
| Saucer, after dinner | 2.00 | 5.00 | 6.00 | 6.00 | 12.00 | |
| Saucer, #1231 | 2.00 | 5.00 | 6.00 | 7.00 | 9.00 | |
| Sugar #500 | 7.00 | 20.00 | 30.00 | 35.00 | 40.00 | |
| Sugar, hotel | 10.00 | 15.00 | 15.00 | 20.00 | 30.00 | |
| Tray, 6", oblong, #500 | 5.00 | 10.00 | 12.00 | 12.00 | 20.00 | |
| Tray, 9", celery | 5.00 | 10.00 | 15.00 | 15.00 | 25.00 | |
| Tray, 12", celery | 7.00 | 15.00 | 17.00 | 17.00 | 35.00 | (Dawn) |
| Tray, 12", 4 pt., #500 variety | 40.00 | 100.00 | 125.00 | 140.00 | 250.00 | 300.00 |

## OLD COLONY, Empress Blank #1401; Caracassone Blank #3390; and Old Dominion Blank #3380, A.H. Heisey & Co., 1930 – 1939

Colors: crystal, "Flamingo" pink, "Sahara" yellow, "Moongleam" green, "Marigold," a deep, amber/yellow, and cobalt

| | Crystal | Flam. | Sahara | Moon. | Marigold |
|---|---|---|---|---|---|
| Bouillon cup, 2 hdld., ftd. | 12.50 | 18.00 | 20.00 | 24.00 | |
| Bowl, finger, #4075 | 5.50 | 10.00 | 11.00 | 14.00 | 18.00 |
| Bowl, ftd., finger, #3390 | 5.50 | 16.00 | 21.00 | 27.50 | |
| Bowl, 4½", nappy | 7.00 | 10.00 | 12.50 | 15.00 | |
| Bowl, 5", ftd., 2 hdld. | 12.50 | 17.50 | 22.50 | 27.50 | |
| Bowl, 6", ftd., 2 hdld., jelly | 15.00 | 20.00 | 25.00 | 32.50 | |
| Bowl, 6", dolp. ftd., mint | 16.00 | 22.00 | 27.50 | 35.00 | |
| Bowl, 7", triplex, dish | 15.00 | 22.00 | 25.00 | 28.00 | |
| Bowl, 7½", dolphin ftd., nappy | 22.00 | 60.00 | 65.00 | 75.00 | |
| Bowl, 8", nappy | 25.00 | 35.00 | 40.00 | 42.50 | |
| Bowl, 8½", ftd., floral, 2 hdld. | 32.00 | 47.00 | 57.50 | 67.50 | |
| Bowl, 9", 3 hdld. | 36.00 | 75.00 | 90.00 | 95.00 | |
| Bowl, 10", rnd., 2 hdld., salad | 32.00 | 47.50 | 57.50 | 65.00 | |
| Bowl, 10", sq., salad, 2 hdld. | 30.00 | 45.00 | 55.00 | 65.00 | |
| Bowl, 10", oval, dessert, 2 hdld. | 30.00 | 40.00 | 50.00 | 62.50 | |
| Bowl, 10", oval, veg. | 30.00 | 34.00 | 42.00 | 50.00 | |
| Bowl, 11", floral, dolphin ft. | 32.00 | 70.00 | 80.00 | 95.00 | |
| Bowl, 13", ftd., flared | 30.00 | 35.00 | 40.00 | 45.00 | |
| Bowl, 13", 2 pt., pickle & olive | 12.50 | 20.00 | 22.50 | 27.50 | |
| Cigarette holder, #3390 (Cobalt $100.00) | 16.00 | 47.50 | 42.50 | 55.00 | |
| Comport, 7", oval, ftd. | 40.00 | 75.00 | 80.00 | 85.00 | |
| Comport, 7", ftd., #3368 | 30.00 | 57.50 | 62.50 | 85.00 | 95.00 |
| Cream soup, 2 hdld. | 12.00 | 20.00 | 22.00 | 27.00 | |
| Creamer, dolphin ft. | 20.00 | 32.00 | 45.00 | 50.00 | |
| Creamer, indiv. | 15.00 | 30.00 | 40.00 | 37.50 | |
| Cup, after dinner | 12.00 | 25.00 | 35.00 | 50.00 | |
| Cup | 10.00 | 26.00 | 32.00 | 38.00 | |
| Decanter, 1 pt. | 150.00 | 300.00 | 275.00 | 525.00 | |
| Flagon, 12 oz., #3390 | 25.00 | 55.00 | 55.00 | 85.00 | |
| Grapefruit, 6" | 15.00 | 23.00 | 30.00 | 35.00 | |
| Grapefruit, ftd., #3380 | 10.00 | 16.00 | 18.00 | 20.00 | 30.00 |
| Ice tub, dolphin ft. | 42.50 | 110.00 | 115.00 | 135.00 | |
| Mayonnaise, 5½", dolp. ft. | 36.00 | 55.00 | 70.00 | 80.00 | |
| Oil, 4 oz., ftd. | 42.50 | 70.00 | 105.00 | 120.00 | |
| Pitcher, 3 pt., #3390 | 90.00 | 245.00 | 210.00 | 400.00 | |
| Pitcher, 3 pt., dolphin ft. | 85.00 | 195.00 | 200.00 | 210.00 | |
| Plate, bouillon | 5.00 | 8.00 | 12.00 | 15.00 | |
| Plate, cream soup | 5.00 | 8.00 | 12.00 | 15.00 | |
| Plate, 4½", rnd. | 3.00 | 6.00 | 7.00 | 8.00 | |
| Plate, 6", rnd. | 6.00 | 12.00 | 15.00 | 18.00 | |
| Plate, 6", sq. | 6.00 | 12.00 | 15.00 | 18.00 | |
| Plate, 7", rnd. | 8.00 | 14.00 | 18.00 | 20.00 | |
| Plate, 7", sq. | 8.00 | 14.00 | 18.00 | 20.00 | |
| Plate, 8", rnd. | 10.00 | 17.00 | 22.00 | 27.00 | |
| Plate, 8", sq. | 10.00 | 17.00 | 22.00 | 27.00 | |
| Plate, 9", rnd. | 15.00 | 22.00 | 25.00 | 28.00 | |
| Plate, 10½", rnd. | 28.50 | 60.00 | 70.00 | 75.00 | |
| Plate, 10½", sq. | 27.50 | 50.00 | 65.00 | 70.00 | |
| Plate, 12", rnd. | 31.00 | 57.50 | 70.00 | 75.00 | |
| Plate, 12", 2 hdld., rnd., muffin | 31.00 | 57.50 | 70.00 | 75.00 | |
| Plate, 12", 2 hdld., rnd., sand. | 31.00 | 57.50 | 70.00 | 75.00 | |
| Plate, 13", 2 hdld., sq., sand. | 35.00 | 40.00 | 45.00 | 50.00 | |
| Plate, 13", 2 hdld., sq., muffin | 35.00 | 40.00 | 45.00 | 50.00 | |
| Platter, 14", oval | 25.00 | 35.00 | 40.00 | 45.00 | |
| Salt & pepper, pr. | 52.50 | 80.00 | 110.00 | 130.00 | |
| Saucer, sq. | 4.00 | 8.00 | 10.00 | 10.00 | |
| Saucer, rnd. | 4.00 | 8.00 | 10.00 | 10.00 | |
| Stem, #3380, 1 oz., cordial | 75.00 | 135.00 | 135.00 | 155.00 | 375.00 |
| Stem, #3380, 2½ oz., wine | 18.00 | 40.00 | 35.00 | 50.00 | 75.00 |
| Stem, #3380, 3 oz., cocktail | 13.00 | 34.00 | 25.00 | 40.00 | 60.00 |
| Stem, #3380, 4 oz., oyster/cocktail | 8.00 | 13.00 | 15.00 | 17.00 | 25.00 |
| Stem, #3380, 4 oz., claret | 20.00 | 50.00 | 40.00 | 55.00 | 65.00 |
| Stem, #3380, 5 oz., parfait | 10.00 | 15.00 | 15.00 | 17.00 | 40.00 |

| | Crystal | Flam. | Sahara | Moon. | Marigold |
|---|---|---|---|---|---|
| Stem, #3380, 6 oz., champagne | 8.00 | 13.00 | 15.00 | 17.00 | 25.00 |
| Stem, #3380, 6 oz., sherbet | 6.00 | 11.00 | 13.00 | 15.00 | 25.00 |
| Stem, #3380, 10 oz., short soda | 7.00 | 18.00 | 15.00 | 22.00 | 30.00 |
| Stem, #3380, 10 oz., tall soda | | 21.00 | 18.00 | 25.00 | 32.50 |
| Stem, #3390, 1 oz., cordial | 50.00 | 130.00 | 125.00 | 165.00 | |
| Stem, #3390, 2½ oz., wine | 12.00 | 20.00 | 27.50 | 35.00 | |
| Stem, #3390, 3 oz., cocktail | 7.00 | 15.00 | 20.00 | 25.00 | |
| Stem, #3390, 3 oz., oyster/cocktail | 7.00 | 15.00 | 20.00 | 25.00 | |
| Stem, #3390, 4 oz., claret | 12.00 | 22.50 | 27.50 | 32.50 | |
| Stem, #3390, 6 oz., champagne | 10.00 | 20.00 | 25.00 | 30.00 | |
| Stem, #3390, 6 oz., sherbet | 10.00 | 20.00 | 25.00 | 30.00 | |
| Stem, #3390, 11 oz., low water | 8.00 | 20.00 | 25.00 | 30.00 | |
| Stem, #3390, 11 oz., tall water | 10.00 | 22.00 | 27.00 | 32.00 | |
| Sugar, dolphin ft. | 17.50 | 30.00 | 45.00 | 50.00 | |
| Sugar, indiv. | 12.50 | 27.50 | 32.50 | 35.00 | |
| Tray, 10", celery | 14.00 | 20.00 | 25.00 | 30.00 | |
| Tray, 12", ctr. hdld., sand. | 35.00 | 65.00 | 75.00 | 85.00 | |
| Tray, 12", ctr. hdld., sq. | 35.00 | 65.00 | 75.00 | 85.00 | |
| Tray, 13", celery | 17.00 | 20.00 | 26.00 | 30.00 | |
| Tray, 13", 2 hdld., hors d'oeuvre | 30.00 | 36.00 | 45.00 | 55.00 | |
| Tumbler, dolp. ft. | 90.00 | 135.00 | 165.00 | 195.00 | |
| Tumbler, #3380, 1 oz., ftd., bar | 22.00 | 37.50 | 42.50 | 52.50 | 55.00 |
| Tumbler, #3380, 2 oz., ftd., bar | 12.00 | 20.00 | 20.00 | 25.00 | 35.00 |
| Tumbler, #3380, 5 oz., ftd., bar | 7.00 | 12.00 | 12.00 | 17.00 | 25.00 |
| Tumbler, #3380, 8 oz., ftd., soda | 10.00 | 21.00 | 18.00 | 25.00 | 32.50 |
| Tumbler, #3380, 10 oz., ftd., soda | 12.00 | 23.00 | 20.00 | 25.00 | 32.50 |
| Tumbler, #3380, 12 oz., ftd., tea | 13.00 | 25.00 | 22.00 | 27.00 | 35.00 |
| Tumbler, #3390, 2 oz., ftd. | 7.00 | 18.00 | 22.50 | 28.00 | |
| Tumbler, #3390, 5 oz., ftd., juice | 7.00 | 15.00 | 20.00 | 25.00 | |
| Tumbler, #3390, 8 oz., ftd., soda | 10.00 | 22.00 | 25.00 | 30.00 | |
| Tumbler, #3390, 12 oz., ftd., tea | 12.00 | 24.00 | 27.00 | 30.00 | |
| Vase, 9", ftd. | 75.00 | 130.00 | 150.00 | 175.00 | |

# OLD SANDWICH, Blank #1404, A.H. Heisey & Co.

Colors: crystal, "Flamingo" pink, "Sahara" yellow, "Moongleam" green, cobalt, amber

Moongleam is the most desirable color to own. Observe Row 4. You are looking at one of the few Moongleam cup and saucers in Old Sandwich.

| | Crystal | Flam. | Sahara | Moon. | Cobalt |
|---|---|---|---|---|---|
| Ash tray, individual | 9.00 | 45.00 | 35.00 | 55.00 | 45.00 |
| Beer mug, 12 oz. | 35.00 | 300.00 | 210.00 | 400.00 | 240.00 |
| Beer mug, 14 oz. | 45.00 | 325.00 | 225.00 | 425.00 | 250.00 |
| * Beer mug, 18 oz. | 50.00 | 400.00 | 270.00 | 475.00 | 300.00 |
| Bottle, catsup, w/#3 stopper (like lg. cruet) | 60.00 | 200.00 | 175.00 | 225.00 | |
| Bowl, finger | 12.00 | 50.00 | 60.00 | 60.00 | |
| Bowl, ftd., popcorn, cupped | 45.00 | 90.00 | 75.00 | 125.00 | |
| Bowl, 11", rnd., ftd., floral | 50.00 | 85.00 | 65.00 | 100.00 | |
| Bowl, 12", oval, ftd., floral | 35.00 | 80.00 | 70.00 | 80.00 | |
| Candlestick, 6" | 45.00 | 100.00 | 90.00 | 150.00 | 235.00 |
| Cigarette holder | 50.00 | 65.00 | 60.00 | 65.00 | |
| Comport, 6" | 40.00 | 95.00 | 90.00 | 100.00 | |
| Creamer, oval | 15.00 | 22.00 | 25.00 | 30.00 | |
| Creamer, 12 oz. | 32.00 | 165.00 | 170.00 | 175.00 | 300.00 |
| Creamer, 14 oz. | 35.00 | 175.00 | 180.00 | 185.00 | |
| Creamer, 18 oz. | 40.00 | 185.00 | 190.00 | 195.00 | |
| Cup | 40.00 | 65.00 | 65.00 | 125.00 | |
| Decanter, 1 pint, w/#98 stopper | 75.00 | 185.00 | 200.00 | 225.00 | 425.00 |
| Floral block, #22 | 15.00 | 25.00 | 30.00 | 35.00 | |
| Oil bottle, 2½ oz., #85 stopper | 65.00 | 100.00 | 95.00 | 140.00 | |
| Parfait, 4½ oz. | 15.00 | 50.00 | 50.00 | 60.00 | |
| Pilsner, 8 oz. | 14.00 | 28.00 | 32.00 | 38.00 | |
| Pilsner, 10 oz. | 16.00 | 32.00 | 37.00 | 42.00 | |
| Pitcher, ½ gallon, ice lip | 85.00 | 175.00 | 165.00 | 185.00 | |
| Pitcher, ½ gallon, reg. | 85.00 | 175.00 | 165.00 | 185.00 | |
| Plate, 6", sq., grnd. bottom | 10.00 | 20.00 | 17.00 | 22.00 | |
| Plate, 7", sq. | 10.00 | 27.00 | 25.00 | 30.00 | |
| Plate, 8", sq. | 15.00 | 30.00 | 27.00 | 32.00 | |
| Salt & pepper, pr. | 40.00 | 65.00 | 75.00 | 85.00 | |
| Saucer | 10.00 | 15.00 | 15.00 | 25.00 | |
| Stem, 2½ oz., wine | 18.00 | 45.00 | 45.00 | 55.00 | |
| Stem, 3 oz., cocktail | 15.00 | 30.00 | 32.00 | 40.00 | |
| Stem, 4 oz., claret | 17.00 | 35.00 | 35.00 | 50.00 | 150.00 |
| Stem, 4 oz., oyster cocktail | 12.00 | 27.00 | 27.00 | 32.00 | |
| Stem, 4 oz., sherbet | 7.00 | 17.00 | 17.00 | 20.00 | |
| Stem, 5 oz., saucer champagne | 12.00 | 32.00 | 32.00 | 35.00 | |
| Stem, 10 oz., low ft. | 20.00 | 30.00 | 35.00 | 40.00 | |
| Sugar, oval | 15.00 | 22.00 | 25.00 | 30.00 | |
| Sundae, 6 oz. | 18.00 | 30.00 | 30.00 | 35.00 | |
| Tumbler, 1½ oz., bar, grnd. bottom | 20.00 | 130.00 | 120.00 | 135.00 | 100.00 |
| Tumbler, 5 oz., juice | 7.00 | 15.00 | 15.00 | 25.00 | |
| Tumbler, 6½ oz., toddy | 10.00 | 22.00 | 22.00 | 25.00 | |
| Tumbler, 8 oz., grnd. bottom, cupped & straight rim | 12.00 | 35.00 | 35.00 | 40.00 | |
| Tumbler, 10 oz. | 15.00 | 40.00 | 40.00 | 45.00 | |
| Tumbler, 10 oz., low ft. | 15.00 | 40.00 | 42.00 | 45.00 | |
| Tumbler, 12 oz., ftd., iced tea | 20.00 | 45.00 | 45.00 | 55.00 | |
| Tumbler, 12 oz., iced tea | 20.00 | 45.00 | 45.00 | 55.00 | |

*Amber; 300.00; Round creamer & sugar, $30.00 ea. piece, (unusual).
Whimsey Basket made from footed soda, $725.00.

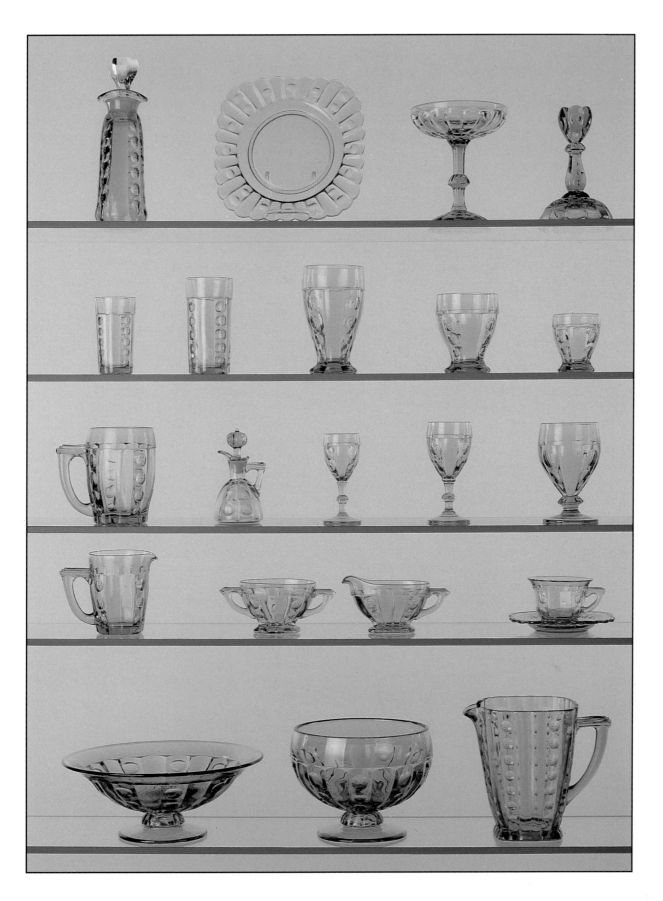

# ORCHID, (Etching #1507) ON WAVERLY BLANK #1519, and QUEEN ANN BLANK #1509,
### A.H. Heisey & Co. 1940 – 1957

Colors: crystal

I had a lot of comments on the ads in the last book; but, the most noticed, by far, was this one from 1945 showing Heisey Orchid. Unfortunately, the printing was bad in some of the copies of the book, but that is supposed to be solved for this book. I never know until I see it in print!

The Universal #3304 cocktail icer and the Fern #1495 mayonnaise and liner are shown separately as pattern shots on page 150. You may have a difficult time acquiring these two items for your collection.

You can see the difference between the Queen Ann and Waverly lemon dishes under Queen Ann on page 163. The Waverly Orchid lemon is rarely seen while the Queen Ann Orchid lemon dish is commonly seen! Price reflects that difference!

| | Crystal |
|---|---|
| Ash tray, 3". | 27.50 |
| Basket, 8½", LARIAT | 750.00 |
| Bell, dinner, #5022 or #5025 | 125.00 |
| Bottle, 8 oz., French dressings | 175.00 |
| Bowl, finger, #3309 or #5025 | 85.00 |
| Bowl, 4½", nappy, QUEEN ANN | 37.50 |
| Bowl, 5½", ftd., mint, QUEEN ANN | 35.00 |
| Bowl, 6", jelly, 2 hdld, QUEEN ANN | 30.00 |
| Bowl, 6" oval, lemon, w/cover, QUEEN ANN | 285.00 |
| Bowl, 6", oval, lemon, w/cover, WAVERLY | 850.00 |
| Bowl, 6½", ftd., honey; cheese, QUEEN ANN | 35.00 |
| Bowl, 6½", ftd., jelly, WAVERLY | 40.00 |
| Bowl, 6½", 2 pt., oval, dressings, WAVERLY | 47.50 |
| Bowl, 7", lily, QUEEN ANN | 85.00 |
| Bowl, 7", salad | 45.00 |
| Bowl, 7", 3 pt., rnd., relish | 45.00 |
| Bowl, 7", ftd., honey; cheese, WAVERLY | 50.00 |
| Bowl, 7", ftd., jelly | 40.00 |
| Bowl, 7", ftd., oval, nut, WAVERLY | 85.00 |
| Bowl, 8", mint, ftd., QUEEN ANN | 60.00 |
| Bowl, 8", nappy, QUEEN ANN | 65.00 |
| Bowl, 8", 2 pt., oval, dressings, ladle | 52.50 |
| Bowl, 8", pt., rnd., relish | 57.50 |
| Bowl, 8½", flared, QUEEN ANN | 65.00 |
| Bowl, 8½", floral, 2 hdld., ftd., QUEEN ANN | 57.50 |
| Bowl, 9", 4 pt., rnd., relish | 70.00 |
| Bowl, 9", ftd., fruit or salad | 125.00 |
| Bowl, 9", gardenia, QUEEN ANN | 60.00 |
| Bowl, 9", salad, WAVERLY | 135.00 |
| Bowl, 9½", crimped floral, QUEEN ANN | 65.00 |
| Bowl, 9½" epergne | 500.00 |
| Bowl, 10", crimped | 70.00 |
| Bowl, 10", deep salad | 120.00 |
| Bowl, 10", gardenia | 70.00 |
| Bowl, 10½", ftd., floral | 110.00 |
| Bowl, 11", shallow, rolled edge | 70.00 |
| Bowl, 11", 3 ftd., floral, seahorse ft. | 145.00 |
| Bowl, 11", 3 pt., oblong, relish | 67.50 |
| Bowl, 11", 4 ftd., oval | 85.00 |
| Bowl, 11", flared | 57.50 |
| Bowl, 11", floral | 57.50 |

| | Crystal |
|---|---|
| Bowl, 11", ftd., floral | 110.00 |
| Bowl, 12", crimped, floral, WAVERLY | 60.00 |
| Bowl, 13", floral | 70.00 |
| Bowl, 13", crimped, floral, WAVERLY | 90.00 |
| Bowl, 13", gardenia | 70.00 |
| Butter, w/cover, ¼ lb., CABOCHON | 315.00 |
| Butter, w/cover, 6", WAVERLY | 170.00 |
| Candleholder, 6", deep epernette, WAVERLY | 350.00 |
| Candlestick, 1-lite, MERCURY | 32.50 |
| Candlestick, 1-lite, QUEEN ANN w/prisms | 125.00 |
| Candlestick, 2-lite, FLAME | 145.00 |
| Candlestick, 5", 2-lite, TRIDENT | 50.00 |
| Candlestick, 2-lite, WAVERLY | 50.00 |
| Candlestick, 3-lite, CASCADE | 75.00 |
| Candlestick, 3-lite, WAVERLY | 87.50 |
| Candy box, w/cover, 6", low ft. | 160.00 |
| Candy, w/cover, 5", high ft., WAVERLY | 180.00 |
| Candy, w/cover, 6", bow knot finial | 165.00 |
| Cheese (comport) & cracker (11½") plate | 115.00 |
| Cheese & cracker, 14" plate | 135.00 |
| Chocolate, w/cover, 5", WAVERLY | 185.00 |
| Cigarette box, w/cover, 4", PURITAN | 135.00 |
| Cigarette holder, #4035 | 60.00 |
| Cigarette holder, w/cover | 125.00 |
| Cocktail icer, w/liner, UNIVERSAL, #3304 | 225.00 |
| Cocktail shaker, pt., #4225 | 275.00 |
| Cocktail shaker, qt., #4036 or #4225 | 225.00 |
| Comport, 5½", blown | 87.50 |
| Comport, 6", low ft., WAVERLY | 45.00 |
| Comport, 6½", low ft., WAVERLY | 47.50 |
| Comport, 7", ftd., oval | 135.00 |
| Creamer, individual | 22.50 |
| Creamer, ftd. | 25.00 |
| Cup, WAVERLY or QUEEN ANN | 40.00 |
| Decanter, oval, sherry, pt. | 225.00 |
| Decanter, pt., ftd. #4036 | 325.00 |
| Decanter, pt., #4036½ | 245.00 |
| Ice bucket, ftd., QUEEN ANN | 285.00 |
| Ice bucket, 2 hdld., WAVERLY | 295.00 |
| Marmalade, w/cover | 225.00 |
| Mayonnaise and liner, #1495, FERN | 245.00 |

# "It's Heisey, Honey!

### *and this has been a 'Heisey family' since I was young as you!"*

HEISEY'S ORCHID ETCHING

BUY WAR BONDS

In the Fall of 1895, Heisey craftsmen produced the first gleaming samples that introduced our crystal to the nation. The "gay nineties" took hand-wrought HEISEY CRYSTAL to its heart—and every succeeding decade has found it in even greater favor with all who love fine things. To-day HEISEY CRYSTAL is offered in a brilliant multitude of pieces and patterns—in tableware and in decorative crystal. Each precious piece has the grace, the sparkling loveliness, the hand-wrought craftsmanship that have brightened the homes of "Heisey families" for all of fifty years.

To be seen at leading stores throughout the nation. A. H. HEISEY & CO., NEWARK, OHIO.

*Heisey's*

HAND·WROUGHT CRYSTAL

# ORCHID, (Etching #1507) ON WAVERLY BLANK #1519 amd QUEEN ANN BLANK #1509,
## A.H. Heisey & Co. 1940 – 1957 (continued)

|  | Crystal |
|---|---|
| Mayonnaise, 5½", 1 hdl. | 40.00 |
| Mayonnaise, 5½", ftd. | 40.00 |
| Mayonnaise, 5½", 1 hdl., div. | 42.50 |
| Mayonnaise, 6½", 1 hdl. | 50.00 |
| Mayonnaise, 6½", 1 hdl., div. | 52.50 |
| Mustard, w/cover, QUEEN ANN | 135.00 |
| Oil, 3 oz., ftd. | 165.00 |
| Pitcher, 73 oz. | 450.00 |
| Pitcher, 64 oz., ice tankard | 525.00 |
| Plate, 6" | 12.50 |
| Plate, 7", mayonnaise | 15.00 |
| Plate, 7", salad | 18.00 |
| Plate, 8", salad, WAVERLY | 21.50 |
| Plate, 10½", dinner | 135.00 |
| Plate, 11", demi-torte | 50.00 |
| Plate, 11", sandwich | 50.00 |
| Plate, 12", ftd., salver, WAVERLY | 225.00 |
| Plate, 12", rnd sandwich, hdld. | 50.00 |
| Plate, 14", ftd., cake or salver | 275.00 |
| Plate, 14", torte, rolled edge | 55.00 |
| Plate, 14", torte, WAVERLY | 45.00 |
| Plate, 14", sandwich, WAVERLY | 65.00 |
| Plate, 15", sandwich, WAVERLY | 65.00 |
| Plate, 15½", QUEEN ANN | 95.00 |
| Salt & pepper, pr. | 60.00 |
| Salt & pepper, ftd., pr., WAVERLY | 65.00 |
| Saucer, WAVERLY or QUEEN ANN | 12.50 |
| Stem, #5022 or #5025, 1 oz., cordial | 125.00 |

|  | Crystal |
|---|---|
| Stem, #5022 or #5025, 2 oz., sherry | 120.00 |
| Stem, #5022 or #5025, 3 oz., wine | 75.00 |
| Stem, #5022 or #5025, 4 oz., oyster cocktail | 57.50 |
| Stem, #5025, 4 oz., cocktail | 40.00 |
| Stem, #5022 or #5025, 4½ oz., claret | 135.00 |
| Stem, #5022 or #5025, 6 oz., saucer champagne | 30.00 |
| Stem, #5022 or #5025, 6 oz., sherbet | 25.00 |
| Stem, #5022 or #5025, 10 oz., low water goblet | 35.00 |
| Stem, #5022 or #5025, 10 oz., water goblet | 42.50 |
| Sugar, individual | 25.00 |
| Sugar, ftd. | 22.50 |
| Toast, w/dome | 350.00 |
| Tray, indiv., creamer/sugar, QUEEN ANN | 85.00 |
| Tray, 12", celery | 47.50 |
| Tray, 13", celery | 50.00 |
| Tumbler, #5022 or #5025, 5 oz., fruit | 55.00 |
| Tumbler, #5022 or #5025, 12 oz., iced tea | 65.00 |
| Vase, 4", ftd., violet, WAVERLY | 95.00 |
| Vase, 6", crimped top | 115.00 |
| Vase, 7", ftd., fan | 85.00 |
| Vase, 7", ftd. | 85.00 |
| Vase, 8", ftd., bud | 195.00 |
| Vase, 8", sq., ftd., bud | 215.00 |
| Vase, 10", sq., ftd., bud | 275.00 |
| Vase, 14" | 650.00 |

# PLANTATION, Blank #1567, A.H. Heisey & Co.

Colors: crystal; rare in amber

Plantation is one of the fastest selling Heisey patterns. It is beginning to nudge ahead of Rose for best selling pattern!

If anyone can figure out how to grasp a goblet the way the model did in the ad on page 155, please let me know.

| | Crystal |
|---|---|
| Ash tray, 3½".......................................... | 35.00 |
| Bowl, 9 qt., Dr. Johnson, punch.................. | 600.00 |
| Bowl, 5", nappy ....................................... | 20.00 |
| Bowl, 5½", nappy ..................................... | 20.00 |
| Bowl, 6½", 2 hdld., jelly........................... | 35.00 |
| Bowl, 6½", flared, jelly ............................. | 45.00 |
| Bowl, 6½", ftd., honey, cupped.................. | 45.00 |
| Bowl, 8", 4 pt., rnd., relish....................... | 60.00 |
| Bowl, 8½", 2 pt., dressing.......................... | 45.00 |
| Bowl, 9", salad ....................................... | 90.00 |
| Bowl, 9½", crimped, fruit or flower............. | 85.00 |
| Bowl, 9½", gardenia.................................. | 85.00 |
| Bowl, 11", 3 part, relish............................ | 45.00 |
| Bowl, 11½", ftd., gardenia ........................ | 80.00 |
| Bowl, 12", crimped, fruit or flower............. | 60.00 |
| Bowl, 13", celery..................................... | 35.00 |
| Bowl, 13", 2 part, celery ........................... | 35.00 |
| Bowl, 13", 5 part, oval relish...................... | 65.00 |
| Bowl, 13", gardenia .................................. | 45.00 |
| Butter, ¼ lb., oblong, w/cover ................... | 95.00 |
| Butter, 5", rnd., (or cov. candy) ................. | 110.00 |
| Candelabrum, w/two #1503 bobeche & 10 "A" prisms........................................ | 110.00 |
| Candle block, hurricane type w/globe ......... | 110.00 |
| Candle block, 1-lite .................................. | 90.00 |
| Candle holder, 5", ftd., epergne ................. | 90.00 |
| Candlestick, 1-lite .................................... | 50.00 |
| Candlestick, 2-lite .................................... | 60.00 |
| Candlestick, 3-lite .................................... | 80.00 |
| Candy box, w/cover, 7" length, flat bottom.. | 135.00 |
| Candy, w/cover, 5", tall, ftd....................... | 175.00 |
| Cheese, w/cover, 5", ftd............................. | 90.00 |
| Cigarette box, w/cover .............................. | 180.00 |
| Coaster, 4" ............................................. | 50.00 |
| Comport, 5"............................................. | 40.00 |
| Comport, 5", w/cover, deep........................ | 100.00 |
| Creamer, ftd. .......................................... | 30.00 |
| Cup........................................................ | 30.00 |

| | Crystal |
|---|---|
| Cup, punch ............................................. | 30.00 |
| Marmalade, w/cover ................................. | 120.00 |
| Mayonnaise, 4½", rolled ft. ....................... | 55.00 |
| Mayonnaise, 5¼", w/liner .......................... | 45.00 |
| Oil bottle, 3 oz., w/#125 stopper ................ | 95.00 |
| Pitcher, ½ gallon, ice lip, blown ................. | 400.00 |
| Plate, coupe (rare) ................................... | 225.00 |
| Plate, 7", salad ....................................... | 20.00 |
| Plate, 8", salad ....................................... | 25.00 |
| Plate, 10½", demi-torte ............................. | 50.00 |
| Plate, 13", ftd., cake salver ....................... | 135.00 |
| Plate, 14", sandwich ................................ | 65.00 |
| Plate, 18", buffet ..................................... | 75.00 |
| Plate, 18", punch bowl liner ....................... | 110.00 |
| Salt & pepper, pr...................................... | 50.00 |
| Saucer ................................................... | 7.00 |
| Stem, 1 oz., cordial.................................. | 125.00 |
| Stem, 3 oz., wine, blown........................... | 75.00 |
| Stem, 3½ oz., cocktail, pressed .................. | 35.00 |
| Stem, 4 oz., fruit/oyster cocktail................ | 35.00 |
| Stem, 4½ oz., claret, blown ....................... | 65.00 |
| Stem, 4½ oz., claret, pressed ..................... | 65.00 |
| Stem, 4½ oz., oyster cocktail, blown ........... | 40.00 |
| Stem, 6½ oz., sherbet/saucer champagne, blown .................................................. | 40.00 |
| Stem, 10 oz., pressed................................ | 50.00 |
| Stem, 10 oz., blown.................................. | 50.00 |
| Sugar, ftd............................................... | 30.00 |
| Syrup bottle, w/drip, cut top ..................... | 80.00 |
| Tray, 8½", condiment/sugar & creamer........ | 25.00 |
| Tumbler, 5 oz., ftd., juice, pressed.............. | 40.00 |
| Tumbler, 5 oz., ftd., juice, blown ................ | 40.00 |
| Tumbler, 10 oz., pressed ........................... | 60.00 |
| Tumbler, 12 oz., ftd., iced tea, pressed ........ | 75.00 |
| Tumbler, 12 oz., ftd., iced tea, blown .......... | 75.00 |
| Vase, 5", ftd., flared ................................. | 50.00 |
| Vase, 9", ftd., flared ................................. | 95.00 |

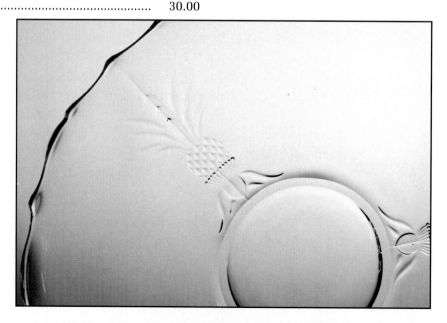

tradition in crystal...

Plantation Ivy...
hospitality's
traditional warmth
captured in
boldly etched
hand blown crystal

the finest in glassware, made in America by hand

**Heisey**
HAND-WROUGHT CRYSTAL

# PLEAT & PANEL, Blank #1170, A.H. Heisey & Co.

Colors: crystal, "Flamingo" pink, "Moongleam" green

Pleat and Panel is another easily recognized Heisey pattern because most pieces carry the familiar H in diamond mark. Stems are marked on the stem itself and not the foot; so look there if you can not find a mark.

Pleat and Panel is not one of Heisey's higher priced patterns. That makes it a good starting pattern for beginning collectors. Notice the color variations in pink and green in the picture. Only Depression Glass is supposed to have color variances. Even Heisey had seconds, but not every Heisey connoisseur is willing to admit that.

| | Crystal | Flam. | Moongleam |
|---|---|---|---|
| Bowl, 4", chow chow.......................... | 5.00 | 10.00 | 12.00 |
| Bowl, 4½", nappy ............................. | 5.00 | 10.00 | 12.00 |
| Bowl, 5", 2 hdld., bouillon.................. | 7.00 | 12.00 | 15.00 |
| Bowl, 5", 2 hdld., jelly ...................... | 9.00 | 12.00 | 15.00 |
| Bowl, 5", lemon, w/cover................... | 10.00 | 25.00 | 30.00 |
| Bowl, 6½", grapefruit/cereal ............. | 5.00 | 13.00 | 16.00 |
| Bowl, 8", nappy ............................... | 10.00 | 30.00 | 35.00 |
| Bowl, 9", oval, vegetable .................. | 12.50 | 30.00 | 35.00 |
| Cheese & cracker set, 10½", tray, w/compote ...................... | 25.00 | 75.00 | 80.00 |
| Compotier, w/cover, 5", hi. ftd........... | 35.00 | 60.00 | 70.00 |
| Creamer, hotel ................................ | 10.00 | 25.00 | 30.00 |
| Cup........................... | 7.00 | 15.00 | 17.50 |
| Marmalade, 4¾".............................. | 10.00 | 25.00 | 27.50 |
| Oil bottle, 3 oz., w/pressed stopper...... | 20.00 | 50.00 | 55.00 |
| Pitcher, 3 pint, ice lip...................... | 45.00 | 130.00 | 145.00 |
| Pitcher, 3 pint............................... | 45.00 | 130.00 | 145.00 |
| Plate, 6"....................................... | 4.00 | 8.00 | 8.00 |
| Plate, 6¾", bouillon underliner............ | 4.00 | 8.00 | 8.00 |
| Plate, 7", bread.............................. | 4.00 | 8.00 | 10.00 |
| Plate, 8", luncheon ......................... | 5.00 | 12.50 | 15.00 |
| Plate, 10¾", dinner ......................... | 15.00 | 42.50 | 47.50 |
| Plate, 14", sandwich........................ | 15.00 | 30.00 | 35.00 |
| Platter, 12", oval ............................ | 15.00 | 35.00 | 40.00 |
| Saucer ........................................ | 3.00 | 5.00 | 5.00 |
| Sherbet, 5 oz., footed...................... | 4.00 | 8.00 | 10.00 |
| Stem, 5 oz., saucer champagne............ | 5.00 | 10.00 | 12.00 |
| Stem, 7½ oz., low foot...................... | 10.00 | 15.00 | 20.00 |
| Stem, 8 oz. .................................. | 12.00 | 20.00 | 25.00 |
| Sugar w/lid, hotel............................ | 10.00 | 25.00 | 30.00 |
| Tray, 10", compartmented spice ........... | 10.00 | 25.00 | 30.00 |
| Tumbler, 8 oz., ground bottom............. | 5.00 | 12.00 | 15.00 |
| Tumbler, 12 oz., tea, ground bottom...... | 7.00 | 17.50 | 22.50 |
| Vase, 8"....................................... | 20.00 | 50.00 | 55.00 |

## PORTIA, Cambridge Glass Company, 1932 – Early 1950's

Colors: crystal, yellow, Heatherbloom, green, amber

| | Crystal |
|---|---|
| Basket, 2 hdld. (upturned sides) | 16.00 |
| Basket, 7", 1 hdld. | 195.00 |
| Bowl, 3½", cranberry | 22.50 |
| Bowl, 3½" sq., cranberry | 22.50 |
| Bowl, 5¼", 2 hdld., bonbon | 15.00 |
| Bowl, 6", 2 pt., relish | 16.00 |
| Bowl, 6", ftd., 2 hdld., bonbon | 16.00 |
| Bowl, 6", grapefruit or oyster | 17.00 |
| Bowl, 6½", 3 pt., relish | 18.00 |
| Bowl, 7", 2 pt., relish | 16.00 |
| Bowl, 7", ftd., bonbon, tab hdld. | 22.00 |
| Bowl, 7", pickle or relish | 22.00 |
| Bowl, 9", 3 pt., celery & relish, tab hdld. | 30.00 |
| Bowl, 9½", ftd., pickle (like corn bowl) | 22.00 |
| Bowl, 10", flared, 4 ftd. | 40.00 |
| Bowl, 11", 2 pt., 2 hdld., "figure 8" relish | 27.50 |
| Bowl, 11", 2 hdld. | 37.50 |
| Bowl, 12", 3 pt., celery & relish, tab hdld. | 35.00 |
| Bowl, 12", 5 pt., celery & relish | 37.50 |
| Bowl, 12", flared, 4 ftd. | 45.00 |
| Bowl, 12", oval, 4 ftd., "ears" handles | 45.00 |
| Bowl, finger, w/liner #3124 | 32.00 |
| Bowl, seafood (fruit cocktail w/liner) | 55.00 |
| Candlestick, 5" | 20.00 |
| Candlestick, 6", 2-lite, "fleur-de-lis" | 35.00 |
| Candlestick, 6", 3-lite | 45.00 |
| Candy box, w/cover, rnd. | 67.50 |
| Cigarette holder, urn shape | 55.00 |
| Cocktail icer, 2 pt. | 65.00 |
| Cocktail shaker, w/stopper | 90.00 |
| Cocktail shaker, 80 oz., hdld. ball w/chrome top | 165.00 |
| Cologne, 2 oz., hdld. ball w/stopper | 85.00 |
| Comport, 5½" | 27.50 |
| Comport, 5⅜", blown | 35.00 |
| Creamer, hdld. ball | 27.50 |
| Creamer, indiv. | 12.50 |
| Cup, ftd. sq. | 18.00 |
| Decanter, 29 oz. ftd., sherry, w/stopper | 175.00 |
| Hurricane lamp, candlestick base | 145.00 |
| Hurricane lamp, keyhole base, w/prisms | 135.00 |
| Ice bucket, w/chrome handle | 65.00 |
| Ivy ball, 5¼" | 35.00 |
| Mayonnaise, div. bowl, w/liner & 2 ladles | 40.00 |
| Mayonnaise, w/liner & ladle | 40.00 |
| Oil, 6 oz., loop hdld., w/stopper | 60.00 |
| Oil, 6 oz., hdld. ball, w/stopper | 65.00 |
| Pitcher, ball | 130.00 |
| Pitcher, Doulton | 300.00 |
| Plate, 6", 2 hdld. | 15.00 |
| Plate, 6½", bread/butter | 7.50 |
| Plate, 8", salad | 12.50 |
| Plate, 8", ftd., 2 hdld. | 17.50 |
| Plate, 8", ftd., bonbon, tab hdld. | 20.00 |
| Plate, 8½", sq. | 15.00 |
| Plate, 10½", dinner | 65.00 |
| Plate, 13", 4 ftd., torte | 35.00 |
| Plate, 13½", 2 hdld., cake | 35.00 |
| Plate, 14", torte | 35.00 |
| Puff box, 3½", ball shape, w/lid | 125.00 |
| Salt & pepper, pr., flat | 25.00 |

| | Crystal |
|---|---|
| Saucer, sq. or rnd. | 3.00 |
| Set: 3 pc. frappe (bowl, 2 plain inserts) | 45.00 |
| Stem, #3121, 1 oz., cordial | 55.00 |
| Stem, #3121, 1 oz., low ftd., brandy | 45.00 |
| Stem, #3121, 2½ oz., wine | 30.00 |
| Stem, #3121, 3 oz., cocktail | 20.00 |
| Stem, #3121, 4½ oz., claret | 37.50 |
| Stem, #3121, 4½ oz., oyster cocktail | 15.00 |
| Stem, #3121, 5 oz., parfait | 35.00 |
| Stem, #3121, 6 oz., low sherbet | 13.50 |
| Stem, #3121, 6 oz., tall sherbet | 15.00 |
| Stem, #3121, 10 oz., goblet | 22.50 |
| Stem, #3124, 3 oz., cocktail | 15.00 |
| Stem, #3124, 3 oz., wine | 25.00 |
| Stem, #3124, 4½ oz., claret | 30.00 |
| Stem, #3124, 7 oz., low sherbet | 14.00 |
| Stem, #3124, 7 oz., tall sherbet | 15.00 |
| Stem, #3124, 10 oz., goblet | 18.00 |
| Stem, #3126, 1 oz., cordial | 55.00 |
| Stem, #3126, 1 oz., low ft., brandy | 45.00 |
| Stem, #3126, 2½ oz., wine | 27.50 |
| Stem, #3126, 3 oz., cocktail | 17.50 |
| Stem, #3126, 4½ oz., claret | 37.50 |
| Stem, #3126, 4½ oz., low ft., oyster cocktail | 12.50 |
| Stem, #3126, 7 oz., low sherbet | 14.00 |
| Stem, #3126, 7 oz., tall sherbet | 15.00 |
| Stem, #3126, 9 oz., goblet | 20.00 |
| Stem, #3130, 1 oz., cordial | 55.00 |
| Stem, #3130, 2½ oz., wine | 25.00 |
| Stem, #3130, 3 oz., cocktail | 17.50 |
| Stem, #3130, 4½ oz., claret | 37.50 |
| Stem, #3130, 4½ oz., fruit/oyster cocktail | 15.00 |
| Stem, #3130, 7 oz., low sherbet | 14.00 |
| Stem, #3130, 7 oz., tall sherbet | 15.00 |
| Stem, #3130, 9 oz., goblet | 22.50 |
| Sugar, ftd., hdld. ball | 25.00 |
| Sugar, indiv. | 11.50 |
| Tray, 11", celery | 27.50 |
| Tumbler, #3121, 2½ oz., bar | 30.00 |
| Tumbler, #3121, 5 oz., ftd., juice | 16.00 |
| Tumbler, #3121, 10 oz., ftd., water | 16.50 |
| Tumbler, #3121, 12 oz., ftd., tea | 25.00 |
| Tumbler, #3124, 3 oz. | 13.00 |
| Tumbler, #3124, 5 oz., juice | 12.50 |
| Tumbler, #3124, 10 oz., water | 15.00 |
| Tumbler, #3124, 12 oz., tea | 22.00 |
| Tumbler, #3126, 2½ oz. | 30.00 |
| Tumbler, #3126, 5 oz., juice | 14.00 |
| Tumbler, #3126, 10 oz., water | 15.00 |
| Tumbler, #3126, 12 oz., tea | 22.00 |
| Tumbler, #3130, 5 oz., juice | 16.00 |
| Tumbler, #3130, 10 oz., water | 15.00 |
| Tumbler, #3130, 12 oz., tea | 22.00 |
| Tumbler, 12 oz., "roly-poly" | 25.00 |
| Vase, 5", globe | 40.00 |
| Vase, 6", ftd. | 45.00 |
| Vase, 8", ftd. | 55.00 |
| Vase, 9", keyhole ft. | 65.00 |
| Vase, 10", bud | 40.00 |
| Vase, 11", flower | 55.00 |
| Vase, 11", pedestal ft. | 65.00 |
| Vase, 12", keyhole ft. | 85.00 |
| Vase, 13", flower | 95.00 |

# PROVINCIAL, Blank #1506, A.H. Heisey & Co.

Colors: crystal, "Limelight" green

"Limelight" green or Zircon prices for Provincial are advancing! Some collectors are beginning to accumulate crystal and forget Zircon. If you find pieces in colors other than crystal or Zircon, you are seeing pieces made by Imperial after they purchased the Heisey moulds in 1957. Some of these other colored pieces still have Heisey marks (H in diamond), but they were made at Imperial after the Heisey plant closed, and are not considered to be Heisey!

|  | Crystal | Limelight Green |
|---|---|---|
| Ash tray, 3" square | 12.50 | |
| Bonbon dish, 7", 2 hdld., upturned sides | 12.00 | 37.50 |
| Bowl, 5 quart, punch | 100.00 | |
| Bowl, individual, nut/jelly | 15.00 | 35.00 |
| Bowl, 4½", nappy | 10.00 | 60.00 |
| Bowl, 5", 2 hdld., nut/jelly | 12.00 | |
| Bowl, 5½", nappy | 12.00 | 40.00 |
| Bowl, 5½", round, hdld., nappy | 15.00 | |
| Bowl, 5½", tri-corner, hdld., nappy | 15.00 | 55.00 |
| Bowl, 10", 4 part, relish | 40.00 | 195.00 |
| Bowl, 12", floral | 30.00 | |
| Bowl, 13", gardenia | 35.00 | |
| Box, 5½", footed, candy, w/cover | 75.00 | 500.00 |
| Butter dish, w/cover | 85.00 | |
| Candle, 1-lite, block | 25.00 | |
| Candle, 3-lite | 60.00 | |
| Candle, 3-lite, #4233, 5", vase | 85.00 | |
| Cigarette box w/cover | 50.00 | |
| Cigarette lighter | 30.00 | |
| Coaster, 4" | 10.00 | |
| Creamer, footed | 20.00 | 95.00 |
| Creamer & sugar, w/tray, individual | 65.00 | |
| Cup, punch | 10.00 | |
| Mayonnaise, 7" (plate, ladle, bowl) | 40.00 | 150.00 |
| Mustard | 90.00 | |
| Oil bottle, 4 oz., #1 stopper | 45.00 | |
| Oil & vinegar bottle, (french dressing) | 60.00 | |
| Plate, 5", footed, cheese | 10.00 | |
| Plate, 7", 2 hdld., snack | 12.00 | |
| Plate, 7", bread | 10.00 | |
| Plate, 8", luncheon | 15.00 | 50.00 |
| Plate, 14", torte | 30.00 | |
| Plate, 18", buffet | 37.50 | 165.00 |
| Salt & pepper, pr. | 25.00 | |
| Stem, 3½ oz., oyster cocktail | 8.00 | |
| Stem, 3½ oz., wine | 15.00 | |
| Stem, 5 oz., sherbet/champagne | 7.00 | |
| Stem, 10 oz. | 15.00 | |
| Sugar, footed | 20.00 | 95.00 |
| Tray, 13", oval, celery | 22.00 | |
| Tumbler, 5 oz., footed, juice | 12.00 | 50.00 |
| Tumbler, 8 oz. | 15.00 | |
| Tumbler, 9 oz., footed | 15.00 | 65.00 |
| Tumbler, 12 oz., footed, iced tea | 17.00 | 75.00 |
| Tumbler, 13", flat, ice tea | 20.00 | |
| Vase, 3½", violet | 30.00 | 95.00 |
| Vase, 4", pansy | 35.00 | |
| Vase, 6", sweet pea | 45.00 | |

# QUEEN ANN, Blank #1509, A.H. Heisey & Co.

Queen Ann is the pattern name given to Empress when it was made in crystal (c. 1938). Pictured for comparison on page 163 is the Empress lemon dish and the Waverly lemon dish. The Waverly lemon dish, shown here with Orchid etching, is rare!

| | Crystal | | Crystal |
|---|---|---|---|
| Ash tray. | 30.00 | Marmalade, w/cover, dolp. ftd. | 50.00 |
| Bonbon, 6". | 10.00 | Mayonnaise, 5½", ftd., w/ladle | 20.00 |
| Bowl, cream soup | 15.00 | Mustard, w/cover | 30.00 |
| Bowl, cream soup, w/sq. liner | 20.00 | Oil bottle, 4 oz. | 35.00 |
| Bowl, frappe, w/center | 20.00 | Plate, bouillon liner | 4.00 |
| Bowl, nut, dolphin ftd., indiv. | 15.00 | Plate, cream soup liner | 5.00 |
| Bowl, 4½", nappy | 5.00 | Plate, 4½" | 5.00 |
| Bowl, 5", preserve, 2 hdld. | 12.00 | Plate, 6" | 5.00 |
| Bowl, 6", ftd., jelly, 2 hdld. | 12.00 | Plate, 6", square | 5.00 |
| Bowl, 6", dolp. ftd., mint | 14.00 | Plate, 7" | 8.00 |
| Bowl, 6", grapefruit, sq. top, grnd. | | Plate, 7", square | 7.00 |
|    bottom | 9.00 | Plate, 8", square | 10.00 |
| Bowl, 6½", oval, lemon, w/cover | 35.00 | Plate, 8" | 9.00 |
| Bowl, 7", 3 pt., relish, triplex | 12.50 | Plate, 9" | 12.00 |
| Bowl, 7", 3 pt., relish, ctr. hand. | 20.00 | Plate, 10½" | 40.00 |
| Bowl, 7½", dolp. ftd., nappy | 25.00 | Plate, 10½", square | 40.00 |
| Bowl, 7½", dolp. ftd., nasturtium | 30.00 | Plate, 12" | 25.00 |
| Bowl, 8", nappy | 22.00 | Plate, 12", muffin, sides upturned | 30.00 |
| Bowl, 8½", ftd., floral, 2 hdld | 30.00 | Plate, 12", sandwich, 2 hdld. | 25.00 |
| Bowl, 9", floral, rolled edge | 22.00 | Plate, 13", hors d'oeuvre, 2 hdld. | 28.00 |
| Bowl, 9", floral, flared | 30.00 | Plate, 13", square, 2 hdld. | 28.00 |
| Bowl, 10", 2 hdld., oval dessert | 30.00 | Platter, 14" | 25.00 |
| Bowl, 10", lion head, floral | 250.00 | Salt & pepper, pr. | 50.00 |
| Bowl, 10", oval, veg. | 27.00 | Saucer, square | 3.00 |
| Bowl, 10", square, salad, 2 hdld. | 30.00 | Saucer, after dinner | 2.00 |
| Bowl, 10", triplex, relish | 20.00 | Saucer. | 3.00 |
| Bowl, 11", dolphin ftd., floral | 32.00 | Stem, 2½ oz., oyster cocktail | 15.00 |
| Bowl, 13", pickle/olive, 2 pt. | 15.00 | Stem, 4 oz., saucer champagne | 20.00 |
| Bowl, 15", dolp. ftd., punch | 400.00 | Stem, 4 oz., sherbet | 15.00 |
| Candlestick, 3", 3 ftd | 45.00 | Stem, 9 oz., Empress stemware, | |
| Candlestick, low, 4 ftd., w/2 hdld. | 15.00 |    unusual | 30.00 |
| Candlestick, 6", dolphin ftd. | 50.00 | Sugar, indiv. | 15.00 |
| Candy, w/cover, 6", dolphin ftd. | 40.00 | Sugar, dolphin ftd., 3 hdld. | 10.00 |
| Comport, 6", ftd. | 25.00 | Tray, condiment & liner for indiv. | |
| Comport, 6", square | 40.00 |    sugar/creamer | 15.00 |
| Comport, 7", oval | 35.00 | Tray, 10", 3 pt., relish | 18.00 |
| Compotier, 6", dolphin ftd. | 70.00 | Tray, 10", 7 pt., hors d'oeuvre | 50.00 |
| Creamer, dolphin ftd. | 15.00 | Tray, 10", celery | 12.00 |
| Creamer, indiv. | 15.00 | Tray, 12", ctr. hdld., sand. | 30.00 |
| Cup | 12.00 | Tray, 12", sq. ctr. hdld., sand. | 32.50 |
| Cup, after dinner | 15.00 | Tray, 13", celery | 16.00 |
| Cup, bouillon, 2 hdld. | 16.00 | Tray, 16", 4 pt., buffet relish | 30.00 |
| Cup, 4 oz., custard or punch | 12.00 | Tumbler, 8 oz., dolp. ftd., unusual | 75.00 |
| Cup, #1401½, has rim as demi-cup | 20.00 | Tumbler, 8 oz., grnd. bottom | 15.00 |
| Grapefruit, w/square liner | 15.00 | Tumbler, 12 oz., tea, grnd. bottom | 18.00 |
| Ice tub, w/metal handles | 40.00 | Vase, 8", flared | 45.00 |
| Jug, 3 pint, ftd. | 70.00 | | |

# RIDGELEIGH, Blank #1469, A.H. Heisey & Co.

Colors: crystal, "Sahara," "Zircon," rare

| | Crystal |
|---|---|
| Ash tray, round | 5.00 |
| Ash tray, square | 4.00 |
| Ash tray, 4", round | 12.00 |
| Ash tray, 6", square | 20.00 |
| Ash trays, bridge set (heart, diamond, spade, club) | 40.00 |
| Basket, bonbon | 11.00 |
| Bottle, rock & rye, w/#104 stopper | 110.00 |
| Bottle, 4 oz., cologne | 85.00 |
| Bottle, 5 oz., bitters, w/tube | 65.00 |
| Bowl, indiv., nut | 9.00 |
| Bowl, oval, indiv., jelly | 12.50 |
| Bowl, indiv., nut, 2 part | 10.50 |
| Bowl, 4½", nappy, bell or cupped | 7.00 |
| Bowl, 4½", nappy, scalloped | 7.00 |
| Bowl, 5", lemon, w/cover | 35.00 |
| Bowl, 5", nappy, straight | 6.50 |
| Bowl, 5", nappy, square | 6.50 |
| Bowl, 6", 2 hdld., divided, jelly | 12.75 |
| Bowl, 6", 2 hdld., jelly | 14.00 |
| Bowl, 7", 2 part, oval, relish | 12.75 |
| Bowl, 8", centerpiece | 22.00 |
| Bowl, 8", nappy, square | 45.00 |
| Bowl, 9", nappy, square | 27.50 |
| Bowl, 9", salad | 30.00 |
| Bowl, 10", flared, fruit | 35.00 |
| Bowl, 10", floral | 35.00 |
| Bowl, 11", centerpiece | 35.00 |
| Bowl, 11", punch | 90.00 |
| Bowl, 11½", floral | 35.00 |
| Bowl, 12", oval, floral | 35.00 |
| Bowl, 12", flared, fruit | 40.00 |
| Bowl, 13", cone, floral | 40.00 |
| Bowl, 14", oblong, floral | 50.00 |
| Bowl, 14", oblong, swan hdld., floral | 110.00 |
| Box, 8", floral | 30.00 |
| Candle block, 3", #1469½ | 20.00 |
| Candle vase, 6" | 30.00 |
| Candlestick, 2", 1-lite | 30.00 |
| Candlestick, 2-lite, bobeche & "A" prisms | 70.00 |
| Candlestick, 7", w/bobeche & "A" prisms | 90.00 |
| Cheese, 6", 2 hdld. | 11.00 |
| Cigarette box, w/cover, oval | 90.00 |
| Cigarette box, w/cover, 6" | 30.00 |
| Cigarette holder, oval, w/2 comp. ashtrays | 60.00 |
| Cigarette holder, round | 7.50 |
| Cigarette holder, square | 7.50 |
| Cigarette holder, w/cover | 20.00 |
| Coaster or cocktail rest | 5.00 |
| Cocktail shaker, 1 qt., w/#1 strainer & #86 stopper | 225.00 |
| Comport, 6", low ft., flared | 16.00 |
| Comport, 6", low ft., w/cover | 30.00 |
| Creamer | 20.00 |
| Creamer, indiv. | 15.00 |
| Cup | 15.00 |
| Cup, beverage | 12.00 |
| Cup, punch | 10.00 |
| Decanter, 1 pint, w/#95 stopper | 175.00 |
| Ice tub, 2 hdld. | 75.00 |
| Marmalade, w/cover, (scarce) | 75.00 |
| Mayonnaise | 35.00 |

| | Crystal |
|---|---|
| Mustard, w/cover | 45.00 |
| Oil bottle, 3 oz., w/#103 stopper | 50.00 |
| Pitcher, ½ gallon, ball shape | 190.00 |
| Pitcher, ½ gallon, ice lip, ball shape | 190.00 |
| Plate, oval, hors d'oeuvres | 70.00 |
| Plate, 2 hdld., ice tub liner | 30.00 |
| Plate, 6", round | 7.00 |
| Plate, 6", scalloped | 7.00 |
| Plate, 6", square | 12.00 |
| Plate, 7", square | 15.00 |
| Plate, 8", round | 17.50 |
| Plate, 8", square | 25.00 |
| Plate, 13½", sandwich | 45.00 |
| Plate, 13½", ftd., torte | 45.00 |
| Plate, 14", salver | 50.00 |
| Salt & pepper, pr. | 30.00 |
| Salt dip, indiv. | 13.00 |
| Saucer | 5.00 |
| Soda, 12 oz., ftd., no knob in stem, (rare) | 50.00 |
| Stem, cocktail, pressed | 22.00 |
| Stem, claret, pressed | 32.00 |
| Stem, oyster cocktail, pressed | 15.00 |
| Stem, sherbet, pressed | 12.00 |
| Stem, saucer champagne, pressed | 20.00 |
| Stem, wine, pressed | 32.00 |
| Stem, 1 oz., cordial, blown | 150.00 |
| Stem, 2 oz., sherry, blown | 85.00 |
| Stem, 2½ oz., wine, blown | 75.00 |
| Stem, 3½ oz., cocktail, blown | 30.00 |
| Stem, 4 oz., claret, blown | 45.00 |
| Stem, 4 oz., oyster cocktail, blown | 25.00 |
| Stem, 5 oz., saucer champagne, blown | 20.00 |
| Stem, 5 oz., sherbet, blown | 15.00 |
| Stem, 8 oz., luncheon, low stem | 25.00 |
| Stem, 8 oz., tall stem | 30.00 |
| Sugar | 20.00 |
| Sugar, indiv. | 12.50 |
| Tray, for indiv. sugar & creamer | 12.50 |
| Tray, 10½", oblong | 30.00 |
| Tray, 11", 3 part, relish | 40.00 |
| Tray, 12", celery & olive, divided | 35.00 |
| Tray, 12", celery | 35.00 |
| Tumbler, 2½ oz., bar, pressed | 35.00 |
| Tumbler, 5 oz., juice, blown | 24.00 |
| Tumbler, 5 oz., soda, ftd., pressed | 22.00 |
| Tumbler, 8 oz., (#1469¾), pressed | 18.00 |
| Tumbler, 8 oz., old-fashioned, pressed | 20.00 |
| Tumbler, 8 oz., soda, blown | 21.00 |
| Tumbler, 10 oz., (#1469½), pressed | 30.00 |
| Tumbler, 12 oz., ftd., soda, pressed | 40.00 |
| Tumbler, 12 oz., soda, (#1469½) pressed | 40.00 |
| Tumbler, 13 oz., iced tea, blown | 22.00 |
| Vase, #1 indiv., cuspidor shape | 25.00 |
| Vase, #2 indiv., cupped top | 22.00 |
| Vase, #3 indiv., flared rim | 27.50 |
| Vase, #4 indiv., fan out top | 35.00 |
| Vase, #5 indiv., scalloped top | 25.00 |
| Vase, 3½" | 22.00 |
| Vase, 6" (also flared) | 17.50 |
| Vase, 8" | 55.00 |
| Vase, 8", triangular (#1469¾) | 55.00 |

# ROMANCE, Etching #341, Fostoria Glass Company, 1942–1986

Colors: crystal

Romance is sometimes confused with Fostoria's crystal June because of the "bow" in the design. Romance is only found in crystal. I will be placing this pattern in the next edition of my new book *Collectible Glassware from the 40's, 50's & 60's....*

| | Crystal |
|---|---|
| Ash tray, 2⅝", indiv., #2364 | 12.50 |
| Bowl, 6", baked apple #2364 | 15.00 |
| Bowl, 8", soup, rimmed, #2364 | 27.50 |
| Bowl, 9", salad, #2364 | 37.50 |
| Bowl, 9¼", ftd. blown, #6023 | 75.00 |
| Bowl, 10", 2 hdld, #2594 | 45.00 |
| Bowl, 10½", salad, #2364 | 42.50 |
| Bowl, 11", shallow, oblong, #2596 | 47.50 |
| Bowl, 12", ftd. #2364 | 55.00 |
| Bowl, 12", lily pond, #2364 | 45.00 |
| Bowl, 13", fruit, #2364 | 52.50 |
| Bowl, 13½", hdld., oval, #2594 | 55.00 |
| Candlestick, 4", #2324 | 17.50 |
| Candlestick, 5", #2596 | 22.50 |
| Candlestick, 5½", #2594 | 25.00 |
| Candlestick, 5½", 2 lite, #6023 | 30.00 |
| Candlestick, 8", 3 lite, #2594 | 42.50 |
| Candy w/ lid, rnd., blown, #2364 | 80.00 |
| Cigarette holder, 2", blown, #2364 | 35.00 |
| Comport, 3¼", cheese, #2364 | 22.50 |
| Comport, 5", #6030 | 22.50 |
| Comport, 8", #2364 | 40.00 |
| Creamer, 3¼", ftd., #2350½ | 17.50 |
| Cup, ftd., #2350½ | 20.00 |
| Ice tub, 4¾", #4132 | 65.00 |
| Ladle, mayonnaise, #2364 | 5.00 |
| Mayonnaise, 5", #2364 | 22.50 |
| Pitcher, 8⅞", 53 oz., ftd., #6011 | 250.00 |
| Plate, 6", #2337 | 8.00 |
| Plate, 6¾", mayonnaise liner, #2364 | 10.00 |
| Plate, 7", #2337 | 10.00 |
| Plate, 8", #2337 | 15.00 |

| | Crystal |
|---|---|
| Plate, 9", #2337 | 47.50 |
| Plate, 11", sandwich, #2364 | 37.50 |
| Plate, 11¼", cracker, #2364 | 25.00 |
| Plate, 14", torte, #2364 | 42.50 |
| Plate, 16", torte, #2364 | 60.00 |
| Plate, crescent salad, #2364 | 40.00 |
| Relish, 8", pickle, #2364 | 22.50 |
| Relish, 10", 3 pt., #2364 | 25.00 |
| Relish, 11", celery, #2364 | 27.50 |
| Salt & pepper, 2⅝", #2364 | 50.00 |
| Saucer, #2350 | 5.00 |
| Stem, 3⅞", ¾ oz., cordial, #6017 | 42.50 |
| Stem, 4½", 6 oz., low sherbet, #6017 | 14.00 |
| Stem, 4⅞", 3½ oz., cocktail, #6017 | 21.50 |
| Stem, 5½", 3 oz., wine, #6017 | 30.00 |
| Stem, 5½", 6 oz., champagne, #6017 | 17.50 |
| Stem, 5⅞", 4 oz., claret, #6017 | 32.50 |
| Stem, 7⅜", 9 oz., goblet, #6017 | 25.00 |
| Sugar, 3⅛", ftd., #2350½ | 16.50 |
| Tray, 11¼", ctr. hdld., #2364 | 32.50 |
| Tumbler, 3⅝", 4 oz., ftd., oyster cocktail, #6017 | 17.50 |
| Tumbler, 4¾", 5 oz., ftd., #6017 | 17.50 |
| Tumbler, 5½", 9 oz., ftd., #6017 | 20.00 |
| Tumbler, 6", 12 oz., ftd., #6017 | 25.00 |
| Vase, 5", #4121 | 39.50 |
| Vase, 6", ftd. bud, #6021 | 37.50 |
| Vase, 6", ftd., #4143 | 47.50 |
| Vase, 6", grnd. bottom, #2619½ | 50.00 |
| Vase, 7½", ftd., #4143 | 60.00 |
| Vase, 7½", grnd. bottom, #2619½ | 65.00 |
| Vase, 9½", grnd. bottom, #2619½ | 85.00 |
| Vase, 10", #2614 | 75.00 |
| Vase, 10", ftd., #2470 | 95.00 |

# ROSALIE, or #731, Cambridge Glass Company, Late 1920's – 1930's

Colors: blue, green, Heatherbloom, pink, red, amber, bluebell, crystal, topaz

Rosalie is one Cambridge pattern that will keep you wondering what new item will be found. Not only do new pieces surface, but unusual colors seem to appear also! Pink, green, and amber are apparently the only colors in which one can amass a large set.

Most of my unusual finds in this pattern end up in a collection in Seattle. That is the new address of the blue ice tub, candy, and Bluebell water goblet in the top picture. The pink wafer tray and marmalade in the bottom photograph made the same trip.

This would be an ideal starting pattern for someone wanting a Cambridge pattern that can be gathered without taking out a loan.

| Item | Blue Pink Green | Amber | Item | Blue Pink Green | Amber |
|---|---|---|---|---|---|
| Bottle, French dressing | 110.00 | 85.00 | Gravy, double, w/platter | 135.00 | 85.00 |
| Bowl, bouillon, 2 hdld. | 25.00 | 15.00 | Ice bucket or pail | 65.00 | 45.00 |
| Bowl, cream soup | 25.00 | 20.00 | Icer, w/liner | 55.00 | 40.00 |
| Bowl, finger, w/liner | 35.00 | 25.00 | Ice tub | 70.00 | 60.00 |
| Bowl, finger, ftd., w/liner | 37.50 | 30.00 | Marmalade | 100.00 | 75.00 |
| Bowl, 3½", cranberry | 27.50 | 22.00 | Mayonnaise, ftd., w/liner | 55.00 | 25.00 |
| Bowl, 3⅝", w/cover, 3 pt. | 47.50 | 37.50 | Nut, 2½", ftd. | 55.00 | 45.00 |
| Bowl, 5½", fruit | 15.00 | 10.00 | Pitcher, 62 oz., #955 | 215.00 | 160.00 |
| Bowl, 5½", 2 hdld., bonbon | 20.00 | 12.00 | Plate, 6¾", bread/butter | 7.00 | 5.00 |
| Bowl, 6¼", 2 hdld., bonbon | 22.50 | 15.00 | Plate, 7", 2 hdld. | 15.00 | 7.00 |
| Bowl, 7", basket, 2 hdld. | 25.00 | 15.00 | Plate, 7½", salad | 10.00 | 6.00 |
| Bowl, 8½", soup | 40.00 | 30.00 | Plate, 8⅜" | 15.00 | 10.00 |
| Bowl, 8½", 2 hdld. | 25.00 | 15.00 | Plate, 9½", dinner | 60.00 | 35.00 |
| Bowl, 8½", w/cover, 3 pt. | 67.50 | 35.00 | Plate, 11", 2 hdld. | 30.00 | 20.00 |
| Bowl, 10" | 37.50 | 25.00 | Platter, 12" | 65.00 | 35.00 |
| Bowl, 10", 2 hdld. | 39.00 | 27.00 | Platter, 15" | 95.00 | 65.00 |
| Bowl, 11" | 40.00 | 25.00 | Relish, 9", 2 pt. | 25.00 | 15.00 |
| Bowl, 11", basket, 2 hdld. | 45.00 | 35.00 | Relish, 11", 2 pt. | 35.00 | 20.00 |
| Bowl, 11½" | 65.00 | 45.00 | Salt dip, 1½", ftd. | 50.00 | 40.00 |
| Bowl, 12", decagon | 95.00 | 75.00 | Saucer | 5.00 | 4.00 |
| Bowl, 13", console | 50.00 | | Stem, 1 oz., cordial, #3077 | 90.00 | 60.00 |
| Bowl, 14", decagon | 225.00 | 165.00 | Stem, 3½ oz., cocktail, #3077 | 20.00 | 15.00 |
| Bowl, 15", oval console | 75.00 | 60.00 | Stem, 6 oz., low sherbet, #3077 | 15.00 | 12.00 |
| Bowl, 15", oval, flanged | 85.00 | 65.00 | Stem, 6 oz., high sherbet, #3077 | 18.00 | 14.00 |
| Bowl, 15½", oval | 95.00 | 70.00 | Stem, 9 oz., water goblet, #3077 | 25.00 | 20.00 |
| Candlestick, 4", 2 styles | 30.00 | 20.00 | Stem, 10 oz., goblet, #801 | 30.00 | 20.00 |
| Candlestick, 5", keyhole | 35.00 | 25.00 | Sugar, ftd. | 16.00 | 13.00 |
| Candlestick, 6", 3-lite keyhole | 55.00 | 35.00 | Sugar shaker | 225.00 | 195.00 |
| Candy and cover, 6" | 100.00 | 65.00 | Tray for sugar shaker/creamer | 30.00 | 20.00 |
| Celery, 11" | 35.00 | 20.00 | Tray, ctr. hdld., for sugar/creamer | 20.00 | 14.00 |
| Cheese & cracker, 11" plate | 65.00 | 40.00 | Tray, 11", ctr. hdld. | 30.00 | 20.00 |
| Comport, 5½", 2 hdld. | 30.00 | 15.00 | Tumbler, 2½ oz., ftd., #3077 | 35.00 | 25.00 |
| Comport, 5¾" | 30.00 | 15.00 | Tumbler, 5 oz., ftd., #3077 | 25.00 | 20.00 |
| Comport, 6", ftd., almond | 40.00 | 25.00 | Tumbler, 8 oz., ftd. #3077 | 25.00 | 16.00 |
| Comport, 6½", low ft. | 40.00 | 25.00 | Tumbler, 10 oz., ftd., #3077 | 27.00 | 20.00 |
| Comport, 6½", high ft. | 40.00 | 25.00 | Tumbler, 12 oz., ftd., #3077 | 35.00 | 25.00 |
| Comport, 6¾" | 45.00 | 30.00 | Vase, 5½", ftd. | 45.00 | 27.50 |
| Creamer, ftd. | 17.00 | 12.00 | Vase, 6" | 55.00 | 40.00 |
| Creamer, ftd., tall, ewer | 35.00 | 25.00 | Vase, 6½", ftd. | 75.00 | 45.00 |
| Cup | 35.00 | 25.00 | Wafer tray | 100.00 | 75.00 |

# ROSE, Etching #1515, on WAVERLY Blank #1519, A.H. Heisey & Co., 1949 – 1957

Colors: crystal

Heisey's Rose pattern had taken over the number one spot from Orchid in collector demand; but presently, Plantation is vying for that position. A cocktail icer (without the insert) is shown as a pattern shot. (The insert obscured the design.) The two styles of ice buckets were the first pieces to sell when we put out almost a complete set at the Heisey show!

| | Crystal | | Crystal |
|---|---|---|---|
| Ash tray, 3" | 37.50 | Cocktail icer, w/liner, #3304, UNIVERSAL .. | 275.00 |
| Bell, dinner, #5072 | 150.00 | Cocktail shaker, #4225, COBEL | 145.00 |
| Bottle, 8 oz., French dressing, blown, #5031 .. | 195.00 | Comport, 6½", low ft., WAVERLY | 60.00 |
| Bowl, finger, #3309 | 95.00 | Comport, 7", oval, ftd., WAVERLY | 130.00 |
| Bowl, 5½", ftd., mint | 35.00 | Creamer, ftd., WAVERLY | 27.50 |
| Bowl, 5¾", ftd., mint, CABOCHON | 75.00 | Creamer, indiv., WAVERLY | 25.00 |
| Bowl, 6", ftd., mint, QUEEN ANN | 45.00 | Cup, WAVERLY | 65.00 |
| Bowl, 6", jelly, 2 hdld., ftd., QUEEN ANN .... | 42.50 | Decanter, 1 pt., #4036½, #101 stopper | 195.00 |
| Bowl, 6", oval, lemon, w/cover, WAVERLY .... | 325.00 | Hurricane lamp, w/12" globe, #5080 | 325.00 |
| Bowl, 6½", 2 pt., oval, dressing, WAVERLY .... | 65.00 | Hurricane lamp, w/12" globe, | |
| Bowl, 6½", ftd., honey/cheese, WAVERLY .... | 60.00 | PLANTATION | 450.00 |
| Bowl, 6½", ftd., jelly, WAVERLY | 45.00 | Ice bucket, dolp. ft., QUEEN ANN | 295.00 |
| Bowl, 6½", lemon, w/cover, WAVERLY | 175.00 | Ice tub, 2 hdld., WAVERLY | 295.00 |
| Bowl, 7", ftd., honey, WAVERLY | 60.00 | Mayonnaise, 5½", 2 hdld., WAVERLY | 55.00 |
| Bowl, 7", ftd., jelly, WAVERLY | 45.00 | Mayonnaise, 5½", div., 1 hdld., WAVERLY ... | 55.00 |
| Bowl, 7", lily, QUEEN ANN | 50.00 | Mayonnaise, 5½", ftd., WAVERLY | 60.00 |
| Bowl, 7", relish, 3 pt., round, WAVERLY | 67.50 | Oil, 3 oz., ftd., WAVERLY | 165.00 |
| Bowl, 7", salad, WAVERLY | 55.00 | Pitcher, 73 oz., #4164 | 575.00 |
| Bowl, 7", salad dressings, QUEEN ANN | 50.00 | Plate, 7", salad, WAVERLY | 20.00 |
| Bowl, 9", ftd., fruit or salad, WAVERLY | 175.00 | Plate, 7", mayonnaise, WAVERLY | 20.00 |
| Bowl, 9", salad, WAVERLY | 95.00 | Plate, 8", salad, WAVERLY | 30.00 |
| Bowl, 9", 4 pt., rnd, relish, WAVERLY | 90.00 | Plate, 10½", dinner WAVERLY | 155.00 |
| Bowl, 9½", crimped, floral, WAVERLY | 65.00 | Plate, 10½", service, WAVERLY | 75.00 |
| Bowl, 10", gardenia, WAVERLY | 70.00 | Plate, 11", sandwich, WAVERLY | 50.00 |
| Bowl, 10", crimped, floral, WAVERLY | 70.00 | Plate, 11", demi-torte, WAVERLY | 65.00 |
| Bowl, 11", 3 pt., relish, WAVERLY | 77.50 | Plate, 12", ftd., salver, WAVERLY | 225.00 |
| Bowl, 11", 3 ftd., floral, WAVERLY | 150.00 | Plate, 15", ftd., cake, WAVERLY | 300.00 |
| Bowl, 11", floral, WAVERLY | 67.50 | Plate, 14", torte, WAVERLY | 90.00 |
| Bowl, 11", oval, 4 ftd., WAVERLY | 150.00 | Plate, 14", sandwich, WAVERLY | 90.00 |
| Bowl, 12", crimped, floral, WAVERLY | 65.00 | Plate, 14", ctr. hdld., sandwich, WAVERLY .. | 215.00 |
| Bowl, 13", crimped, floral, WAVERLY | 110.00 | Salt & pepper, ftd., pr., WAVERLY | 65.00 |
| Bowl, 13", floral, WAVERLY | 80.00 | Saucer, WAVERLY | 15.00 |
| Bowl, 13", gardenia, WAVERLY | 80.00 | Stem, #5072, 1 oz., cordial | 145.00 |
| Butter, w/cover, 6", WAVERLY | 185.00 | Stem, #5072, 3 oz., wine | 115.00 |
| Butter, w/cover, ¼ lb., CABOCHON | 295.00 | Stem, #5072, 3½ oz., oyster cocktail, ftd. ..... | 32.50 |
| Candlestick, 1-lite, #112 | 40.00 | Stem, #5072, 4 oz., claret, | 125.00 |
| Candlestick, 2-lite, FLAME | 70.00 | Stem, #5072, 4 oz., cocktail | 45.00 |
| Candlestick, 3-lite, #142, CASCADE | 80.00 | Stem, #5072, 6 oz., sherbet | 27.50 |
| Candlestick, 3-lite, WAVERLY | 90.00 | Stem, #5072, 6 oz., saucer champagne | 35.00 |
| Candlestick, 5", 2-lite, #134, TRIDENT | 65.00 | Stem, #5072, 9 oz., water | 45.00 |
| Candlestick, 6", epergnette, deep, | | Sugar, indiv., WAVERLY | 25.00 |
| WAVERLY | 400.00 | Sugar, ftd., WAVERLY | 22.50 |
| Candy, w/cover, 5", ftd., WAVERLY | 165.00 | Tumbler, #5072, 5 oz., ftd., juice | 47.50 |
| Candy, w/cover, 6", low, bowknot cover | 170.00 | Tumbler, #5072, 12 oz., ftd., tea | 55.00 |
| Candy, w/cover, 6¼", #1951, CABOCHON ... | 155.00 | Tray, indiv. creamer/sugar, QUEEN ANN ..... | 55.00 |
| Celery tray, 12", WAVERLY | 60.00 | Vase, 3½", ftd., violet, WAVERLY | 100.00 |
| Celery tray, 13", WAVERLY | 67.50 | Vase, 4", ftd., violet, WAVERLY | 110.00 |
| Cheese compote, 4½", & cracker (11" plate) | | Vase, 7", ftd., fan, WAVERLY | 110.00 |
| WAVERLY | 145.00 | Vase, 8", #4198 | 120.00 |
| Cheese compote, 5½", & cracker (12" plate) | | Vase, 8", sq., ftd., urn | 120.00 |
| QUEEN ANNE | 145.00 | Vase, 10", #4198 | 200.00 |
| Chocolate, w/cover, 5", WAVERLY | 150.00 | Vase, 10", sq., ftd, urn | 140.00 |
| Cigarette holder, #4035 | 95.00 | Vase, 12", sq., ftd., urn | 225.00 |

# ROSE POINT, Cambridge Glass Company, 1936 – 1953

One of the major problems confronting new collectors is recognizing the different blanks on which Rose Point is found. With the shelf shots on page 173, I will try to clarify blank identification.

Row 1: #3400 cup and saucer, #3900 plate, #3400 plate, #3900 cup and saucer

Row 2: #3500 cup and saucer, plate, cereal, individual sugar and creamer (so called "pie crust edge")

Row 3: #3500 ftd. water tumbler, claret, cocktail, ftd. juice tumbler, oyster cocktail, short wine, cordial, tall sherbet, short sherbet

Row 4: oyster cocktail, wine, cordial, #3121 brandy, pressed cordial, Pristine cocktail, #7966 cordial, cordial, cocktail, #3106 wine

The Pristine cocktail in Row 4 is the first stemware piece of Rose Point to show up on that blank. On the bottom of page 175 in the foreground is a flat soup and on page 177 is the punch set that is missing in most collections. Take a last view of the pressed Rose Point stem with etched Rose Point top that will be retired after this book. Those were found in Texas a few years ago; but none have been seen since. I need to find a cordial in that style!

Throughout the photographs are many unusual and rare pieces, but to show them, I have little space to mention them. Enjoy!

| | Crystal | | Crystal |
|---|---|---|---|
| Ash tray, stack set on metal pole, #1715 | 225.00 | Bowl, 9½", ftd., w/hdl. (#3500/115) | 125.00 |
| Ash tray, 2½", sq. #721 | 32.50 | Bowl, 9½", 2 hdld. (#3400/34) | 67.50 |
| Ash tray, 3¼" (#3500/124) | 32.50 | Bowl, 9½", 2 part, blown (#225) | 375.00 |
| Ash tray, 3¼", sq. (#3500/129) | 55.00 | Bowl, 2 hdld. (#3400/1185) | 70.00 |
| Ash tray, 3½" (#3500/125) | 35.00 | Bowl, 10", 2 hdld. (#3500/28) | 77.50 |
| Ash tray, 4" (#3500/126) | 40.00 | Bowl, 10", 4 tab ftd., flared (#3900/54) | 60.00 |
| Ash tray, 4", oval (#3500/130) | 85.00 | Bowl, 10½", crimp edge, #1351 | 85.00 |
| Ash tray, 4¼" (#3500/127) | 45.00 | Bowl, 10½", flared (#3400/168) | 65.00 |
| Ash tray, 4½" (#3500/128) | 50.00 | Bowl, 10½", 3 part, #222 | 195.00 |
| Ash tray, 4½", oval (#3500/131) | 65.00 | Bowl, 10½", 3 part (#1401/122) | 245.00 |
| Basket, 3", favor (#3500/79) | 275.00 | Bowl, 11", ftd. (#3500/16) | 100.00 |
| Basket, 5", 1 hdld. (#3500/51) | 200.00 | Bowl, 11", ftd., fancy edge (#3500/19) | 125.00 |
| Basket, 6", 1 hdld. (#3500/52) | 245.00 | Bowl, 11", 4 ftd., oval (#3500/109) | 325.00 |
| Basket, 6", 2 hdld. (#3400/1182) | 35.00 | Bowl, 11", 4 ftd., shallow, fancy edge | |
| Basket, 6", sq., ftd., 2 hdld (#3500/55) | 37.50 | (#3400/48) | 85.00 |
| Basket, 7", 1 hdld., #119 | 395.00 | Bowl, 11", fruit (#3400/1188) | 90.00 |
| Basket, 7", wide (#3500/56) | 50.00 | Bowl, 11", low foot (#3400/3) | 145.00 |
| Basket, sugar, w/handle and tongs (#3500/13) | 275.00 | Bowl, 11", tab hdld. (#3900/34) | 67.50 |
| Bell, dinner, #3121 | 145.00 | Bowl, 11½", ftd., w/tab hdl. (#3900/28) | 70.00 |
| Bowl, 3", 4 ftd., nut (#3400/71) | 70.00 | Bowl, 12", crimped, pan (Pristine #136) | 275.00 |
| Bowl, 3½", bonbon, cupped, deep (#3400/204) | 80.00 | Bowl, 10", salad (Pristine #427) | 135.00 |
| Bowl, 3½", cranberry (#3400/70) | 85.00 | Bowl, 12", 4 ftd., oval (#3400/1240) | 110.00 |
| Bowl, 5", hdld. (#3500/49) | 35.00 | Bowl, 12", 4 ftd., oval, w/"ears" hdl. | |
| Bowl, 5" fruit (#3500/10) | 42.50 | (#3900/65) | 85.00 |
| Bowl, 5" fruit, blown #1534 | 75.00 | Bowl, 12", 4 ftd., fancy rim oblong (#3400/160) | 85.00 |
| Bowl, 5¼" fruit (#3400/56) | 42.50 | Bowl, 12", 4 ftd., flared (#3400/4) | 70.00 |
| Bowl, 5½", nappy (#3400/56) | 42.50 | Bowl, 12", 4 tab ftd., flared (#3900/62) | 72.50 |
| Bowl, 5½", 2 hdld., bonbon (#3400/1179) | 32.00 | Bowl, 12", ftd., (#3500/17) | 110.00 |
| Bowl, 5½", 2 hdld., bonbon (#3400/1180) | 30.00 | Bowl, 12", ftd., oblong (#3500/118) | 155.00 |
| Bowl, 6", bonbon, crimped (#3400/203) | 85.00 | Bowl, 12", ftd., oval w/hdl. (#3500/21) | 195.00 |
| Bowl, 6", bonbon, cupped, shallow (#3400/205) | 80.00 | Bowl, 12½", flared, rolled edge (#3400/2) | 145.00 |
| Bowl, 6", cereal (#3400/53) | 77.50 | Bowl, 12½", 4 ftd., #993 | 85.00 |
| Bowl, 6", cereal (#3400/10) | 77.50 | Bowl, 13", #1398 | 110.00 |
| Bowl, 6", cereal (#3500/11) | 77.50 | Bowl, 13", 4 ftd., narrow, crimped (#3400/47) | 120.00 |
| Bowl, 6", hdld. (#3500/50) | 42.50 | Bowl, 13", flared (#3400/1) | 67.50 |
| Bowl, 6", 2 hdld. (#1402/89) | 40.00 | Bowl, 14", 4 ftd., crimp edge, oblong, #1247 | 135.00 |
| Bowl, 6", 2 hdld., ftd., bonbon (#3500/54) | 35.00 | Bowl, 18", crimped, pan, (Pristine #136) | 595.00 |
| Bowl, 6", 4 ftd., fancy rim (#3400/136) | 145.00 | Bowl, cream soup, w/liner (#3400) | 145.00 |
| Bowl, 6½" bonbon, crimped (#3400/202) | 85.00 | Bowl, cream soup, w/liner (#3500/2) | 155.00 |
| Bowl, 7", bonbon, crimped, shallow | | Bowl, finger, w/liner, #3106 | 85.00 |
| (#3400/201) | 110.00 | Bowl, finger, w/liner, #3121 | 85.00 |
| Bowl, 7", tab hdld., ftd., bonbon (#3900/130) | 35.00 | Butter, w/cover, round, #506 | 177.50 |
| Bowl, 8", ram's head, squared (#3500/27) | 325.00 | Butter, w/cover, 5" (#3400/52) | 170.00 |
| Bowl, 8½", rimmed soup, #361 | 250.00 | Butter dish, ¼ lb. (#3900/52) | 285.00 |
| Bowl, 8½", 3 part, #221 | 150.00 | Candelabrum, 2-lite w/bobeches & prisms, | |
| Bowl, 9", 4 ftd., (#3400/135) | 200.00 | #1268 | 125.00 |
| Bowl, 9", ram's head (#3500/25) | 345.00 | Candelabrum, 2-lite (#3500/94) | 95.00 |
| Bowl, 9½", pickle (like corn), #477 | 50.00 | Candelabrum, 3-lite, #1338 | 60.00 |

| | Crystal |
|---|---|
| Candelabrum, 5½", 3-lite w/#19 bobeche & #1 prisms, #1545 ................................................ | 100.00 |
| Candelabrum, 6½", 2-lite, w/bobeches & prisms, (Martha #496) ............................................ | 160.00 |
| Candle, torchere, cup ft. (#3500/90) .................. | 175.00 |
| Candle, torchere, flat ft. (#3500/88) .................. | 160.00 |
| Candlestick, (Pristine #500) .............................. | 125.00 |
| Candlestick, sq. base & lites (#1700/501) ........... | 165.00 |
| Candlestick, 2½" (#3500/108) ............................ | 30.00 |
| Candlestick, 3½", #628 .................................... | 35.00 |
| Candlestick, 4", #627 ...................................... | 52.50 |
| Candlestick, 4", ram's head (#3500/74) ............. | 95.00 |
| Candlestick, 5", 1-lite keyhole (#3400/646) ........ | 30.00 |
| Candlestick, 5", inverts to comport (#3900/68) ... | 52.50 |
| Candlestick, 5½", 2-lite (Martha #495) ............... | 55.00 |
| Candlestick, 6" (#3500/31) ............................... | 87.50 |
| Candlestick, 6", 2-lite keyhole (#3400/647) ......... | 37.50 |
| Candlestick, 6", 2-lite (#3900/72) ..................... | 42.50 |
| Candlestick, 6", 3-lite (#3900/74) ..................... | 47.50 |
| Candlestick, 6", 3-lite keyhole (#3400/638) ........ | 45.00 |
| Candlestick, 6", 3-tiered lite, #1338 .................. | 65.00 |
| Candlestick, 6½", Calla Lily, #499 .................... | 92.50 |
| Candlestick, 7", #3121 .................................... | 70.00 |
| Candlestick, 7½", w/prism (Martha #497) ........... | 130.00 |
| Candy box, w/cover, 5", apple shape, #316 ......... | 850.00 |
| Candy box, w/cover, 5⅜", #1066 stem ............... | 150.00 |
| Candy box, w/cover, 5⅜", tall stem, (#3121/3) ..... | 140.00 |
| Candy box, w/cover, 5⅜", short stem, (#3121/4) .. | 155.00 |
| Candy box, w/cover, blown, 5⅜" (#3500/103) ...... | 155.00 |
| Candy box, w/cover, 6", ram's head (#3500/78) ... | 250.00 |
| Candy box, w/rose finial, 6", 3 ftd., #300 .......... | 265.00 |
| Candy box, w/cover, 7" (#3400/9) ...................... | 135.00 |
| Candy box, w/cover, 7", round, 3 pt. #103 .......... | 155.00 |
| Candy box, w/cover, 8", 3 pt. (#3500/57) ........... | 75.00 |
| Candy box, w/cover, rnd. (#3900/165) ................ | 100.00 |
| Celery, 12" (#3400/652) ................................... | 45.00 |
| Celery, 12" (#3500/652) ................................... | 47.50 |
| Celery, 12", 5 pt. (#3400/67) ............................ | 75.00 |
| Celery, 14", 4 pt., 2 hdld. (#3500/97) ................ | 145.00 |
| Celery & relish, 9", 3 pt. (#3900/125) ................ | 50.00 |
| Celery & relish, 12", 3 pt. (#3900/126) .............. | 60.00 |
| Celery & relish, 12", 5 pt. (#3900/120) .............. | 67.50 |
| Cheese (5" comport) & cracker (13" plate) (#3900/135) ................................................ | 115.00 |
| Cheese (5½" comport) & cracker (11½" plate) (#3400/6) .................................................. | 115.00 |
| Cheese (6" comport) & cracker (12" plate) (#3500/162) ................................................ | 135.00 |
| Cheese dish, w/cover, 5", #980 ........................ | 425.00 |
| Cigarette box, w/cover, #615 ............................ | 120.00 |
| Cigarette box, w/cover, #747 ............................ | 150.00 |
| Cigarette holder, oval, w/ash tray ft., #1066 ....... | 160.00 |
| Cigarette holder, round, w/ash tray ft., #1337 ..... | 140.00 |
| Coaster, 3½", #1628 ....................................... | 52.50 |
| Cocktail icer, 2 pc. (#3600) ............................. | 72.50 |
| Cocktail shaker, metal top (#3400/157) .............. | 165.00 |
| Cocktail shaker, metal top (#3400/175) .............. | 135.00 |
| Cocktail shaker, 12 oz., metal top, #97 .............. | 295.00 |
| Cocktail shaker, 32 oz., w/glass stopper, #101 .... | 175.00 |
| Cocktail shaker, 46 oz., metal top, #98 .............. | 150.00 |
| Cocktail shaker, 48 oz., glass stopper, #102 ........ | 160.00 |
| Comport, 5" (#3900/135) ................................. | 42.50 |

| | Crystal |
|---|---|
| Comport, 5", 4 ftd., (#3400/74) ........................ | 67.50 |
| Comport, 5½", scalloped edge (#3900/136) ......... | 55.00 |
| Comport, 5⅜", blown (#3500/101) ..................... | 62.50 |
| Comport, 5⅜", blown, #3121 stem ..................... | 60.00 |
| Comport, 5⅜", blown, #1066 stem ..................... | 67.50 |
| Comport, 6" (#3500/36) ................................... | 120.00 |
| Comport, 6" (#3500/111) .................................. | 140.00 |
| Comport, 6", 4 ftd., (#3400/13) ........................ | 37.50 |
| Comport, 7", 2 hdld. (#3500/37) ....................... | 115.00 |
| Comport, 7", keyhole (#3400/29) ...................... | 130.00 |
| Comport, 7", keyhole, low (#3400/28) ................ | 80.00 |
| Creamer (#3400/68) ........................................ | 20.00 |
| Creamer (#3500/14) ........................................ | 22.00 |
| Creamer, flat #137 .......................................... | 115.00 |
| Creamer, flat, #944 ......................................... | 135.00 |
| Creamer, ftd., (#3400/16) ................................ | 90.00 |
| Creamer, ftd., (#3900/41) ................................ | 20.00 |
| Creamer, indiv. (#3500/15) pie crust edge .......... | 25.00 |
| Creamer, indiv. (#3900/40) scalloped edge .......... | 20.00 |
| Cup, 3 styles (#3400/54, #3500/1, #3900/17) ...... | 30.00 |
| Cup, 5 oz., punch, #488 .................................. | 37.50 |
| Cup, after dinner (#3400/69) ............................ | 255.00 |
| Decanter, 12 oz., ball, w/stopper (#3400/119) ..... | 240.00 |
| Decanter, 14 oz., ftd., #1320 ........................... | 415.00 |
| Decanter, 26 oz., sq., #1380 ............................ | 415.00 |
| Decanter, 28 oz., tall, #1372 ............................ | 575.00 |
| Decanter, 28 oz., w/stopper, #1321 ................... | 300.00 |
| Decanter, 32 oz., ball, w/stopper (#3400/92) ....... | 375.00 |
| Dressing bottle, flat, #1263 ............................. | 275.00 |
| Dressing bottle, ftd., #1261 ............................. | 310.00 |
| Epergne (candle w/vases) (#3900/75) ................. | 210.00 |
| Grapefruit, w/liner, #187 ................................. | 115.00 |
| Hat, 5", #1704 ............................................... | 425.00 |
| Hat, 6", #1703 ............................................... | 425.00 |
| Hat, 8", #1702 ............................................... | 475.00 |
| Hat, 9", #1701 ............................................... | 550.00 |
| Honey dish, w/cover (#3500/139) ...................... | 275.00 |
| Hot plate or trivet ......................................... | 65.00 |
| Hurricane lamp, w/prisms, #1613 ...................... | 325.00 |
| Hurricane lamp, candlestick base, #1617 ............ | 195.00 |
| Hurricane lamp, keyhole base, w/prisms, #1603 ..................................................... | 215.00 |
| Hurricane lamp, 8", etched chimney, #1601 ....... | 225.00 |
| Hurricane lamp, 10", etched chimney & base, #1604 ..................................................... | 275.00 |
| Ice bucket (#1402/52) ..................................... | 195.00 |
| Ice bucket, w/chrome hand. (#3900/671) ............ | 135.00 |
| Ice pail, #1705 .............................................. | 215.00 |
| Ice pail (#3400/851) ....................................... | 120.00 |
| Ice tub, (Pristine), #671 ................................. | 195.00 |
| Icer, cocktail, #968 or #18 .............................. | 72.50 |
| Marmalade, 8 oz., #147 ................................... | 135.00 |
| Marmalade, w/cover, 7 oz., ftd., #157 ................ | 170.00 |
| Mayonnaise (sherbet type w/ladle) #19 ............... | 52.50 |
| Mayonnaise, div., w/liner & 2 ladles (#3900/111) ................................................ | 75.00 |
| Mayonnaise, 3 pc. (#3400/11) .......................... | 67.50 |
| Mayonnaise, 3 pc. (#3900/129) ........................ | 65.00 |
| Mayonnaise, w/liner & ladle (#3500/59) ............. | 75.00 |
| Mustard, 3 oz., #151 ...................................... | 135.00 |
| Mustard, 4½ oz., ftd., #1329 ........................... | 310.00 |
| Oil, 2 oz., ball, w/stopper (#3400/96) ................ | 75.00 |

| | Crystal | | Crystal |
|---|---|---|---|
| Oil, 6 oz., ball, w/stopper (#3400/99) | 115.00 | Relish, 7½", 4 pt. (#3500/70) | 37.50 |
| Oil, 6 oz., hdld (#3400/193) | 90.00 | Relish, 7½", 4 pt., 2 hdld. (#3500/62) | 55.00 |
| Oil, 6 oz., loop hdld., w/stopper (#3900/100) | 125.00 | Relish, 8", 3 pt., 3 hdld. (#3400/91) | 37.50 |
| Oil, 6 oz., w/stopper, ftd., hdld. (#3400/161) | 210.00 | Relish, 10", 2 hdld. (#3500/85) | 70.00 |
| Pickle, 9" (#3400/59) | 60.00 | Relish, 10", 3 pt., 2 hdld. (#3500/86) | 52.50 |
| Pickle or relish, 7", (#3900/123) | 35.00 | Relish, 10", 3 pt., 4 ftd., 2 hdld. (#3500/64) | 52.50 |
| Pitcher, 20 oz., (#3900/117) | 235.00 | Relish, 10", 4 pt., 4 ftd., (#3500/65) | 62.50 |
| Pitcher, 20 oz. w/ice lip, #70 | 235.00 | Relish, 10", 4 pt., 2 hdld. (#3500/87) | 60.00 |
| Pitcher, 32 oz. (#3900/118) | 295.00 | Relish, 11", 2 pt., 2 hdld. (#3400/89) | 77.50 |
| Pitcher, 32 oz. martini (slender) w/metal insert, (#3900/114) | 425.00 | Relish, 11", 3 pt. (#3400/200) | 57.50 |
| Pitcher, 60 oz., martini, #1408 | 1,850.00 | Relish, 12", 5 pt. (#3400/67) | 75.00 |
| Pitcher, 76 oz. (#3900/115) | 195.00 | Relish, 12", 5 pt., (Pristine #419) | 225.00 |
| Pitcher, 76 oz., ice lip (#3400/100) | 200.00 | Relish, 12", 6 pc. (#3500/67) | 215.00 |
| Pitcher, 76 oz., ice lip (#3400/152) | 285.00 | Relish, 14", w/cover, 4 pt., 2 hdld. (#3500/142) | 425.00 |
| Pitcher, 80 oz., ball (#3400/38) | 195.00 | Relish, 15", 4 pt., hdld. (#3500/113) | 185.00 |
| Pitcher, 80 oz., ball (#3900/116) | 210.00 | Salt & pepper, egg shape, pr., #1468 | 85.00 |
| Pitcher, 80 oz., Doulton (#3400/141) | 275.00 | Salt & pepper, individual, rnd., glass base, pr., #1470 | 80.00 |
| Pitcher, nite set, 2 pc., w/tumbler insert top, #103 | 550.00 | Salt & pepper, individual, w/chrome tops, pr., #360 | 65.00 |
| Plate, 6", bread/butter (#3400/60) | 13.50 | Salt & pepper, lg., rnd., glass base, pr., #1471 | 80.00 |
| Plate, 6", bread/butter (#3500/3) | 15.00 | Salt & pepper, w/chrome tops, pr., #395 | 165.00 |
| Plate, 6", 2 hdld. (#3400/1181) | 20.00 | Salt & pepper, w/chrome tops, pr. (#3400/37) | 165.00 |
| Plate, 6⅛" canape #693 | 155.00 | Salt & pepper, w/chrome tops, pr., ftd. (#3400/77) | 50.00 |
| Plate, 6½", bread/butter (#3900/20) | 13.50 | Salt & pepper w/chrome tops, pr., flat (#3900/1177) | 40.00 |
| Plate, 7½" (#3500/4) | 15.00 | Sandwich tray, 11", center handled (#3400/10) | 135.00 |
| Plate, 7½", salad (#3400/176) | 15.00 | Saucer, after dinner (#3400/69) | 55.00 |
| Plate, 8", salad (#3900/22) | 20.00 | Saucer, 3 styles (#3400, #3500, #3900) | 5.00 |
| Plate, 8", 2 hdld., ftd., (#3500/161) | 42.50 | Stem, #3104, 3½ oz., cocktail | 275.00 |
| Plate, 8", tab hdld., ftd., bonbon (#3900/131) | 37.50 | Stem, #3106, ¾ oz., brandy | 110.00 |
| Plate, 8½", breakfast (#3400/62) | 20.00 | Stem, #3106, 1 oz., cordial | 110.00 |
| Plate, 8½", salad (#3500/5) | 20.00 | Stem, #3106, 1 oz., pousse cafe | 120.00 |
| Plate, 9½" crescent salad #485 | 235.00 | Stem, #3106, 2 oz., sherry | 45.00 |
| Plate, 9½", luncheon (#3400/63) | 40.00 | Stem, #3106, 2½ oz., wine | 45.00 |
| Plate, 10½", dinner (#3400/64) | 125.00 | Stem, #3106, 3 oz., cocktail | 35.00 |
| Plate, 10½" dinner (#3900/24) | 125.00 | Stem, #3106, 4½ oz., claret | 50.00 |
| Plate, 11", 2 hdld. (#3400/35) | 50.00 | Stem, #3106, 5 oz., oyster cocktail | 32.50 |
| Plate, 12", 4 ftd., service (#3900/26) | 70.00 | Stem, #3106, 7 oz., high sherbet | 30.00 |
| Plate, 12", ftd. (#3500/39) | 90.00 | Stem, #3106, 7 oz., low sherbet | 25.00 |
| Plate, 12½", 2 hdld. (#3400/1186) | 65.00 | Stem, #3106, 10 oz., water goblet | 35.00 |
| Plate, 13", rolled edge, ftd. (#3900/33) | 70.00 | Stem, #3121, 1 oz., brandy | 115.00 |
| Plate, 13", 4 ftd., torte (#3500/110) | 125.00 | Stem, #3121, 1 oz., cordial | 70.00 |
| Plate, 13", ftd., cake (Martha #170) | 235.00 | Stem, #3121, 3 oz., cocktail | 32.50 |
| Plate, 13", torte (#3500/38) | 175.00 | Stem, #3121, 3½ oz., wine | 60.00 |
| Plate, 13½", #242 | 145.00 | Stem, #3121, 4½ oz., claret | 90.00 |
| Plate, 13½", rolled edge, #1397 | 70.00 | Stem, #3121, 4½ oz., low oyster cocktail | 37.50 |
| Plate, 13½", tab hdld., cake (#3900/35) | 70.00 | Stem, #3121, 5 oz., low ft. parfait | 75.00 |
| Plate, 14", rolled edge (#3900/166) | 65.00 | Stem, #3121, 6 oz., low sherbet | 20.00 |
| Plate, 14", service (#3900/167) | 75.00 | Stem, #3121, 6 oz., tall sherbet | 22.00 |
| Plate, 14", torte (#3400/65) | 125.00 | Stem, #3121, 10 oz., water | 30.00 |
| Plate, 18", punch bowl liner (Martha #129) | 475.00 | Stem, #3500, 1 oz., cordial | 70.00 |
| Punch bowl, 15", Martha #478 | 3,250.00 | Stem, #3500, 2½ oz., wine | 57.50 |
| Punch set, 15-pc. (Martha) | 4,125.00 | Stem, #3500, 3 oz., cocktail | 35.00 |
| Relish, 5½", 2 pt. (#3500/68) | 25.00 | Stem, #3500, 4½ oz., claret | 80.00 |
| Relish, 5½", 2 pt., hdld. (#3500/60) | 30.00 | Stem, #3500, 4½ oz., low oyster cocktail | 37.50 |
| Relish, 6", 2 pt. (#3400/90) | 32.50 | Stem, #3500, 5 oz., low ft. parfait | 75.00 |
| Relish, 6", 2 pt., 1 hdl. (#3400/1093) | 85.00 | Stem, #3500, 7 oz., low ft. sherbet | 18.00 |
| Relish, 6½", 3 pt. (#3500/69) | 32.50 | Stem, #3500, 7 oz., tall sherbet | 24.00 |
| Relish, 6½", 3 pt., hdld. (#3500/61) | 37.50 | Stem, #3500, 10 oz. water | 30.00 |
| Relish, 7", 2 pt. (#3900/124) | 37.50 | | |
| Relish, 7½", 3 pt., center hdld. (#3500/71) | 135.00 | | |

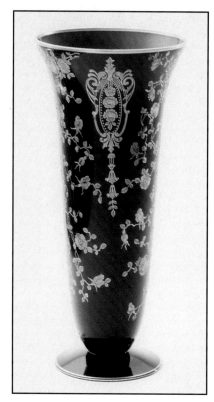

**ROSE POINT**

| | Crystal |
|---|---|
| Stem, #37801, 4 oz., cocktail | 45.00 |
| Stem, #7801, 4 oz. cocktail, plain stem | 40.00 |
| Stem, #7966, 1 oz., cordial, plain ft. | 135.00 |
| Stem, #7966, 2 oz., sherry, plain ft. | 95.00 |
| Sugar (#3400/68) | 20.00 |
| Sugar (#3500/14) | 20.00 |
| Sugar, flat, #137 | 110.00 |
| Sugar, flat, #944 | 135.00 |
| Sugar, ftd. (#3400/16) | 85.00 |
| Sugar, ftd. (#3900/41) | 20.00 |
| Sugar, indiv. (#3500/15) pie crust edge | 22.50 |
| Sugar, indiv. (#3900/40) scalloped edge | 21.50 |
| Syrup, w/drip stop top, #1670 | 375.00 |
| Tray, 6", 2 hdld., sq. (#3500/91) | 170.00 |
| Tray, 12", 2 hdld., oval, service (#3500/99) | 210.00 |
| Tray, 12", rnd. (#3500/67) | 150.00 |
| Tray, 13", 2 hdld., rnd. (#3500/72) | 150.00 |
| Tray, sugar/creamer, (#3900/37) | 25.00 |
| Tumbler, #498, 2 oz., straight side | 100.00 |
| Tumbler, #498, 5 oz., straight side | 45.00 |
| Tumbler, #498, 8 oz., straight side | 45.00 |
| Tumbler, #498, 10 oz., straight side | 45.00 |
| Tumbler, #498, 12 oz., straight side | 50.00 |
| Tumbler, #3000, 3½ oz., cone, ftd. | 90.00 |
| Tumbler, #3000, 5 oz., cone, ftd. | 110.00 |
| Tumbler, #3106, 3 oz., ftd. | 25.00 |
| Tumbler, #3106, 5 oz., ftd. | 25.00 |
| Tumbler, #3106, 9 oz., ftd. | 25.00 |
| Tumbler, #3106, 12 oz., ftd. | 32.00 |
| Tumbler, #3121, 2½ oz., ftd. | 65.00 |

| | Crystal |
|---|---|
| Tumbler, #3121, 5 oz., low ft., juice | 35.00 |
| Tumbler, #3121, 10 oz., low ft., water | 27.50 |
| Tumbler, #3121, 12 oz., low ft., ice tea | 32.50 |
| Tumbler, #3400/1341, 1 oz., cordial | 95.00 |
| Tumbler, #3400/92, 2½ oz. | 100.00 |
| Tumbler, #3400/38, 5 oz. | 90.00 |
| Tumbler, #3400/38, 12 oz. | 50.00 |
| Tumbler, #3900/115, 13 oz. | 42.00 |
| Tumbler, #3500, 2½ oz., ftd. | 55.00 |
| Tumbler, #3500, 5 oz., low ft., juice | 35.00 |
| Tumbler, #3500, 10 oz., low ft., water | 27.50 |
| Tumbler, #3500, 13 oz., low ftd. | 35.00 |
| Tumbler, #3500, 12 oz., tall ft., ice tea | 32.50 |
| Tumbler, #7801, 5 oz., ftd. | 35.00 |
| Tumbler, #7801, 12 oz., ftd., ice tea | 50.00 |
| Tumbler, #3900/117, 5 oz. | 45.00 |
| Tumbler, #3400/115, 13 oz. | 45.00 |
| Urn, 10", w/cover (#3500/41) | 500.00 |
| Urn, 12", w/cover (#3500/42) | 625.00 |
| Vase, 5", #1309 | 67.50 |
| Vase, 5", globe (#3400/102) | 70.00 |
| Vase, 5", ftd., #6004 | 45.00 |
| Vase, 6", high ftd., flower, #6004 | 50.00 |
| Vase, 6", #572 | 130.00 |
| Vase, 6½", globe (#3400/103) | 80.00 |
| Vase, 7", ivy, ftd., ball, #1066 | 225.00 |
| Vase, 8", #1430 | 150.00 |
| Vase, 8", flat, flared, #797 | 125.00 |
| Vase, 8", ftd. (#3500/44) | 110.00 |
| Vase, 8", high ftd., flower, #6004 | 55.00 |
| Vase, 9", ftd., keyhole, #1237 | 85.00 |
| Vase, 9", ftd., #1620 | 115.00 |
| Vase, 9½" ftd., keyholde, #1233 | 75.00 |
| Vase, 10", ball bottom, #400 | 165.00 |
| Vase, 10", bud, #1528 | 80.00 |
| Vase, 10", cornucopia (#3900/575) | 175.00 |
| Vase, 10", flat, #1242 | 125.00 |
| Vase, 10", ftd., #1301 | 75.00 |
| Vase, 10", ftd., #6004 | 75.00 |
| Vase, 10", ftd. (#3500/45) | 150.00 |
| Vase, 10", slender, #274 | 55.00 |
| Vase, 11", ftd., flower, #278 | 115.00 |
| Vase, 11", ped. ftd., flower, #1299 | 135.00 |
| Vase, 12", ftd., #6004 | 85.00 |
| Vase, 12", ftd., keyhole, #1234 | 85.00 |
| Vase, 12", ftd., keyhole, #1238 | 135.00 |
| Vase, 13", ftd., flower, #279 | 200.00 |
| Vase 18", #1336 | 1,800.00 |
| Vase, sweet pea, #629 | 250.00 |

# ROYAL, Plate Etching #273, Fostoria Glass Company, 1925 – 1932

Colors: amber, black, blue, green

Royal is a Fostoria pattern that is often confused with Vesper since both designs are similar and both are found in the same colors on the #2350 blank. There are more collectors for Vesper right now because that pattern has been more publicized than Royal. New collectors are finding that the less expensive Royal is comparable to Vesper in many ways, but kinder to the cash flow.

Don't ever pass up a buy on the covered cheese, cologne bottle, or the pitchers. Both the amber and green can be collected in sets; but only a few pieces can be found in blue and black. Fostoria's blue color found with Royal etching was called "Blue" as opposed to the "Azure" blue which is the lighter color found with June, Kashmir, or Versailles etchings. You can see how attractive the Blue is from the photograph. It is a shame that there is not more of it available.

Although some production of Royal supposedly continued until 1934, the January 1, 1933, Fostoria Catalogue no longer listed pieces as being for sale. I am adjusting my cutoff date for production to 1932 until someone can prove otherwise. If you ever have access to a May 1928, copy of *House and Garden*, there is an interesting Fostoria advertisement there.

| | *Amber, Green | | *Amber, Green |
|---|---|---|---|
| Ash tray, #2350, 3½" | 22.50 | Ice bucket, #2378 | 45.00 |
| Bowl, #2350, bouillon, flat | 11.00 | Mayonnaise, #2315 | 25.00 |
| Bowl, #2350½, bouillon, ftd. | 12.50 | Pickle, 8", #2350 | 20.00 |
| Bowl, #2350, cream soup, flat | 15.00 | Pitcher, #1236 | 365.00 |
| Bowl, #2350½, cream soup, ftd. | 17.50 | Pitcher, #5000, 48 oz. | 265.00 |
| Bowl, #869, 4½", finger | 16.00 | Plate, 8½", deep soup/underplate | 35.00 |
| Bowl, #2350, 5½", fruit | 12.00 | Plate, #2350, 6", bread/butter | 3.00 |
| Bowl, #2350, 6½", cereal | 17.00 | Plate, #2350, 7½", salad | 4.00 |
| Bowl, #2267, 7", ftd. | 30.00 | Plate, #2350, 8½", luncheon | 8.00 |
| Bowl, #2350, 7¾", soup | 18.00 | Plate, #2321, 8¾, Maj Jongg (canape) | 35.00 |
| Bowl, #2350, 8", nappy | 30.00 | Plate, #2350, 9½", small dinner | 13.00 |
| Bowl, #2350, 9", nappy | 32.00 | Plate, #2350, 10½", dinner | 27.50 |
| Bowl, #2350, 9", oval, baker | 37.50 | Plate, #2350, 13", chop | 27.50 |
| Bowl, #2324, 10", ftd. | 40.00 | Plate, #2350, 15", chop | 40.00 |
| Bowl, #2350, 10", salad | 35.00 | Platter, #2350, 10½" | 30.00 |
| Bowl, #2350, 10½", oval, baker | 45.00 | Platter, #2350, 12" | 45.00 |
| Bowl, #2315, 10½", ftd. | 45.00 | Platter, #2350, 15½" | 85.00 |
| Bowl, #2329, 11", console | 22.00 | Salt and pepper, #5100, pr. | 60.00 |
| Bowl, #2297, 12", deep | 22.00 | Sauce boat, w/liner | 125.00 |
| Bowl, #2329, 13", console | 30.00 | Saucer, #2350/#2350½ | 3.00 |
| Bowl, #2324, 13", ftd. | 45.00 | Saucer, #2350, demi | 5.00 |
| Bowl, #2371, 13", oval, w/flower frog | 100.00 | Server, #2287, 11", center hdld. | 25.00 |
| Butter, w/cover #2350 | 235.00 | Stem, #869, ¾ oz., cordial | 65.00 |
| Candlestick, #2324, 4" | 14.00 | Stem, #869, 2¾ oz., wine | 27.50 |
| Candlestick, #2324, 9" | 45.00 | Stem, #869, 3 oz., cocktail | 22.50 |
| Candy, w/cover, #2331, 3 part | 60.00 | Stem, #869, 5½ oz., oyster cocktail | 15.00 |
| Candy, w/cover, ftd., ½ lb. | 150.00 | Stem, #869, 5½ oz., parfait | 30.00 |
| Celery, #2350, 11" | 25.00 | Stem, #869, 6 oz., low sherbet | 12.50 |
| Cheese, w/cover/plate #2276 (plate 11") | 115.00 | Stem, #869, 6 oz., high sherbet | 16.00 |
| Cologne, #2322, tall | 30.00 | Stem, #869, 9 oz., water | 20.00 |
| Cologne, #2323, short | 25.00 | Sugar, flat, w/lid | 155.00 |
| Cologne/powder jar combination | 200.00 | Sugar, #2315, ftd., flat | 17.00 |
| Comport, #1861½, 6", jelly | 25.00 | Sugar, #2350½, ftd. | 12.00 |
| Comport, #2327, 7" | 28.00 | Sugar lid, #2350½ | 100.00 |
| Comport, #2358, 8" wide | 30.00 | Tumbler, #869, 5 oz., flat | 22.50 |
| Creamer, flat | 14.00 | Tumbler, #859, 9 oz., flat | 25.00 |
| Creamer, #2315½, ftd., fat | 18.00 | Tumbler, #859, 12 oz., flat | 30.00 |
| Creamer, #2350½, ftd. | 13.00 | Tumbler, #5000, 2½ oz., ftd. | 27.50 |
| Cup, #2350, flat | 12.00 | Tumbler, #5000, 5 oz., ftd. | 14.00 |
| Cup, #2350½, ftd. | 13.00 | Tumbler, #5000, 9 oz., ftd. | 16.00 |
| Cup, #2350, demi | 22.50 | Tumbler, #5000, 12 oz., ftd. | 25.00 |
| Egg cup, #2350 | 27.50 | Vase, #2324, urn, ftd. | 75.00 |
| Grapefruit, w/insert | 75.00 | Vase, #2292, flared | 90.00 |

* Add 50% more for blue or black!

180

# RUBA ROMBIC, Consolidated Lamp and Glass Company

Colors: Smokey topaz, Jungle green, French Crystal, Silver grey, Lilac, Sunshine, Jade; some milk glass, Apple green, black

Ruba Rombic is a pattern that I have tried to add to this book for several editions, but never had the opportunity to photograph a set until now. The color shown here is Smokey Topaz, priced below with the Jungle Green.

If you look up rombic, you will find that it means irregular in shape, an apropos name for this pattern. I've found collectors either love it or hate it. There seems to be no in between!

This pattern was displayed sporadically for years at Depression Glass shows; but in the last few years advanced Art Deco collectors and museums have started buying Ruba Rombic, and the prices have soared out of the reach of the average collector. Those who purchased pieces prior to this surge in collecting can make a tidy sum on their collections now.

The cased glass (thin layer of white applied on the inside) color column in the prices below includes three colors. They are: Lilac (lavender), Sunshine (yellow), and Jade (green). The French crystal is a white applied color except that the raised edges are crystal with no white coloring at all. The Silver is sometimes referred as Grey Silver.

Thanks to Kevin Kiley and Bob Aibel's Moderne Gallery in Philadelphia for help in pricing and photographing Ruba Rombic.

| | Smokey Topaz/ Jungle Green | Cased Colors | French Crystal/ Silver | | Smokey Topaz/ Jungle Green | Cased Colors | French Crystal/ Silver |
|---|---|---|---|---|---|---|---|
| Ash tray, 3½" | 800.00 | 1000.00 | 1200.00 | Light, wall sconce | | 1500.00 | 1500.00 |
| Bon bon, flat, 3 part | 250.00 | 350.00 | 400.00 | Pitcher, 8¼" | 2500.00 | 3000.00 | 4000.00 |
| Bottle, decanter, 9" | 1800.00 | 2200.00 | 2500.00 | Plate, 7" | 75.00 | 100.00 | 150.00 |
| Bottle, perfume, 4¾" | 1200.00 | 1500.00 | 1800.00 | Plate, 8" | 75.00 | 100.00 | 150.00 |
| Bottle, toilet, 7½" | 1800.00 | 2200.00 | 2500.00 | Plate, 10" | 250.00 | 275.00 | 300.00 |
| Bowl, 3", almond | 225.00 | 250.00 | 300.00 | Plate, 15" | 2000.00 | 2200.00 | 2400.00 |
| Bowl, 8", cupped | 1500.00 | 1800.00 | 2000.00 | Relish, 2 part | 350.00 | 450.00 | 500.00 |
| Bowl, 9", flared | 1500.00 | 1800.00 | 2000.00 | Sugar | 200.00 | 250.00 | 300.00 |
| Bowl, 12", oval | 1800.00 | 2200.00 | 2500.00 | Sundae | 100.00 | 135.00 | 150.00 |
| Bowl, bouillon | 175.00 | 250.00 | 275.00 | Tray for decanter set | 2000.00 | 2250.00 | 2500.00 |
| Bowl, finger | 95.00 | 125.00 | 140.00 | Tumbler, 2 oz., flat, 2¾" | 100.00 | 125.00 | 150.00 |
| Box, cigarette 3½" x 4¼" | 850.00 | 1250.00 | 1500.00 | Tumbler, 3 oz., ftd | 125.00 | 150.00 | 175.00 |
| Box, powder, 5", round | 850.00 | 1250.00 | 1500.00 | Tumbler, 9 oz., flat | 125.00 | 175.00 | 200.00 |
| Candlestick, 2½" high, pr. | 500.00 | 650.00 | 750.00 | Tumbler, 10 oz., ftd. | 175.00 | 300.00 | 350.00 |
| Celery, 10", 3 part | 1000.00 | 1250.00 | 1400.00 | Tumbler, 12 oz., flat | 175.00 | 300.00 | 350.00 |
| Comport, 7", wide | 1000.00 | 1250.00 | 1400.00 | Tumbler, 15 oz., ftd., 7" | 350.00 | 450.00 | 500.00 |
| Creamer | 200.00 | 250.00 | 300.00 | Vase, 6" | 850.00 | 1000.00 | 1500.00 |
| Light, ceiling fixture, 10" | | 1500.00 | 1500.00 | Vase, 9½" | 2000.00 | 3000.00 | 5000.00 |
| Light, ceiling fixture, 16" | | 2500.00 | 2500.00 | Vase, 16" | 10000.00 | 12000.00 | 12000.00 |
| Light, table light | | 1200.00 | 1200.00 | | | | |

# SANDWICH, #41, Duncan & Miller Glass Company, 1924 – 1955

Colors: crystal, amber, pink, green, red, cobalt blue

Lancaster Colony continues to make some of this for their lines today. The bright blue, green, and amberina are from Duncan moulds (made by Indiana) and were sold by Montgomery Ward in the early 1970's. Tiffin also made some Sandwich pieces in milk glass. Stemware abounds and is as economical to use as newly made stemware. I have included some original Duncan catalogue reprints on pages 187-189. Hopefully, these will add to your enjoyment of the book!

| | Crystal | | Crystal |
|---|---|---|---|
| Ash tray, 2½" x 3¾", rect. | 10.00 | Bowl, 10", lily, vertical edge | 50.00 |
| Ash tray, 2⅜", sq. | 8.00 | Bowl, 11", cupped nut | 52.50 |
| Basket, 6½", w/loop hdld. | 115.00 | Bowl, 11½", crimped flower | 55.00 |
| Basket, 10", crimped, w/loop hdl. | 165.00 | Bowl, 11½", gardenia | 45.00 |
| Basket, 10", oval, w/loop hdl. | 165.00 | Bowl, 11½", ftd., crimped fruit | 60.00 |
| Basket, 11½", w/loop hdl. | 225.00 | Bowl, 12", fruit, flared edge | 45.00 |
| Bonbon, 5", heart shape, w/ring hdl. | 15.00 | Bowl, 12", shallow salad | 40.00 |
| Bonbon, 5½", heart shape, hdld. | 15.00 | Bowl, 12", oblong console | 40.00 |
| Bonbon, 6", heart shape, w/ring hdl. | 20.00 | Bowl, 12", epergne, w/ctr. hole | 75.00 |
| Bonbon, 7½", ftd., w/cover | 40.00 | Butter, w/cover, ¼ lb. | 37.50 |
| Bowl, 2½", salted almond | 8.00 | Cake stand, 11½", ftd., rolled edge | 90.00 |
| Bowl, 3½", nut | 8.50 | Cake stand, 12", ftd., rolled edge, plain pedestal | 75.00 |
| Bowl, 4", finger | 12.50 | Cake stand, 13", ftd., plain pedestal | 75.00 |
| Bowl, 5½", hdld. | 15.00 | Candelabra, 10", 1-lite, w/bobeche & prisms | 75.00 |
| Bowl, 5½", ftd., grapefruit, w/rim liner | 15.00 | Candelabra, 10", 3-lite, w/bobeche & prisms | 165.00 |
| Bowl, 5½", ftd., grapefruit, w/fruit cup liner | 15.00 | Candelabra, 16", 3-lite, w/bobeche & prisms | 225.00 |
| Bowl, 5", 2 pt., nappy | 12.00 | Candlestick, 4", 1-lite | 14.00 |
| Bowl, 5", ftd., crimped ivy | 27.50 | Candlestick, 4", 1-lite, w/bobeche & stub. prisms | 32.50 |
| Bowl, 5", fruit | 10.00 | Candlestick, 5", 3-lite | 40.00 |
| Bowl, 5", nappy, w/ring hdl. | 12.00 | Candlestick, 5", 3-lite, w/bobeche & stub. prisms | 95.00 |
| Bowl, 6", 2 pt., nappy | 14.00 | | |
| Bowl, 6", fruit salad | 12.00 | Candlestick, 5", 2-lite, w/bobeche & stub. prisms | 75.00 |
| Bowl, 6", grapefruit, rimmed edge | 15.00 | | |
| Bowl, 6", nappy, w/ring hdl. | 17.50 | Candlestick, 5", 2-lite | 25.00 |
| Bowl, 10", salad, deep | 70.00 | | |
| Bowl, 10", 3 pt., fruit | 80.00 | | |

| | Crystal |
|---|---|
| Candy, 6" square | 350.00 |
| Candy box, w/cover, 5", flat | 40.00 |
| Candy jar, w/cover, 8½", ftd. | 55.00 |
| Cheese, w/cover (cover 4¾", plate 8") | 100.00 |
| Cheese/cracker (3" compote, 13" plate) | 50.00 |
| Cigarette box, w/cover, 3½" | 22.00 |
| Cigarette holder, 3", ftd. | 27.50 |
| Coaster, 5" | 12.00 |
| Comport, 2¼" | 15.00 |
| Comport, 3¼", low ft., crimped candy | 20.00 |
| Comport, 3¼", low ft., flared candy | 17.50 |
| Comport, 4¼", ftd. | 20.00 |
| Comport, 5", low ft. | 20.00 |
| Comport, 5½", ftd., low crimped | 25.00 |
| Comport, 6", low ft., flared | 22.50 |
| Condiment set (2 cruets; 3¾" salt & pepper; 4 pt. tray) | 95.00 |
| Creamer, 4", 7 oz., ftd. | 9.00 |
| Cup, 6 oz., tea | 10.00 |
| Epergne, 9", garden | 95.00 |
| Epergne, 12", 3 pt., fruit or flower | 225.00 |
| Jelly, 3", indiv. | 7.00 |
| Mayonnaise set, 3 pc.: ladle, 5" bowl, 7" plate | 32.00 |
| Oil bottle, 5¾" | 35.00 |
| Pan, 6¾" x 10½", oblong, camelia | 60.00 |
| Pitcher, 13 oz., metal top | 60.00 |
| Pitcher, w/ice lip, 8", 64 oz. | 130.00 |
| Plate, 3", indiv. jelly | 6.00 |
| Plate, 6", bread/butter | 6.00 |
| Plate, 6½", finger bowl liner | 8.00 |
| Plate, 7", dessert | 7.50 |
| Plate, 8", mayonnaise liner, w/ring | 7.00 |
| Plate, 8", salad | 10.00 |
| Plate, 9½", dinner | 35.00 |
| Plate, 11½", hdld., service | 35.00 |
| Plate, 12", torte | 45.00 |
| Plate, 12", ice cream, rolled edge | 55.00 |
| Plate, 12", deviled egg | 65.00 |
| Plate, 13", salad dressing, w/ring | 32.00 |
| Plate, 13", service | 50.00 |
| Plate, 13", service, rolled edge | 55.00 |
| Plate, 13", cracker, w/ring | 27.50 |
| Plate, 16", lazy susan, w/turntable | 95.00 |
| Plate, 16", hostess | 95.00 |
| Relish, 5½", 2 pt., rnd., ring hdl. | 15.00 |
| Relish, 6", 2 pt., rnd., ring hdl. | 17.00 |
| Relish, 7", 2 pt., oval | 20.00 |
| Relish, 10", 4 pt., hdld. | 25.00 |

| | Crystal |
|---|---|
| Relish, 10", 3 pt., oblong | 27.50 |
| Relish, 10½", 3 pt., oblong | 27.50 |
| Relish, 12", 3 pt. | 37.50 |
| Salad dressing set: (2 ladles; 5" ftd. mayonnaise; 13" plate w/ring) | 80.00 |
| Salad dressing set: (2 ladles; 6" ftd. div. bowl; 8" plate w/ring) | 65.00 |
| Salt & pepper, 2½", w/glass tops, pr. | 18.00 |
| Salt & pepper, 2½", w/metal tops, pr. | 18.00 |
| Salt & pepper, 3¾", w/metal top (on 6" tray), 3 pc. | 30.00 |
| Saucer, 6", w/ring | 4.00 |
| Stem, 2½", 6 oz., ftd., fruit cup/jello | 11.00 |
| Stem, 2¾", 5 oz., ftd., oyster cocktail | 15.00 |
| Stem, 3½", 5 oz., sundae (flared rim) | 12.00 |
| Stem, 4¼", 3 oz., cocktail | 15.00 |
| Stem, 4¼", 5 oz., ice cream | 12.50 |
| Stem, 4¼", 3 oz., wine | 20.00 |
| Stem, 5¼", 4 oz., ftd., parfait | 30.00 |
| Stem, 5¼", 5 oz., champagne | 20.00 |
| Stem, 6", 9 oz., goblet | 18.50 |
| Sugar, 3¼", ftd., 9 oz. | 8.00 |
| Sugar, 5 oz. | 7.50 |
| Sugar (cheese) shaker, 13 oz., metal top | 65.00 |
| Tray, oval (for sugar/creamer) | 10.00 |
| Tray, 6" mint, rolled edge, w/ring hdl. | 17.50 |
| Tray, 7", oval, pickle | 15.00 |
| Tray, 7", mint, rolled edge, w/ring hdl. | 20.00 |
| Tray, 8", oval | 18.00 |
| Tray, 8", for oil/vinegar | 20.00 |
| Tray, 10", oval, celery | 18.00 |
| Tray, 12", fruit epergne | 50.00 |
| Tray, 12", ice cream, rolled edge | 45.00 |
| Tumbler, 3¾", 5 oz., ftd., juice | 12.00 |
| Tumbler, 4¾", 9 oz., ftd., water | 14.00 |
| Tumbler, 5¼", 13 oz., flat, iced tea | 20.00 |
| Tumbler, 5¼", 12 oz., ftd., iced tea | 17.50 |
| Urn, w/cover, 12", ftd. | 125.00 |
| Vase, 3", ftd., crimped | 17.50 |
| Vase, 3", ftd., flared rim | 15.00 |
| Vase, 4", hat shape | 20.00 |
| Vase, 4½", flat base, crimped | 25.00 |
| Vase, 5", ftd., flared rim | 22.50 |
| Vase, 5", ftd., crimped | 25.00 |
| Vase, 5", ftd., fan | 35.00 |
| Vase, 7½", epergne, threaded base | 55.00 |
| Vase, 10", ftd. | 60.00 |

DUNCAN

**EARLY AMERICAN
SANDWICH
No. 41 PATTERN**

Duncan

Washington, Pa.    1-1-43

No. 41
9 oz. Goblet
Height—6"

No. 41
5 oz. Saucer
Champagne
Height—5¼"

No. 41
3 oz. Wine
Height—4½"

No. 41
3 oz. Cocktail
Height—4¼"

No. 41
5 oz. Ice Cream
Height—4¼"

No. 41
5 oz. Flared Sundae
Height—3½"

No. 41
3 in. Ind. Jelly

No. 41
½ gal. Ice Lip Jug
Height—8"

No. 41
6 oz. Fruit Cup or Jello
Height—2½"

No. 41
5 oz. Oyster Cocktail
Height—2¾"

No. 41
13 oz. Ice Tea
Tumbler—Straight
Height—5¼"

No. 41
12 oz. Ftd. Ice Tea
Height—5½"

No. 41
9 oz. Ftd. Tumbler
Height—4¾"

No. 41
5 oz. Ftd. Orange Juice
Height—3¼"

No. 41
4 oz. Parfait
Height—5¼"

THE DUNCAN & MILLER GLASS CO.

15

DUNCAN

**EARLY AMERICAN
SANDWICH
No. 41 PATTERN**

Washington, Pa.   1-1-43

THE DUNCAN & MILLER GLASS CO.

No. 41
6 in. Tall Hld.
Basket

No. 41
5 in. Ftd. Ivy Bowl

No. 41
4½ in. Crimped Vase

No. 41
5 in. Ftd. Vase Crimped
Also made 3 in. size

No. 41
11½ in. Crimped Flower Bowl
Height—3½"

No. 41
10 in. Lily Bowl
Height—2"

No. 41
10 in. Ftd. Vase

No. 41
12 in. Urn and Cover

DUNCAN
**EARLY AMERICAN
SANDWICH
No. 41 PATTERN**

No. 1-B-41—3 Light
Candelabrum W/U Prisms
Height—10"   Width—13"
2 Bobeches

No. 1-41—1 Light
Candelabrum W/U Prisms
Height—10"

No. 1-41—1 Light
Hurricane Lamp Candelabrum
W/Prisms
Height—15"

No. 1-C-41—3 Light
Candelabrum W/U Prisms
Height—16"   Width—13"
3 Bobeches

# SATURN, Blank #1485, A.H. Heisey & Co.

Colors: crystal, "Zircon" or "Limelight" green, charcoal or smoke

"Limelight" and "Zircon" are the same color. Originally made in 1937, this color was called "Zircon." In 1955, it was made again by Heisey, but called "Limelight."

Zircon prices continue to skyrocket in Saturn!

Let me know what you think of the shelf shot set-ups!

| | Crystal | Zircon/ Limelight |
|---|---|---|
| Ash tray | 10.00 | 150.00 |
| Bitters bottle, w/short tube, blown | 35.00 | |
| Bowl, baked apple | 7.00 | 65.00 |
| Bowl, finger | 5.00 | |
| Bowl, rose, lg. | 40.00 | |
| Bowl, 4½", nappy | 5.00 | |
| Bowl, 5", nappy | 7.00 | |
| Bowl, 5", whipped cream | 15.00 | 150.00 |
| Bowl, 7", pickle | 15.00 | |
| Bowl, 9", 3 part, relish | 17.50 | |
| Bowl, 10", celery | 15.00 | |
| Bowl, 11", salad | 40.00 | 140.00 |
| Bowl, 12", fruit, flared rim | 35.00 | 100.00 |
| Bowl, 13", floral, rolled edge | 37.00 | |
| Bowl, 13", floral | 37.00 | |
| Candelabrum, w/"e" ball drops, 2-lite | 125.00 | 500.00 |
| Candle block, 2-lite | 95.00 | 325.00 |
| Candlestick, 3", ftd., 1-lite | 30.00 | 500.00 |
| Comport, 7" | 50.00 | 550.00 |
| Creamer | 17.00 | 150.00 |
| Cup | 10.00 | 150.00 |
| Hostess Set, 8 pc. (low bowl w/ftd. ctr. bowl, 3 toothpick holders & clips) | 55.00 | 300.00 |
| Marmalade, w/cover | 45.00 | 500.00 |
| Mayonnaise | 8.00 | 80.00 |
| Mustard, w/cover and paddle | 45.00 | 325.00 |
| Oil bottle, 2 oz., w/#1 stopper | 55.00 | 350.00 |
| Pitcher, 70 oz., w/ice lip, blown | 65.00 | 500.00 |
| Pitcher, juice | 40.00 | 300.00 |
| Plate, 6" | 3.00 | 35.00 |
| Plate, 7", bread | 5.00 | 45.00 |
| Plate, 8", luncheon | 7.00 | 55.00 |
| Plate, 13", torte | 25.00 | |
| Plate, 15", torte | 30.00 | |
| Salt & pepper, pr. | 45.00 | 550.00 |
| Saucer | 5.00 | 30.00 |
| Stem, 3 oz., cocktail | 10.00 | 60.00 |
| Stem, 4 oz., fruit cocktail or oyster cocktail, no ball in stem, ftd. | 8.00 | 75.00 |
| Stem, 4½ oz., sherbet | 5.00 | 70.00 |
| Stem, 5 oz., parfait | 10.00 | 110.00 |
| Stem, 6 oz., saucer champagne | 5.00 | 95.00 |
| Stem, 10 oz. | 12.00 | 90.00 |
| Sugar | 17.00 | 150.00 |
| Sugar shaker (pourer) | 80.00 | |
| Sugar, w/cover, no handles | 25.00 | |
| Tray, tidbit, 2 sides turned as fan | 25.00 | 80.00 |
| Tumbler, 5 oz., juice | 7.00 | 120.00 |
| Tumbler, 7 oz., old-fashioned | 10.00 | |
| Tumbler, 8 oz., old-fashioned | 10.00 | |
| Tumbler, 9 oz., luncheon | 12.00 | |
| Tumbler, 10 oz. | 17.50 | 70.00 |
| Tumbler, 12 oz., soda | 10.00 | 150.00 |
| Vase, violet | 22.00 | 85.00 |
| Vase, 8½", flared | 25.00 | 175.00 |
| Vase, 8½", straight | 25.00 | 175.00 |
| Vase, 10½" | | 230.00 |

# SEVILLE, Fostoria Glass Company, 1926 – 1931

Colors: amber, green

Fostoria's Seville is a pattern that has been widely ignored by the collecting world. It would be a great starting point for someone wanting to collect an inexpensive Elegant pattern. It would probably not stay inexpensive for long as there is not that much to go around. Green would be easier to obtain than amber. The butter dish, pitcher, grapefruit and liner, and sugar lid are all troublesome to find; be on the lookout for them.

| | Amber | Green | | Amber | Green |
|---|---|---|---|---|---|
| Ash tray, #2350, 4" | 17.50 | 22.50 | Grapefruit, #945½, blown | 40.00 | 45.00 |
| Bowl, #2350, fruit, 5½" | 10.00 | 12.00 | Grapefruit, #945½, liner, blown | 30.00 | 35.00 |
| Bowl, #2350, cereal, 6½" | 16.00 | 18.00 | Grapefruit, #2315, molded | 22.50 | 25.00 |
| Bowl, #2350, soup, 7¾" | 17.50 | 20.00 | Ice bucket, #2378 | 50.00 | 52.00 |
| Bowl, #2315, low foot, 7" | 16.00 | 18.00 | Pickle, #2350, 8" | 13.50 | 15.00 |
| Bowl, #2350, vegetable | 20.00 | 25.00 | Pitcher, #5084, ftd. | 235.00 | 265.00 |
| Bowl, #2350, nappy, 9" | 30.00 | 35.00 | Plate, #2350, bread and butter, 6" | 3.50 | 4.00 |
| Bowl, #2350, oval, baker, 9" | 25.00 | 30.00 | Plate, #2350, salad, 7½" | 5.00 | 5.50 |
| Bowl, #2315, flared, 10½", ftd. | 25.00 | 30.00 | Plate, #2350, luncheon, 8½" | 6.00 | 6.50 |
| Bowl, #2350, oval, baker, 10½" | 35.00 | 40.00 | Plate, #2321, Maj Jongg (canape), | | |
| Bowl, 10", ftd. | 35.00 | 40.00 | 8¾" | 35.00 | 40.00 |
| Bowl, #2350, salad, 10" | 30.00 | 35.00 | Plate, #2350, sm. dinner, 9½" | 12.00 | 13.50 |
| Bowl, #2329, rolled edge, console, | | | Plate, #2350, dinner, 10½" | 32.50 | 40.00 |
| 11" | 27.50 | 32.50 | Plate, #2350, chop, 13¾" | 30.00 | 35.00 |
| Bowl, #2297, deep, flared, 12" | 30.00 | 32.50 | Plate, #2350, round, 15" | 35.00 | 40.00 |
| Bowl, #2371, oval, console, 13" | 35.00 | 40.00 | Plate, #2350, cream soup liner | 5.00 | 6.00 |
| Bowl, #2329, rolled edge, console, | | | Platter, #2350, 10½" | 22.50 | 25.00 |
| 13" | 30.00 | 32.50 | Platter, #2350, 12" | 35.00 | 40.00 |
| Bowl, #2350, bouillon, flat | 13.50 | 15.00 | Platter, #2350, 15" | 70.00 | 80.00 |
| Bowl, #2350½, bouillon, ftd. | 14.00 | 16.00 | Salt and pepper shaker, #5100, pr. | 60.00 | 65.00 |
| Bowl, #2350, cream soup, flat | 14.50 | 16.00 | Sauce boat liner, #2350 | 25.00 | 27.50 |
| Bowl, #2350½, cream soup, ftd. | 15.50 | 17.00 | Sauce boat, #2350 | 55.00 | 72.50 |
| Bowl, #869/2283, finger, w/6" liner | 17.50 | 20.00 | Saucer, #2350 | 3.00 | 3.00 |
| Butter, w/cover, #2350, round | 185.00 | 235.00 | Saucer, after dinner, #2350 | 5.00 | 5.00 |
| Candlestick, #2324, 2" | 15.00 | 17.50 | Stem, #870, cocktail | 15.00 | 16.00 |
| Candlestick, #2324, 4" | 12.50 | 15.00 | Stem, #870, cordial | 65.00 | 70.00 |
| Candlestick, #2324, 9" | 25.00 | 30.00 | Stem, #870, high sherbet | 15.00 | 16.00 |
| Candy jar, w/cover, #2250, | | | Stem, #870, low sherbet | 12.50 | 13.50 |
| ½ lb., ftd. | 95.00 | 120.00 | Stem, #870, oyster cocktail | 16.50 | 17.50 |
| Candy jar, w/cover, #2331, 3 pt., flat | 65.00 | 80.00 | Stem, #870, parfait | 30.00 | 35.00 |
| Celery, #2350, 11" | 15.00 | 17.50 | Stem, #870, water | 20.00 | 22.50 |
| Cheese and cracker, #2368, | | | Stem, #870, wine | 22.50 | 25.00 |
| (11" plate) | 40.00 | 45.00 | Sugar cover, #2350½ | 80.00 | 100.00 |
| Comport, #2327, 7½", | | | Sugar, fat, ftd., #2315 | 13.50 | 14.50 |
| (twisted stem) | 20.00 | 25.00 | Sugar, ftd., #2350½ | 12.50 | 13.50 |
| Comport, #2350, 8" | 27.50 | 35.00 | Tray, 11", center handled, #2287 | 27.50 | 30.00 |
| Creamer, #2315½, flat, ftd. | 13.50 | 15.00 | Tumbler, #5084, ftd., 2 oz. | 35.00 | 37.50 |
| Creamer, #2350½, ftd. | 12.50 | 13.50 | Tumbler, #5084, ftd., 5 oz. | 13.50 | 15.00 |
| Cup, #2350, after dinner | 25.00 | 30.00 | Tumbler, #5084, ftd., 9 oz. | 15.00 | 16.50 |
| Cup, #2350, flat | 10.00 | 12.50 | Tumbler, #5084, ftd., 12 oz. | 18.00 | 20.00 |
| Cup, #2350½, ftd. | 10.00 | 12.50 | Urn, small, #2324 | 75.00 | 95.00 |
| Egg cup, #2350 | 30.00 | 35.00 | Vase, #2292, 8" | 55.00 | 65.00 |

# "SPIRAL FLUTES," Duncan & Miller Glass Company, Introduced 1924

Colors: amber, green, pink, crystal

This Duncan pattern has been ignored by new collectors. Three items are easily found: the 6¾" flanged bowls, 7 oz. footed tumblers, and 7½" plates; after that, there is little found effortlessly. There is more green available than other colors.

| | Amber, Green, Pink | | Amber, Green, Pink |
|---|---|---|---|
| Bowl, 2", almond | 11.00 | Ice tub, handled | 45.00 |
| Bowl, 3¾", bouillon | 15.00 | Lamp, 10½", countess | 250.00 |
| Bowl, 4⅜", finger | 6.00 | Mug, 6½", 9 oz., handled | 27.50 |
| Bowl, 4¾", ftd., cream soup | 15.00 | Mug, 7", 9 oz., handled | 35.00 |
| Bowl, 4" w., mayonnaise | 17.50 | Oil, w/stopper, 6 oz. | 165.00 |
| Bowl, 5", nappy | 6.00 | Pickle, 8⅝" | 12.00 |
| Bowl, 6½", cereal, sm. flange | 32.50 | Pitcher, ½ gal. | 165.00 |
| Bowl, 6¾", grapefruit | 7.50 | Plate, 6", pie | 3.00 |
| Bowl, 6", handled nappy | 22.00 | Plate, 7½", salad | 4.00 |
| Bowl, 6", handled nappy, w/cover | 75.00 | Plate, 8⅜", luncheon | 4.00 |
| Bowl, 7", nappy | 15.00 | Plate, 10⅜", dinner | 22.50 |
| Bowl, 7½", flanged (baked apple) | 22.50 | Plate, 13⅝", torte | 27.50 |
| Bowl, 8", nappy | 17.50 | Plate, w/star, 6", (fingerbowl item) | 6.00 |
| Bowl, 8½", flanged (oyster plate) | 22.50 | Platter, 11" | 32.50 |
| Bowl, 9", nappy | 27.50 | Platter, 13" | 42.50 |
| Bowl, 10", oval, veg., two styles. | 42.50 | Relish, 10" x 7⅜", oval, 3 pc. (2 inserts) | 75.00 |
| Bowl, 10½", lily pond | 40.00 | Saucer | 3.00 |
| Bowl, 11¾" w. x 3¾" t., console, flared | 30.00 | Saucer, demi | 5.00 |
| Bowl, 11", nappy | 30.00 | Seafood sauce cup, 3" w. x 2½" h. | 25.00 |
| Bowl, 12", cupped console | 30.00 | Stem, 3¾", 3½ oz., wine | 17.50 |
| Candle, 3½" | 15.00 | Stem, 3¾", 5 oz., low sherbet | 8.00 |
| Candle, 7½" | 55.00 | Stem, 4¾", 6 oz., tall sherbet | 12.00 |
| Candle, 9½" | 65.00 | Stem, 5⅝", 4½ oz., parfait | 17.50 |
| Candle, 11½" | 100.00 | Stem, 6¼", 7 oz., water | 17.50 |
| Celery, 10¾" x 4¾" | 17.50 | Sugar, oval | 8.00 |
| * Chocolate jar, w/cover | 225.00 | Sweetmeat, w/cover, 7½" | 100.00 |
| Cigarette holder, 4" | 30.00 | Tumbler, 3⅜", ftd., 2½ oz., cocktail (no stem) | 7.00 |
| Comport, 4⅜" | 15.00 | | |
| Comport, 6⅝" | 17.50 | Tumbler, 4¼", 8 oz., flat | 30.00 |
| Comport, 9", low ft., flared | 55.00 | Tumbler, 4⅜", ftd., 5½ oz., juice (no stem) | 14.00 |
| Console stand, 1½" h. x 4⅝" w. | 12.00 | Tumbler, 4¾", 7 oz., flat, soda | 32.50 |
| Creamer, oval | 8.00 | Tumbler, 5⅛", ftd., 7 oz., water (1 knob) | 8.00 |
| Cup | 9.00 | Tumbler, 5⅛", ftd., 9 oz., water (no stem) | 20.00 |
| Cup, demi | 25.00 | Tumbler, 5½", 11 oz., gingerale | 60.00 |
| * Fernery, 10" x 5½", 4 ftd., flower box | 350.00 | Vase, 6½" | 12.00 |
| Grapefruit, ftd. | 20.00 | Vase, 8½" | 17.50 |
| | | Vase, 10½" | 25.00 |

*Crystal, $135.00

# STANHOPE, #1483, A.H. Heisey Co., 1936 – 1941

Colors: crystal, some blown stemware in Zircon

Stanhope is a Heisey pattern that has caught the eye of some Deco collectors. This has sparked some life into prices that were fairly stagnant.

The colored insert handles of black or red (round knobs) drive some people to distraction; others think they look great. If everyone liked the same thing...!

A word of explanation for those who asked. The T knobs are like wooden dowel rods that act as horizontal handles.

|  | Crystal |
|---|---|
| Ash tray, indiv. | 20.00 |
| Bottle, oil, 3 oz. w or w/o rd. knob | 275.00 |
| Bowl, 6" mint, 2 hdld., w or w/o rd. knobs | 15.00 |
| Bowl, 6" mint, 2 pt., 2 hdld., w or w/o rd. knobs | 15.00 |
| Bowl, 11" salad | 45.00 |
| Bowl, finger #4080 (blown, plain) | 5.00 |
| Bowl, floral, 11", 2 hdld. w or w/o "T" knobs | 45.00 |
| Candelabra, 2-lite, w bobeche & prisms | 135.00 |
| Candy box & lid, rnd., w or w/o rd. knob | 160.00 |
| Cigarette box & lid, w or w/o rd. knob | 45.00 |
| Creamer, 2 hdld., w or w/o rd. knobs | 25.00 |
| Cup, w or w/o rd. knob | 15.00 |
| Ice tub, 2 hdld., w or w/o "T" knobs | 45.00 |
| Jelly, 6", 1 hdld., w or w/o rd. knobs | 20.00 |
| Jelly, 6", 3 pt., 1 hdld., w or w/o rd. knobs | 20.00 |
| Nappy, 4½", 1 hdld. w or w/o rd. knob | 15.00 |
| Nut, indiv., 1 hdld., w or w/o rd. knob | 25.00 |
| Plate, 7" | 7.50 |
| Plate, 12" torte, 2 hdld. w or w/o "T" knobs | 30.00 |
| Plate, 15" torte, rnd. or salad liner | 32.50 |
| Relish, 11" triplex buffet, 2 hdld., w or w/o "T" knobs | 30.00 |
| Relish, 12" 4 pt., 2 hdld., w or w/o "T" knobs | 35.00 |
| Relish, 12", 5 pt., 2 hdld. w or w/o "T" knobs | 35.00 |
| Salt & pepper, #60 top | 45.00 |
| Saucer | 5.00 |
| Stem, 1 oz. cordial #4083 (blown) | 70.00 |
| Stem, 2½ oz. pressed wine | 20.00 |
| Stem, 2½ oz. wine, #4083 | 25.00 |
| Stem, 3½ oz. cocktail #4083 | 20.00 |
| Stem, 3½ oz. pressed cocktail | 10.00 |
| Stem, 4 oz. claret #4083 | 25.00 |
| Stem, 4 oz. oyster cocktail #4083 | 10.00 |
| Stem, 5½ oz. pressed saucer champagne | 15.00 |
| Stem, 5½ oz. saucer champagne #4083 | 15.00 |
| Stem, 9 oz. pressed goblet | 20.00 |
| Stem, 10 oz. goblet #4083 | 22.50 |
| Stem, 12 oz. pressed soda | 25.00 |
| Sugar, 2 hdld., w or w/o rd. knobs | 25.00 |
| Tray, 12" celery, 2 hdld. w or w/o "T" knobs | 12.50 |
| Tumbler, 5 oz. soda #4083 | 20.00 |
| Tumbler, 8 oz. soda #4083 | 22.50 |
| Tumbler, 12 oz. soda #4083 | 25.00 |
| Vase, 7" ball | 50.00 |
| Vase, 9", 2 hdld., w or w/o "T" knobs | 45.00 |

# SUNRISE MEDALLION, "Dancing Girl" #758, Morgantown Glass Works, Late 1920's – Early 1930's

Colors: pink, green, blue, crystal

The Morgantown Collectors of America have been at pains to broadcast the actual name of this pattern, Sunrise Medallion (etching #758).

Measurements in most glassware catalogues were in ounces only. The twisted stem items (#7642½) are slightly taller than their plain stem (#7630) counterparts. Measurements given below are from the #7630 line. I have been unable to obtain measurements on the twisted stemware items; if you have some, I would appreciate having measurements.

I just bought six little footed tumblers in Seattle. It cost me one to have the other five shipped. That is the trouble with friends who are collectors, they can talk you out of any piece of glass that they want for their collection. In any case, these stand 2⁷⁄₁₆" to 2⁹⁄₁₆" tall and hold 4 ozs. These have been called oyster cocktails, but they are more like juice or bar tumblers to me.

The green and pink sugar bowls need creamers if you spot one for me! The blue creamer and sugar pictured below have found a new home in California.

The Morgantown Collectors of America's address is 420 First Ave. N.W., Plainview, MN 55964. If you would like more information about Morgantown Glass, please contact them!

| | Crystal | Blue | Pink/ Green |
|---|---|---|---|
| Bowl, finger, ftd. | | 65.00 | |
| Creamer | | 295.00 | 250.00 |
| Cup | 40.00 | 90.00 | 80.00 |
| Parfait, 5 oz. | 55.00 | 100.00 | 80.00 |
| Pitcher | | 400.00 | |
| Plate, 5⅞", sherbet | 6.00 | 12.50 | 10.00 |
| Plate, 7½", salad | 10.00 | 25.00 | 20.00 |
| Plate, 8⅜" | 12.50 | 30.00 | 22.50 |
| Saucer | 15.00 | 22.50 | 17.50 |
| Stem, 1½ oz., cordial | 100.00 | 250.00 | 175.00 |
| Stem, 2½ oz., wine | 45.00 | 85.00 | 55.00 |
| Stem, 4¾", 7 oz., sherbet or champagne | 25.00 | 45.00 | 30.00 |
| Stem, 6⅛", cocktail | 30.00 | 65.00 | 40.00 |
| Stem, 7¾", 9 oz., water | 35.00 | 70.00 | 45.00 |
| Sugar | | 275.00 | 235.00 |
| Tumbler, 2½", 4 oz., ftd. | 25.00 | 150.00 | |
| Tumbler, 4¼", 5 oz., ftd. | 45.00 | 55.00 | 35.00 |
| Tumbler, 4¾", 9 oz., ftd. | 20.00 | 60.00 | 40.00 |
| Tumbler, 5½", 11 oz., ftd. | 35.00 | 85.00 | 65.00 |
| Vase, 6" tall, 5" wide | | | 250.00 |
| Vase, 10", slender, bud | 65.00 | | 125.00 |
| Vase, 10", bulbous bottom | | | 195.00 |

# TEAR DROP, #301, Duncan & Miller Glass Company, 1936 – 1955

Colors: crystal

    I still have trouble selling stemware in Tear Drop; but finding dinner plates and serving pieces is not getting any easier. Even cordials are easily found when compared to finding cordials in other patterns. This is another good starting pattern for beginners. I have included reprints of original Duncan catalogues on pages 203-205.

| | Crystal | | Crystal |
|---|---|---|---|
| Ash tray, 3" indiv. | 6.00 | Coaster/ashtray, 3", rolled edge | 7.00 |
| Ash tray, 5" | 8.00 | Comport, 4¾", ftd. | 12.00 |
| Bonbon, 6", 4 hdld. | 12.00 | Comport, 6", low foot., hdld. | 15.00 |
| Bottle, w/stopper, 12", bar | 125.00 | Condiment set: 5 pc. (salt/pepper, 2 | |
| Bowl, 4¼", finger | 7.00 |    3 oz. cruets, 9", 2 hdld. tray) | 95.00 |
| Bowl, 5", fruit nappy | 6.00 | Creamer, 3 oz. | 5.00 |
| Bowl, 5", 2 hdld., nappy | 8.00 | Creamer, 6 oz. | 6.00 |
| Bowl, 6", dessert, nappy | 6.00 | Creamer, 8 oz. | 8.00 |
| Bowl, 6", fruit, nappy | 6.00 | Cup, 2½ oz., demi | 10.00 |
| Bowl, 7", fruit, nappy | 7.00 | Cup, 6 oz., tea | 6.00 |
| Bowl, 7", 2 hdld., nappy | 10.00 | Flower basket, 12", loop hdl. | 115.00 |
| Bowl, 8" x 12", oval, flower | 40.00 | Ice bucket, 5½" | 60.00 |
| Bowl, 9", salad | 25.00 | Marmalade, w/cover, 4" | 35.00 |
| Bowl, 9", 2 hdld., nappy | 20.00 | Mayonnaise, 4½" (2 hdld. bowl, ladle, | |
| Bowl, 10", crimped console, 2 hdld. | 27.50 |    6" plate) | 27.50 |
| Bowl, 10", flared, fruit | 25.00 | Mayonnaise set, 3 pc. (4½" bowl, ladle, | |
| Bowl, 11½", crimped, flower | 30.00 |    8" hdld. plate) | 32.50 |
| Bowl, 11½", flared, flower | 30.00 | Mustard jar, w/cover, 4¼" | 35.00 |
| Bowl, 12", salad | 40.00 | Nut dish, 6", 2 pt. | 10.00 |
| Bowl, 12", crimped, low foot | 37.00 | Oil bottle, 3 oz. | 20.00 |
| Bowl, 12", ftd., flower | 45.00 | Olive dish, 4¼", 2 hdld., oval | 15.00 |
| Bowl, 12", sq., 4 hdld. | 42.50 | Olive dish, 6", 2 pt. | 15.00 |
| Bowl, 13", gardenia | 35.00 | Pickle dish, 6" | 15.00 |
| Bowl, 15½", 2½ gal. punch | 95.00 | Pitcher, 5", 16 oz., milk | 50.00 |
| Butter, w/cover, ¼ lb., 2 hdld. | 22.00 | Pitcher, 8½", 64 oz., w/ice lip | 105.00 |
| Cake salver, 13", ftd. | 45.00 | Plate, 6", bread/butter | 4.00 |
| Canape set: (6" plate w/ring, 4 oz., ftd., | | Plate, 6", canape | 10.00 |
|    cocktail) | 25.00 | Plate, 7", 2 hdld., lemon | 12.50 |
| Candlestick, 4" | 9.00 | Plate, 7½", salad | 5.00 |
| Candlestick, 7", 2-lite, ball loop ctr. | 18.00 | Plate, 8½", luncheon | 7.00 |
| Candlestick, 7", lg. ball ctr. w/bobeches, | | Plate, 10½", dinner | 35.00 |
|    prisms | 35.00 | Plate, 11", 2 hdld. | 27.50 |
| Candy basket, 5½" x 7½", 2 hdld., oval | 70.00 | Plate, 13", 4 hdld. | 25.00 |
| Candy box, w/cover, 7", 2 pt., 2 hdld. | 50.00 | Plate, 13", salad liner, rolled edge | 27.50 |
| Candy box, w/cover, 8", 3 pt., 3 hdld. | 55.00 | Plate, 13", torte, rolled edge | 30.00 |
| Candy dish, 7½", heart shape | 22.00 | Plate, 14", torte | 35.00 |
| Celery, 11", 2 hdld. | 15.00 | Plate, 14", torte, rolled edge | 35.00 |
| Celery, 11", 2 pt., 2 hdld. | 18.00 | Plate, 16", torte, rolled edge | 37.50 |
| Celery, 12", 3 pt. | 20.00 | Plate, 18", lazy susan | 60.00 |
| Cheese & cracker (3½" comport, 11" | | Plate, 18", punch liner, rolled edge | 50.00 |
|    2 hdld. plate) | 45.00 | | |

| | Crystal | | Crystal |
|---|---|---|---|
| Relish, 7", 2 pt., 2 hdld. | 15.00 | Sugar, 8 oz. | 8.00 |
| Relish, 7½", 2 pt., heart shape | 18.00 | Sweetmeat, 5½", star shape, 2 hdld. | 30.00 |
| Relish, 9", 3 pt., 3 hdld. | 27.50 | Sweetmeat, 6½", ctr. hdld. | 30.00 |
| Relish, 11", 3 pt., 2 hdld. | 27.50 | Sweetmeat, 7", star shape, 2 hdld. | 37.50 |
| Relish, 12", 3 pt. | 27.50 | Tray, 5½", ctr. hdld. (for mustard jar) | 11.00 |
| Relish, 12", 5 pt., rnd. | 27.50 | Tray, 6", 2 hdld. (for salt/pepper) | 10.00 |
| Relish, 12", 6 pt., rnd. | 27.50 | Tray, 7¾", ctr. hdld. (for cruets) | 12.50 |
| Relish, 12", sq., 4 pt., 4 hdld. | 27.50 | Tray, 8", 2 hdld. (for oil/vinegar) | 12.50 |
| Salad set, 6" (compote, 11" hdld. plate) | 37.50 | Tray, 8", 2 hdld. (for sugar/creamer) | 7.50 |
| Salad set, 9", (2 pt. bowl, 13" rolled edge plate) | 70.00 | Tray, 10", 2 hdld (for sugar/creamer) | 8.00 |
| Salt & pepper, 5" | 25.00 | Tumbler, 2¼", 2 oz., flat, whiskey | 16.00 |
| Saucer, 4½", demi | 3.00 | Tumbler, 2¼", 2 oz., ftd., whiskey | 12.00 |
| Saucer, 6" | 1.50 | Tumbler, 3", 3 oz., ftd., whiskey | 12.00 |
| Stem, 2½", 5 oz., ftd., sherbet | 5.00 | Tumbler, 3¼", 3½ oz., flat, juice | 6.00 |
| Stem, 2¾", 3½ oz., ftd., oyster cocktail | 7.50 | Tumbler, 3¼", 7 oz., flat, old-fashioned | 11.00 |
| Stem, 3½", 5 oz., sherbet | 6.00 | Tumbler, 3½", 5 oz., flat, juice | 6.00 |
| Stem, 4", 1 oz., cordial | 30.00 | Tumbler, 4", 4½ oz., ftd., juice | 8.00 |
| Stem, 4½", 1¾ oz., sherry | 30.00 | Tumbler, 4¼", 9 oz., flat | 8.00 |
| Stem, 4½", 3½ oz., cocktail | 15.00 | Tumbler, 4½", 8 oz., flat, split | 8.00 |
| Stem, 4¾", 3 oz., wine | 18.00 | Tumbler, 4½", 9 oz., ftd. | 8.00 |
| Stem, 5", 5 oz., champagne | 10.00 | Tumbler, 4¾", 10 oz., flat, hi-ball | 10.00 |
| Stem, 5½", 4 oz., claret | 17.50 | Tumbler, 5", 8 oz., ftd., party | 9.00 |
| Stem, 5¾", 9 oz. | 10.00 | Tumbler, 5¼", 12 oz., flat, iced tea | 15.00 |
| Stem, 6¼", 8 oz., ale | 15.00 | Tumbler, 5¾", 14 oz., flat, hi-ball | 17.50 |
| Stem, 7", 9 oz. | 14.00 | Tumbler, 6", 14 oz., iced tea | 17.50 |
| Sugar, 3 oz. | 5.00 | Urn, w/cover, 9", ftd. | 110.00 |
| Sugar, 6 oz. | 6.00 | Vase, 9", ftd., fan | 25.00 |
| | | Vase, 9", ftd., round | 37.50 |

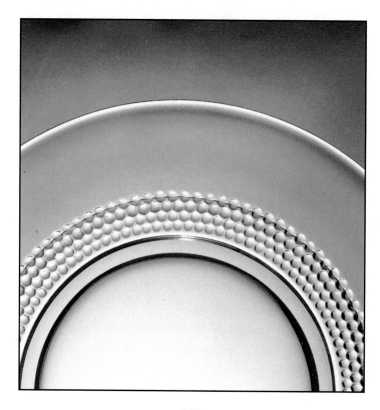

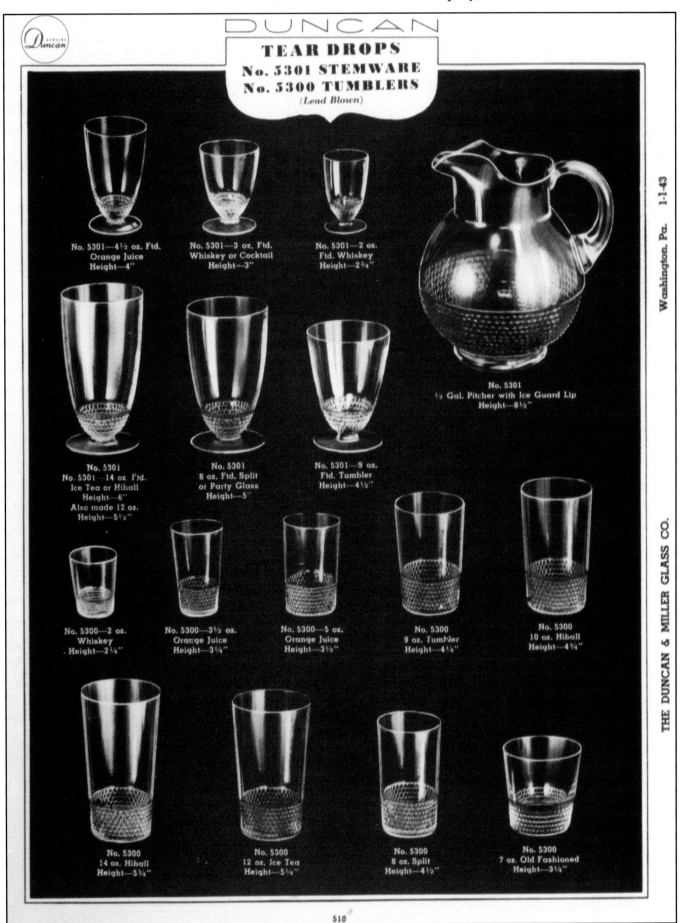

DUNCAN

**TEAR DROPS**
No. 5301 STEMWARE
No. 5300 TUMBLERS
(Lead Blown)

No. 5301—4½ oz. Ftd.
Orange Juice
Height—4"

No. 5301—3 oz. Ftd.
Whiskey or Cocktail
Height—3"

No. 5301—2 oz.
Ftd. Whiskey
Height—2¾"

No. 5301
½ Gal. Pitcher with Ice Guard Lip
Height—8½"

No. 5301
No. 5301—14 oz. Ftd.
Ice Tea or Hiball
Height—6"
Also made 12 oz.
Height—5½"

No. 5301
8 oz. Ftd. Split
or Party Glass
Height—5"

No. 5301—9 oz.
Ftd. Tumbler
Height—4½"

No. 5300—2 oz.
Whiskey
Height—2¼"

No. 5300—3½ oz.
Orange Juice
Height—3¼"

No. 5300—5 oz.
Orange Juice
Height—3½"

No. 5300
9 oz. Tumbler
Height—4¼"

No. 5300
10 oz. Hiball
Height—4¾"

No. 5300
14 oz. Hiball
Height—5¾"

No. 5300
12 oz. Ice Tea
Height—5¼"

No. 5300
8 oz. Split
Height—4½"

No. 5300
7 oz. Old Fashioned
Height—3¼"

Washington, Pa.   1-1-43

THE DUNCAN & MILLER GLASS CO.

510

203

DUNCAN

**TEAR DROP**
No. 301 PATTERN

No. 301
3 in. Individual Ash Tray

No. 301
3 in. Coaster or Ash Tray

No. 301
5 in. Ash Tray

No. 301
Bar Bottle & Stopper
Height—12"

No. 301
6 in. Canape Plate with Ring

No. 520½
4 oz. Ftd. Cocktail
Height, Cocktail—3½"

No. 301
6 in. Ice Bucket
Height—6½"  Diameter—5½"

No. 301
6 in. Low Foot Comport
Height—4"

Washington, Pa.    1-1-43

THE DUNCAN & MILLER GLASS CO.

DUNCAN

**TEAR DROP**
*Lead Blown Stemware*
**NO. 5301 PATTERN**

No. 5301
9 oz. Goblet
Height—7″

No. 5301
5 oz. Saucer
Champagne
Height—5″

No. 5301
3½ oz.
Liquor Cocktail
Height—4½″

No. 5301
4 oz. Claret
Height—5½″

No. 5301
3 oz. Wine
Height—4¾″

No. 5301
1¾ oz. Sherry
Height—4½″

No. 5301
1 oz. Cordial
Height—4″

No. 5301
Finger Bowl
Height—2¼″
Diameter—4¼″

No. 5301
9 oz.
Luncheon Goblet
Height—5¾″

No. 5301
5 oz.
Ice Cream
Height—3½″

No. 5301
5 oz. Ftd.
Sherbet
Height—2½″

No. 5301
3½ oz. Ftd.
Oyster Cocktail
Height—2¾″

No. 5301
8 oz.
Ale Goblet
Height—6¼″

Washington, Pa.    1-1-43

THE DUNCAN & MILLER GLASS CO.

# TROJAN, Fostoria Glass Company, 1929 – 1944

Colors: "Rose" pink, "Topaz" yellow; some green seen

Trojan has been hot recently. Both yellow and pink have been selling very well. I sold a yellow set to a fellow dealer who almost sold it all at the first show to which he took it.

Serving pieces are difficult to find, but stemware is fairly abundant except for the clarets. I can say that clarets are almost nonexistent in any pattern. If you need them, you had better buy them whenever you find them.

The yellow vase in the bottom photo is #4105 while the pink one is #2417. That should clarify that problem for those of you who asked.

Trojan would be ideal for someone who wishes a wealth of pieces to collect. The variety of occasional pieces is outstanding for those who decorate with their glassware.

| | Rose | Topaz | | Rose | Topaz |
|---|---|---|---|---|---|
| Ash tray, #2350, lg. | 50.00 | 40.00 | Ice dish liner (tomato, crab, fruit) | | |
| Ash tray, #2350, sm. | 30.00 | 25.00 | #2451 | 20.00 | 10.00 |
| Bottle, salad dressing, #2983 | 465.00 | 300.00 | Mayonnaise ladle | 30.00 | 30.00 |
| Bowl, baker, #2375, 9" | | 60.00 | Mayonnaise, w/liner, #2375 | 60.00 | 50.00 |
| Bowl, bonbon, #2375 | | 13.00 | Oil, ftd., #2375 | 325.00 | 235.00 |
| Bowl, bouillon, #2375, ftd. | | 18.00 | Oyster, cocktail, #5099, ftd. | 30.00 | 27.50 |
| Bowl, cream soup, #2375, ftd. | 27.50 | 22.00 | Parfait, #5099 | 70.00 | 50.00 |
| Bowl, finger, #869/2283, | | | Pitcher, #5000 | 375.00 | 285.00 |
| w/6¼" liner | 45.00 | 40.00 | Plate, #2375, canape | 30.00 | 20.00 |
| Bowl, lemon, #2375 | 18.00 | 16.00 | Plate, #2375, bread/butter, 6" | 6.00 | 5.00 |
| Bowl, #2394, 3 ftd., 4½", mint. | 25.00 | 22.00 | Plate, #2375, salad, 7½" | 9.00 | 8.00 |
| Bowl, #2375, fruit, 5" | 20.00 | 18.00 | Plate, 2375, cream soup or | | |
| Bowl, #2354, 3 ftd., 6" | 30.00 | 35.00 | mayo liner, 7½", | 9.00 | 8.00 |
| Bowl, cereal, #2375, 6½" | 37.50 | 27.50 | Plate, #2375, luncheon, 8¾" | 17.50 | 15.00 |
| Bowl, soup, #2375, 7" | 65.00 | 55.00 | Plate, #2375, sm., dinner, 9½" | 22.50 | 17.50 |
| Bowl, lg. dessert, #2375, 2-handled | 65.00 | 55.00 | Plate, #2375, cake, handled, 10" | 35.00 | 32.50 |
| Bowl, #2395, 10" | 90.00 | 65.00 | Plate, #2375, grill, rare, 10¼" | 90.00 | 80.00 |
| Bowl, #2395, scroll, 10" | 65.00 | 55.00 | Plate, #2375, dinner, 10¼" | 70.00 | 50.00 |
| Bowl, combination #2415, | | | Plate, #2375, chop, 13" | 50.00 | 45.00 |
| w/candleholder handles, | 175.00 | 135.00 | Plate, #2375, round, 14" | 55.00 | 45.00 |
| Bowl, #2375, centerpiece, flared | | | Platter, #2375, 12" | 65.00 | 55.00 |
| optic, 12" | 45.00 | 40.00 | Platter, #2375, 15" | 135.00 | 110.00 |
| Bowl, #2394, centerpiece, ftd., 12" | 45.00 | 40.00 | Relish, #2375, 8½" | | 15.00 |
| Bowl, #2375, centerpiece, | | | Relish, #2350, 3 pt., rnd., 8¾" | 45.00 | 40.00 |
| mushroom, 12" | 45.00 | 40.00 | Sauce boat, #2375 | 115.00 | 95.00 |
| Candlestick, #2394, 2" | 18.00 | 16.00 | Sauce plate, #2375 | 45.00 | 40.00 |
| Candlestick, #2375, flared, 3" | 20.00 | 18.00 | Saucer, #2375, after dinner | 10.00 | 10.00 |
| Candlestick, #2395½, scroll, 5" | 60.00 | 55.00 | Saucer, #2375 | 6.00 | 5.00 |
| Candy, w/cover, #2394, ¼ lb. | 250.00 | 225.00 | Shaker, #2375, pr., ftd. | 95.00 | 75.00 |
| Candy, w/cover, #2394, ½ lb. | 175.00 | 135.00 | Sherbet, #5099, high, 6" | 25.00 | 20.00 |
| Celery, #2375, 11½" | 35.00 | 27.50 | Sherbet, #5099, low, 4¼" | 20.00 | 16.00 |
| Cheese & cracker, set, #2375, #2368 | 65.00 | 60.00 | Sugar, #2375½, ftd. | 22.50 | 20.00 |
| Comport, 5299 or #2400, 6" | 35.00 | 30.00 | Sugar cover, #2375½ | 125.00 | 95.00 |
| Comport, #2375, 7" | 45.00 | 40.00 | Sugar pail, #2378 | 155.00 | 110.00 |
| Creamer, #2375, ftd. | 22.50 | 20.00 | Sugar, tea, #2375½ | 55.00 | 45.00 |
| Creamer, tea, #2375½ | 55.00 | 45.00 | Sweetmeat, #2375 | 15.00 | 15.00 |
| Cup, after dinner, #2375 | 45.00 | 35.00 | Tray, 11", ctr. hdld, #2375 | 35.00 | 32.50 |
| Cup, #2375½, ftd. | 20.00 | 18.00 | Tray, #2429, service & lemon insert | | 225.00 |
| Decanter, #2439, 9" | 850.00 | 750.00 | Tumbler, #5099, ftd., 2½ oz. | 55.00 | 40.00 |
| Goblet, claret, #5099, 4 oz., 6" | 120.00 | 75.00 | Tumbler, #5099, ftd., 5 oz., 4½" | 30.00 | 25.00 |
| Goblet, cocktail, #5099, 3 oz., 5¼" | 30.00 | 27.50 | Tumbler, #5099, ftd., 9 oz., 5¼" | 22.50 | 17.50 |
| Goblet, cordial, #5099, ¾ oz., 4" | 95.00 | 70.00 | Tumbler, #5099, ftd., 12 oz., 6" | 37.50 | 30.00 |
| Goblet, water, #5299, 10 oz., 8¼" | 37.50 | 27.50 | Vase, #2417, 8" | 145.00 | 120.00 |
| Goblet, wine, #5099, 3 oz., 5½" | 55.00 | 45.00 | Vase, #4105, 8" | 215.00 | 160.00 |
| Grapefruit, #5282½ | 55.00 | 45.00 | Vase, #2369, 9" | | 210.00 |
| Grapefruit liner, #945½ | 50.00 | 40.00 | Whipped cream bowl, #2375 | 15.00 | 12.00 |
| Ice bucket, #2375 | 75.00 | 65.00 | Whipped cream pail, #2378 | 135.00 | 115.00 |
| Ice dish, #2451, #2455 | 45.00 | 35.00 | Note: See page 99 for stem identification. | | |

# TWIST, Blank #1252, A.H. Heisey & Co.

Colors: crystal, "Flamingo" pink, "Moongleam" green, "Marigold" amber/yellow; "Sahara" yellow; some "Alexandrite" (rare)

Twist (on the cover of the last book) caused one dealer to comment, "I haven't been able to keep it in stock since your book came out!"

| | Crystal | Pink | Green | Sahara | Marigold / Alexandrite |
|---|---|---|---|---|---|
| Baker, 9", oval | 10.00 | 20.00 | 25.00 | 60.00 | |
| Bonbon | 5.00 | 12.00 | 17.00 | 30.00 | |
| Bonbon, 6", 2 hdld. | 5.00 | 12.00 | 17.00 | 30.00 | |
| Bottle, French dressing | 35.00 | 75.00 | 95.00 | 125.00 | |
| Bowl, cream soup/bouillon | 15.00 | 25.00 | 32.00 | 50.00 | |
| Bowl, ftd., almond/indiv. sugar | 15.00 | 30.00 | 37.50 | 60.00 | |
| Bowl, indiv. nut | 5.00 | 20.00 | 27.50 | 45.00 | |
| Bowl, 4", nappy | 5.00 | 12.00 | 16.00 | 17.00 | |
| Bowl, 6", 2 hdld. | 7.00 | 15.00 | 18.00 | 20.00 | |
| Bowl, 6", 2 hdld., jelly | 7.00 | 15.00 | 18.00 | 20.00 | |
| Bowl, 6", 2 hdld., mint | 7.00 | 15.00 | 18.00 | 20.00 | |
| Bowl, 8", low ftd. | 25.00 | 35.00 | 40.00 | 65.00 | |
| Bowl, 8", nappy, grnd. bottom | 12.00 | 25.00 | 30.00 | 40.00 | |
| Bowl, 8", nasturtium, rnd. | 35.00 | 60.00 | 70.00 | 80.00 | 400.00 |
| Bowl, 8", nasturtium, oval | 35.00 | 60.00 | 70.00 | 80.00 | |
| Bowl, 9", floral | 25.00 | 35.00 | 40.00 | 65.00 | |
| Bowl, 9", floral, rolled edge | 30.00 | 35.00 | 40.00 | 65.00 | |
| Bowl, 12", floral, oval, 4 ft. | 30.00 | 40.00 | 50.00 | 65.00 | |
| Bowl, 12", floral, rnd., 4 ft. | 30.00 | 40.00 | 50.00 | 65.00 | |
| Candlestick, 2", 1-lite | 12.00 | 25.00 | 30.00 | 60.00 | |
| Cheese dish, 6", 2 hdld. | 5.00 | 10.00 | 17.50 | 20.00 | |
| Claret, 4 oz. | 15.00 | 30.00 | 40.00 | 50.00 | |
| Cocktail shaker, metal top | | | 400.00 | | |
| Comport, 7", tall | 25.00 | 60.00 | 85.00 | 150.00 | |
| Creamer, hotel, oval | 25.00 | 35.00 | 45.00 | 50.00 | |
| Creamer, individual (unusual) | 18.00 | 35.00 | 35.00 | 65.00 | |
| Creamer, zigzag handles, ftd. | 20.00 | 30.00 | 37.50 | 60.00 | |
| Cup, zigzag handles | 10.00 | 25.00 | 32.00 | 35.00 | |
| Grapefruit, ftd. | 15.00 | 25.00 | 35.00 | 60.00 | |
| Ice tub | 25.00 | 65.00 | 85.00 | 125.00 | |
| Ice Bucket | | | | | 300.00 |
| Pitcher, 3 pint | 50.00 | 110.00 | 160.00 | | |
| Mayonnaise | 20.00 | 40.00 | 45.00 | 40.00 | |
| Mayonnaise, #1252½ | 20.00 | 35.00 | 45.00 | 50.00 | |
| Mustard, w/cover, spoon | 30.00 | 80.00 | 90.00 | 100.00 | |
| Oil bottle, 2½ oz., w/#78 stopper | 40.00 | 70.00 | 90.00 | | |
| Oil bottle, 4 oz., w/#78 stopper | 40.00 | 70.00 | 90.00 | | |
| Plate, cream soup liner | 5.00 | 7.00 | 10.00 | 15.00 | |
| Plate, 8", Kraft cheese | 15.00 | 30.00 | 40.00 | 60.00 | |
| Plate, 8", grnd. bottom | 7.00 | 12.00 | 15.00 | 25.00 | |
| Plate, 10" utility, 3 ft. | 25.00 | 30.00 | 42.00 | | |
| Plate, 12", 2 hdld., sandwich | 25.00 | 40.00 | 50.00 | 55.00 | |
| Plate, 12", muffin, 2 hdld., turned sides | 30.00 | 40.00 | 55.00 | 65.00 | |
| Plate, 13", 3 part, relish | 10.00 | 17.00 | 22.00 | 35.00 | |
| Platter, 12" | 15.00 | 40.00 | 60.00 | 75.00 | |
| Salt & pepper, 2 styles | 35.00 | 65.00 | 135.00 | 150.00 | |
| Saucer | 3.00 | 5.00 | 7.00 | 10.00 | |
| Stem, 2½ oz., wine, 2 block stem | 15.00 | 30.00 | 35.00 | 40.00 | |
| Stem, 3 oz., oyster cocktail, ftd. | 5.00 | 15.00 | 22.00 | 25.00 | |
| Stem, 3 oz., cocktail, 2 block stem | 5.00 | 15.00 | 22.00 | 25.00 | |
| Stem, 5 oz., saucer champagne, 2 block stem | 7.00 | 16.00 | 22.00 | 25.00 | |
| Stem, 5 oz., sherbet, 2 block stem | 7.50 | 12.00 | 18.00 | 22.50 | |
| Stem, 9 oz., luncheon (1 block in stem), also made 2 block stem 9 oz. | 20.00 | 25.00 | 40.00 | 50.00 | |
| Sugar, ftd. | 20.00 | 30.00 | 37.50 | 60.00 | |
| Sugar, hotel, oval | 25.00 | 35.00 | 40.00 | 50.00 | |
| Sugar, individual (unusual) | 18.00 | 35.00 | 38.00 | 65.00 | |
| Sugar, w/cover, zigzag handles | 15.00 | 27.00 | 40.00 | 70.00 | |
| Tray, 7", pickle, grnd. bottom | 7.00 | 15.00 | 22.00 | 25.00 | |
| Tray, 10", celery | 10.00 | 20.00 | 27.00 | 30.00 | |
| Tray, 13", celery | 12.00 | 25.00 | 37.00 | 50.00 | |
| Tumbler, 5 oz., soda, flat bottom | 4.00 | 12.00 | 20.00 | 25.00 | |
| Tumbler, 6 oz., ftd. soda | 5.00 | 13.00 | 20.00 | 25.00 | |
| Tumbler, 8 oz., flat, grnd. bottom | 9.00 | 20.00 | 25.00 | 35.00 | |
| Tumbler, 8 oz., soda, straight & flared | 9.00 | 20.00 | 25.00 | 35.00 | |
| Tumbler, 9 oz., ftd. soda | 10.00 | 17.00 | 25.00 | 35.00 | |
| Tumbler, 12 oz., iced tea, flat bottom | 12.00 | 30.00 | 40.00 | 50.00 | |
| Tumbler, 12 oz., ftd. iced tea | 15.00 | 30.00 | 40.00 | 50.00 | |

# VALENCIA, Cambridge Glass Company

Colors: crystal, pink

Another Cambridge pattern often confused with Valencia is Minerva. Notice in the pattern shot of Valencia that the lines in the pattern are perpendicular to each other. On Minerva, the lines in the pattern meet on a diagonal.

Collectors are just beginning to recognize Valencia. It was not nationally distributed in the large quantities that Rose Point and Caprice were. Many of the Cambridge blanks used for Rose Point are found etched with Valencia. Some of the more unusual and interesting pieces pictured include the covered honey dish, six-piece relish on #3500, 12" plate, and the 15" long, three-part, two-handled relish. All of these pieces are highly coveted in Rose Point, but are only beginning to be noticed in Valencia. These pieces are, of course, rarer in Valencia than the highly promoted Rose Point. Yet there are thousands of collectors searching for Rose Point and only a few looking for Valencia; so, there is an immense discrepancy in price on identical pieces in these patterns **due to demand**.

That metal-handled piece in the center of the photo behind the squared honey dish was called a sugar basket by Cambridge. This is similar to Fostoria's sugar pail. Terminology used by different companies sometimes causes today's collectors problems figuring which piece is called what.

| | Crystal | | Crystal |
|---|---|---|---|
| Ash tray, #3500/124, 3¼", round. | 10.00 | Relish, #1402/91, 8", 3 comp. | 25.00 |
| Ash tray, #3500/126, 4", round | 14.00 | Relish, #3500/64, 10", 3 comp. | 27.50 |
| Ash tray, #3500/128, 4½", round | 18.00 | Relish, #3500/65, 10", 4 comp. | 30.00 |
| Basket, #3500/55, 6", 2 hdld., ftd. | 22.00 | Relish, #3500/67, 12", 6 pc. | 95.00 |
| Bowl, #3500/49, 5", hdld. | 18.00 | Relish, #3500/112, 15", 3 pt./2 hdld. | 85.00 |
| Bowl, #3500/37, 6", cereal | 20.00 | Relish, #3500/13, 15", 4 pt./2 hdld. | 85.00 |
| Bowl, #1402/89, 6", 2 hdld. | 18.00 | Salt and pepper, #3400/18 | 50.00 |
| Bowl, #1402/88, 6", 2 hdld., div. | 20.00 | Saucer, #3500/1 | 3.00 |
| Bowl, #3500/115, 9½", 2 hdld., ftd. | 35.00 | Stem, #1402, cordial | 65.00 |
| Bowl, #1402/82, 10" | 32.50 | Stem, #1402, wine | 30.00 |
| Bowl, #1402/88, 11" | 35.00 | Stem, #1402, cocktail | 20.00 |
| Bowl, #1402/95, salad dressing, div. | 40.00 | Stem, #1402, claret | 40.00 |
| Bowl, #1402/100, finger, w/liner | 30.00 | Stem, #1402, oyster cocktail | 16.00 |
| Bowl, #3500, ftd., finger | 27.50 | Stem, #1402, low sherbet | 12.50 |
| Candy dish, w/cover, #3500/103 | 90.00 | Stem, #1402, tall sherbet | 15.00 |
| Celery, #1402/94, 12" | 30.00 | Stem, #1402, goblet | 20.00 |
| Cigarette holder, #1066, ftd. | 38.00 | Stem, #3500, cordial | 65.00 |
| Comport, #3500/36, 6" | 27.50 | Stem, #3500, wine, 2½ oz. | 27.50 |
| Comport, #3500/37, 7" | 40.00 | Stem, #3500, cocktail, 3 oz | 18.00 |
| Creamer, #3500/14 | 15.00 | Stem, #3500, claret, 4½ oz. | 40.00 |
| Creamer, #3500/15, individual | 17.50 | Stem, #3500, oyster cocktail, 4½ oz. | 15.00 |
| Cup, #3500/1 | 17.50 | Stem, #3500, low sherbet, 7 oz. | 12.50 |
| Decanter, #3400/92, 32 oz., ball | 125.00 | Stem, #3500, tall sherbet, 7 oz. | 15.00 |
| Decanter, #3400/119, 12 oz., ball | 95.00 | Stem, #3500, goblet, long bowl | 20.00 |
| Honey dish, w/cover, #3500/139 | 110.00 | Stem, #3500, goblet, short bowl | 18.00 |
| Ice pail, #1402/52 | 65.00 | Sugar, #3500/14 | 15.00 |
| Mayonnaise, #3500/59, 3 pc. | 40.00 | Sugar, #3500/15, individual | 17.50 |
| Nut, #3400/71, 3", 4 ftd. | 55.00 | Sugar basket, #3500/13 | 95.00 |
| Perfume, #3400/97, 2 oz., perfume | 95.00 | Tumbler, #3400/92, 2½ oz. | 17.50 |
| Plate, #3500/167, 7½", salad | 10.00 | Tumbler, #3400/100, 13 oz. | 20.00 |
| Plate, #3500/5, 8½", breakfast | 12.00 | Tumbler, #3400/115, 14 oz. | 22.00 |
| Plate, #1402, 11½", sandwich, hdld. | 22.50 | Tumbler, #3500, 2½ oz., ftd. | 17.50 |
| Plate, #3500/39, 12", ftd. | 27.50 | Tumbler, #3500, 3 oz., ftd. | 14.00 |
| Plate, #3500/67, 12" | 22.50 | Tumbler, #3500, 5 oz., ftd. | 12.50 |
| Plate, #3500/38, 13", torte | 25.00 | Tumbler, #3500, 10 oz., ftd. | 14.00 |
| Pitcher, 80oz., Doulton #3400/141 | 275.00 | Tumbler, #3500, 12 oz., ftd. | 18.00 |
| Relish, #3500/68, 5½", 2 comp. | 17.50 | Tumbler, #3500, 13 oz., ftd. | 17.50 |
| Relish, #3500/69, 6½", 3 comp. | 20.00 | Tumbler, #3500, 16 oz., ftd. | 20.00 |

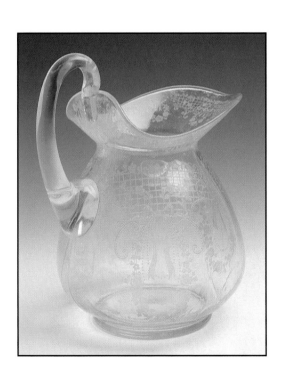

# VERSAILLES, Fostoria Glass Company, 1928 – 1944

Colors: blue, yellow, pink, green

I have tried to list all Fostoria line numbers for each piece of Versailles. These numbers can also be utilized for items in June.

If you order or ship through ads, you should know the following: liners for cream soups and mayonnaise liners are the same piece; two handled cake plates come with and without an indent in the center. The indented version also serves as a plate for one of two styles of cheese comports; bonbon, lemon dish, sweetmeat, and whipped cream bowls all come with loop or bow handles; and sugars come with a straight and ruffled top. The ruffled top requires a lid.

The sugar and creamer were set upon the lemon tray in the green Versailles photo. There is a plain, six sided insert that fits in the center which is not shown here. The 7" soup bowl shown next to this tray is the nemesis of many collectors.

Be sure to see page 99 for Fostoria stems. Many people confuse them because their heights are so similar. Shapes are more important. Clarets are the most difficult stem to find; cordials are the next most troublesome.

| | Pink, Green | Blue | Yellow |
|---|---|---|---|
| Ash tray, #2350 | 24.00 | 30.00 | 25.00 |
| Bottle, #2083, salad dressing, crystal glass top | 295.00 | 600.00 | 345.00 |
| Bottle, #2375, salad dressing, w/ sterling top or colored top | 350.00 | 650.00 | 375.00 |
| Bowl, #2375, baker, 9" | 55.00 | 110.00 | 55.00 |
| Bowl, #2375, bonbon | 15.00 | 22.50 | 17.50 |
| Bowl, #2375, bouillon, ftd. | 20.00 | 32.00 | 20.00 |
| Bowl, #2375, cream soup, ftd. | 22.00 | 27.50 | 20.00 |
| Bowl, #869/2283, finger, w/6" liner | 35.00 | 50.00 | 35.00 |
| Bowl, lemon | 15.00 | 22.00 | 17.50 |
| Bowl, 4½", mint, 3 ftd. | 25.00 | 35.00 | 25.00 |
| Bowl, #2375, fruit, 5" | 17.50 | 25.00 | 20.00 |
| Bowl, #2394, 3 ftd., 6" | | | 30.00 |
| Bowl, #2375, cereal, 6½" | 22.50 | 35.00 | 25.00 |
| Bowl, #2375, soup, 7" | 50.00 | 70.00 | 50.00 |
| Bowl, #2375, lg., dessert, 2 hdld. | 45.00 | 85.00 | 40.00 |
| Bowl, #2375, baker, 10" | 45.00 | 85.00 | 40.00 |
| Bowl, #2395, centerpiece, scroll, 10" | 45.00 | 65.00 | 45.00 |
| Bowl, #2375, centerpiece, flared top, 12" | 35.00 | 55.00 | 40.00 |
| Bowl, #2394, ftd., 12" | 35.00 | 55.00 | 45.00 |
| Bowl, #2375½, oval, centerpiece 13" | 50.00 | 75.00 | |
| Candlestick, #2394, 2" | 20.00 | 22.50 | 17.50 |
| Candlestick, #2395, 3" | 17.50 | 27.50 | 20.00 |
| Candlestick, #2395½, scroll, 5" | 30.00 | 45.00 | 30.00 |
| Candy, w/cover, #2331, 3 pt. | 145.00 | 195.00 | |
| Candy, w/cover, #2394, ¼ lb. | | | 185.00 |
| Candy, w/cover, #2394, ½ lb. | | | 160.00 |
| Celery, #2375, 11½" | 35.00 | 95.00 | 40.00 |
| Cheese & cracker, #2375 or #2368, set | 65.00 | 95.00 | 65.00 |
| Comport, #5098, 3" | 25.00 | 35.00 | 25.00 |
| Comport, #5099/2400, 6" | 30.00 | 45.00 | 30.00 |
| Comport, #2375, 7" | 32.50 | 55.00 | |
| Comport, #2400, 8" | 65.00 | 100.00 | |
| Creamer, #2375½, ftd. | 17.50 | 22.50 | 15.00 |
| Creamer, #2375½, tea | 42.50 | 55.00 | 42.50 |
| Cup, #2375, after dinner | 35.00 | 50.00 | 35.00 |
| Cup, #2375½, ftd. | 17.50 | 21.00 | 19.00 |
| Decanter, #2439, 9" | 900.00 | 1,600.00 | 600.00 |
| Goblet, cordial, #5098 or #5099, ¾ oz., 4" | 80.00 | 95.00 | 65.00 |
| Goblet, #5098 or #5099, claret, 4 oz., 6" | 70.00 | 120.00 | 70.00 |
| Goblet, cocktail, #5098 or #5099, 3 oz., 5¼" | 25.00 | 37.50 | 28.00 |
| Goblet, water, #5098 or #5099, 10 oz., 8¼" | 27.50 | 37.50 | 30.00 |
| Goblet, wine, #5098 or #5099, 3 oz., 5½" | 40.00 | 70.00 | 45.00 |
| Grapefruit, #5082½ | 45.00 | 70.00 | 40.00 |

| | Pink, Green | Blue | Yellow |
|---|---|---|---|
| Grapefruit liner, #945½ | 40.00 | 50.00 | 35.00 |
| Ice bucket, #2375 | 62.50 | 80.00 | 75.00 |
| Ice dish, #2451 | 30.00 | 45.00 | 30.00 |
| Ice dish liner (tomato, crab, fruit), #2451 | 20.00 | 20.00 | 10.00 |
| Mayonnaise, w/liner, #2375 | 35.00 | 50.00 | 40.00 |
| Mayonnaise ladle | 30.00 | 40.00 | 30.00 |
| Oil, #2375, ftd. | 350.00 | 525.00 | 300.00 |
| Oyster cocktail, #5098 or #5099 | 22.50 | 32.50 | 25.00 |
| Parfait, #5098 or #5099 | 35.00 | 45.00 | 35.00 |
| Pitcher, #5000 | 295.00 | 425.00 | 325.00 |
| Plate, #2375, bread/butter, 6" | 4.00 | 5.00 | 4.00 |
| Plate, #2375, canape, 6" | 20.00 | 35.00 | 30.00 |
| Plate, #2375, salad, 7½" | 6.00 | 10.00 | 7.00 |
| Plate, #2375, cream soup or mayo liner, 7½" | 6.00 | 10.00 | 7.00 |
| Plate, #2375, luncheon, 8¾" | 8.00 | 12.50 | 9.00 |
| Plate, #2375, sm., dinner, 9½" | 17.50 | 32.50 | 20.00 |
| Plate, #2375, cake, 2 hdld., 10" | 26.00 | 37.50 | 30.00 |
| Plate, #2375, dinner, 10¼" | 60.00 | 85.00 | 55.00 |
| Plate, #2375, chop, 13" | 50.00 | 75.00 | 45.00 |
| Platter, #2375, 12" | 65.00 | 80.00 | 65.00 |
| Platter, #2375, 15" | 95.00 | 135.00 | 95.00 |
| Relish, #2375, 8½" | 30.00 | 40.00 | 35.00 |
| Sauce boat, #2375 | 75.00 | 120.00 | 75.00 |
| Sauce boat plate, #2375 | 20.00 | 35.00 | 20.00 |
| Saucer, #2375, after dinner | 5.00 | 7.50 | 5.00 |
| Saucer, #2375 | 4.00 | 6.00 | 5.00 |
| Shaker, #2375, pr., ftd. | 90.00 | 140.00 | 85.00 |
| Sherbet, #5098/5099, high, 6" | 20.00 | 27.50 | 22.50 |
| Sherbet, #5098/5099, low, 4¼" | 20.00 | 25.00 | 22.00 |
| Sugar, #2375½, ftd. | 15.00 | 20.00 | 15.00 |
| Sugar cover, #2375½ | 135.00 | 175.00 | 120.00 |
| Sugar pail, #2378 | 145.00 | 200.00 | 135.00 |
| Sugar, #2375½, tea | 42.50 | 55.00 | 42.50 |
| Sweetmeat, #2375 | 14.00 | 18.00 | 15.00 |
| Tray, #2375, ctr. hdld., 11" | 30.00 | 45.00 | 35.00 |
| Tray, service & lemon | 300.00 | 395.00 | 215.00 |
| Tumbler, flat, old-fashioned (pink only) | 90.00 | | |
| Tumbler, flat, tea (pink only) | 95.00 | | |
| Tumbler, #5098 or #5099 2½ oz., ftd., | 32.50 | 50.00 | 37.50 |
| Tumbler, #5098 or #5099, 5 oz., ftd., 4½", | 20.00 | 30.00 | 22.00 |
| Tumbler, #5098 or #5099, 9 oz., ftd., 5¼", | 20.00 | 32.50 | 21.50 |
| Tumbler, #5098 or #5099 12 oz., ftd., 6", | 30.00 | 50.00 | 27.50 |
| Vase, #2417, 8" | | | 150.00 |
| Vase, #4100, 8" | 125.00 | 225.00 | |
| Vase, #2385, fan, ftd., 8½" | 110.00 | 195.00 | |
| Whipped cream bowl, #2375 | 15.00 | 18.00 | 13.00 |
| Whipped cream pail, #2378 | 110.00 | 155.00 | 110.00 |

Note: See page 99 for stem identification.

# VESPER, Fostoria Glass Company, 1926 – 1934

Colors: amber, green; some blue

I have finally found enough blue and green Vesper to be able to have a photograph of each of these! Blue Vesper has devotees, but their one complaint is that there is a none to be found on the market at a price they are willing to pay! Rarely found and attractive glassware often gets priced "out of sight" as one collector put it! Green is more easily found, but that is not as desirable as is blue!

Amber Vesper is not as collected as some other Fostoria colors; but as you can see here, this amber pattern has a multitude of pieces! Many are easily found; others will take some patience and searching. Etched amber Fostoria patterns may be the "sleepers" in the Elegant glass collecting field. I've seen gorgeous table settings made with amber glass. A dealer from the West Coast informed me that decorators are buying amber glass for the first time in ten years. They buy **color** to decorate what the furniture and carpet people are pushing in years to come. Do not be surprised to see moneyed people starting to buy amber Elegant glassware in the next few years! They are going to be buying more for color than what the glass is, but the key word is **buying!**

The amber butter dish was the only one known in the last book. Another one was found in Texas the first of the year, but before it could be marketed, it was broken into a few hundred pieces. So, for now, there is still only this one known! It is shown in the top picture on page 217. Behind the butter is a finger bowl and liner and sauce boat and liner. Other companies called these gravy boats, but Fostoria always listed them as sauce boats.

An 8¾" canape plate, which is large by most standards, is shown on the left in the second photo on page 217. This has a sherbet on the off center ring and was called a Maj Jongg set by Fostoria. They are quite rare. In front of that set are an egg cup and the #2315 moulded grapefruit, which also doubled as a mayonnaise. The blown style of grapefruit with the etched liner is shown in the foreground. Some companies called these shrimp dishes. You filled the inside compote with shrimp or fruit and put ice in the larger container to keep it chilled. Since ice was a valuable commodity in those days, only the well-to-do had these items and that results in short supplies today.

| | Green | Amber | Blue |
|---|---|---|---|
| Ash tray, #2350, 4" ................................................ | 25.00 | 30.00 | |
| Bowl, #2350, bouillon, ftd. ................................. | 12.00 | 17.50 | 25.00 |
| Bowl, #2350, cream soup, flat............................ | 25.00 | 30.00 | |
| Bowl, #2350, cream soup, ftd.............................. | 20.00 | 20.00 | 30.00 |
| Bowl, #2350, fruit, 5½"........................................ | 10.00 | 12.50 | 22.50 |
| Bowl, #2350, cereal, sq. or rnd., 6½" .................. | 18.00 | 20.00 | 30.00 |
| Bowl, #2267, low, ftd., 7" .................................... | 20.00 | 25.00 | |
| Bowl, #2350, soup, shallow, 7¾" ........................ | 22.00 | 32.50 | 45.00 |
| Bowl, soup, deep, 8¼" .......................................... | | 35.00 | |
| Bowl, 8"................................................................. | 30.00 | 40.00 | |
| Bowl, #2350, baker, oval, 9"................................. | 60.00 | 70.00 | 85.00 |
| Bowl, #2350, baker, oval, 10½"............................ | 75.00 | 85.00 | 110.00 |
| Bowl, #2375, flared bowl, 10½"............................ | 35.00 | 35.00 | |
| Bowl, #2329, console, rolled edge, 11"................. | 35.00 | 37.50 | |
| Bowl, #2375, 3 ftd., 12½"..................................... | 40.00 | 42.50 | |
| Bowl, #2371, oval, 13"........................................... | 40.00 | 45.00 | |
| Bowl, #2329, rolled edge, 13"............................... | 40.00 | 45.00 | |
| Bowl, #2329, rolled edge, 15"............................... | 45.00 | 50.00 | |
| Butter dish, #2350................................................ | | 800.00 | |
| Candlestick, #2324, 2"........................................... | 17.50 | 25.00 | |
| Candlestick, #2394, 3"........................................... | 15.00 | 17.50 | 35.00 |
| Candlestick, #2324, 4"........................................... | 15.00 | 20.00 | |
| Candlestick, #2394, 9"........................................... | 55.00 | 90.00 | 90.00 |
| Candy jar, w/cover, #2331, 3 pt. .......................... | 100.00 | 100.00 | 200.00 |
| Candy jar, w/cover, #2250, ftd., ½ lb...................... | 225.00 | 175.00 | |
| Celery, #2350 ....................................................... | 17.00 | 22.00 | 32.50 |
| Cheese, #2368, ftd. .............................................. | 18.00 | 20.00 | |
| Comport, 6"............................................................ | 22.50 | 25.00 | 40.00 |

| | Green | Amber | Blue |
|---|---|---|---|
| Comport, #2327, (twisted stem), 7½" | 27.50 | 30.00 | 50.00 |
| Comport, 8" | 40.00 | 50.00 | 60.00 |
| Creamer, #2350½, ftd. | 14.00 | 20.00 | |
| Creamer, #2315½, fat, ftd. | 18.00 | 22.00 | 30.00 |
| Creamer, #2350½, flat | | 22.00 | |
| Cup, #2350 | 14.00 | 15.00 | 30.00 |
| Cup, #2350, after dinner | 35.00 | 35.00 | 70.00 |
| Cup, #2350½, ftd. | 14.00 | 15.00 | |
| Egg cup, #2350 | | 40.00 | |
| Finger bowl and liner, #869/2283, 6" | 27.50 | 30.00 | 45.00 |
| Grapefruit, #5082½, blown | 45.00 | 45.00 | 75.00 |
| Grapefruit liner, #945½, blown | 40.00 | 40.00 | 45.00 |
| Grapefruit, #2315, molded | 50.00 | 55.00 | |
| Ice bucket, #2378 | 60.00 | 67.50 | |
| Oyster cocktail, #5100 | 16.00 | 20.00 | 35.00 |
| Pickle, #2350 | 22.00 | 25.00 | 35.00 |
| Pitcher, #5100, ftd. | 295.00 | 325.00 | 500.00 |
| Plate, #2350, bread/butter, 6" | 4.50 | 5.00 | 10.00 |
| Plate, #2350, salad, 7½" | 6.00 | 6.50 | 14.00 |
| Plate, #2350, luncheon, 8½" | 7.50 | 8.50 | 17.50 |
| Plate, #2321, Maj Jongg (canape), 8¾" | | 45.00 | |
| Plate, #2350, sm., dinner, 9½" | 18.00 | 20.00 | 25.00 |
| Plate, dinner, 10½" | 30.00 | 37.50 | |
| Plate, #2287, ctr. hand., 11" | 22.50 | 25.00 | 50.00 |
| Plate, chop, 13¾" | 32.00 | 37.50 | 75.00 |
| Plate, #2350, server, 15" | 55.00 | 65.00 | 95.00 |
| Plate, w/indent for cheese, 11" | 18.00 | 20.00 | |
| Platter, #2350, 10½" | 35.00 | 40.00 | |
| Platter, #2350, 12" | 50.00 | 60.00 | 95.00 |
| Platter, #2350, 15", | 85.00 | 95.00 | 125.00 |
| Salt & pepper, #5100, pr. | 65.00 | 75.00 | |
| Sauce boat, w/liner, #2350 | 115.00 | 125.00 | |
| Saucer, #2350, after dinner | 9.00 | 10.00 | 20.00 |
| Saucer, #2350 | 4.00 | 4.50 | 5.00 |
| Stem, #5093, high sherbet | 16.00 | 17.50 | 30.00 |
| Stem, #5093, water goblet | 25.00 | 27.50 | 40.00 |
| Stem, #5093, low sherbet | 15.00 | 17.00 | 25.00 |
| Stem, #5093, parfait | 32.50 | 37.50 | 50.00 |
| Stem, #5093, cordial, ¾ oz. | 70.00 | 75.00 | 110.00 |
| Stem, #5093, wine, 2¾ oz. | 35.00 | 37.50 | 50.00 |
| Stem, #5093, cocktail, 3 oz. | 25.00 | 27.50 | 40.00 |
| Sugar, #2350½, flat | | 20.00 | |
| Sugar, #2315, fat ftd. | 18.00 | 20.00 | 30.00 |
| Sugar, #2350½, ftd. | 14.00 | 16.00 | |
| Sugar, lid | 175.00 | 165.00 | |
| Tumbler, #5100, ftd., 2 oz. | 30.00 | 40.00 | 55.00 |
| Tumbler, #5100, ftd., 5 oz. | 15.00 | 20.00 | 35.00 |
| Tumbler, #5100, ftd., 9 oz. | 16.00 | 20.00 | 40.00 |
| Tumbler, #5100, ftd., 12 oz. | 22.00 | 30.00 | 50.00 |
| Urn, #2324, small | 65.00 | 80.00 | |
| Urn, large | 75.00 | 90.00 | |
| Vase, #2292, 8" | 85.00 | 90.00 | 145.00 |
| Vanity set, combination cologne/ powder & stopper | 200.00 | 225.00 | 300.00 |

Note: See stemware identification on page 99.

# VICTORIAN, #1425 A.H. Heisey Co., 1933 – 1953

Colors: crystal, Sahara, Cobalt, rare in pale Zircon

Victorian, by Heisey, was only made in the colors listed. If you find pink, green, or amber Victorian in your travels, then you have Imperial's contribution to this pattern from 1964 and 1965. These colors are marked with the H in diamond trademark, but they were made from Heisey moulds after the company was no longer in business.

The first Heisey I ever bought at a yard sale was pink Victorian. It was marked Heisey, so I couldn't understand why it would not sell at the flea market for a reasonable price. Two years later someone explained to me that it really wasn't Heisey regardless of the mark. (Because of that, I turned down sixty-seven pieces of marked cobalt Heisey for $1.00 each that a lady had bought for $.10 each. I learned my mistake a couple of weeks later, but it was all sold by then!)

Imperial also made about ten pieces in crystal, but they can not be differentiated from the original Heisey... and they aren't as discriminated against by Heisey collectors as are the colored pieces!

| | Crystal | | Crystal |
|---|---|---|---|
| Bottle, 3 oz. oil | 45.00 | Plate, 21" buffet or punch bowl liner, | 100.00 |
| Bottle, 27 oz. rye | 150.00 | Relish, 11", 3 pt. | 45.00 |
| Bottle, French dressing | 65.00 | Salt & pepper | 40.00 |
| Bowl, 10½" floral | 40.00 | Stem, 2½ oz. wine | 20.00 |
| Bowl, finger | 15.00 | Stem, 3 oz. claret | 20.00 |
| Bowl, punch | 250.00 | Stem, 5 oz. oyster cocktail | 15.00 |
| Bowl, rose | 75.00 | Stem, 5 oz. saucer champagne | 17.50 |
| Bowl, triplex w/flared or cupped rim | 80.00 | Stem, 5 oz. sherbet | 15.00 |
| Butter dish, ¼ lb. | 65.00 | Stem, 9 oz. goblet (one ball) | 20.00 |
| Candlestick, 2-lite | 110.00 | Stem, 9 oz. high goblet (two ball) | 22.50 |
| Cigarette box, 4" | 50.00 | Sugar | 25.00 |
| Cigarette box, 6" | 75.00 | Tray, 12" celery | 25.00 |
| Cigarette holder & ash tray, ind. | 20.00 | Tray, condiment (s/p & mustard) | 150.00 |
| Comport, 5" | 45.00 | Tumbler, 2 oz. bar | 35.00 |
| Comport, 6", 3 ball stem | 80.00 | Tumbler, 5 oz. soda (straight or | |
| Compote, cheese (for center sandwich) | 20.00 | curved edge) | 15.00 |
| Creamer | 25.00 | Tumbler, 8 oz. old-fashioned | 30.00 |
| Cup, punch, 5 oz. | 10.00 | Tumbler, 10 oz. w/rim foot | 20.00 |
| Decanter and stopper, 32 oz., | 50.00 | Tumbler, 12 oz. ftd. soda | 25.00 |
| Jug, 54 oz. | 225.00 | Tumbler, 12 oz. soda (straight or | |
| Nappy, 8" | 30.00 | curved edge) | 22.50 |
| Plate, 6" liner for finger | 10.00 | Vase, 4" | 25.00 |
| Plate, 7" | 20.00 | Vase, 5½" | 35.00 |
| Plate, 8" | 30.00 | Vase, 6" ftd. | 45.00 |
| Plate, 12" cracker | 75.00 | Vase, 9" ftd. w/flared rim | 65.00 |
| Plate, 13" sandwich | 80.00 | | |

# WAVERLY, Blank #1519, A.H. Heisey & Co.

Colors: crystal; rare in amber

This Heisey blank is known more for its use with etched Orchid or Rose than for itself.

| | **Crystal** |
|---|---:|
| Bowl, 6", oval, lemon, w/cover | 30.00 |
| Bowl, 6½", 2 hdld., ice | 50.00 |
| Bowl, 7", 3 part, relish, oblong | 25.00 |
| Bowl, 7", salad | 17.00 |
| Bowl, 9", 4 part, relish, round | 25.00 |
| Bowl, 9", fruit | 20.00 |
| Bowl, 9", vegetable | 20.00 |
| Bowl, 10", crimped edge | 25.00 |
| Bowl, 10", gardenia | 20.00 |
| Bowl, 11", seahorse foot, floral | 65.00 |
| Bowl, 12", crimped edge | 35.00 |
| Bowl, 13", gardenia | 25.00 |
| Box, 5", chocolate, w/cover | 60.00 |
| Box, 5" tall, ftd., w/cover, seahorse hand. | 85.00 |
| Box, 6", candy, w/bow tie knob | 45.00 |
| Box, trinket, lion cover (rare) | 600.00 |
| Butter dish, w/cover, 6", square | 65.00 |
| Candleholder, 1-lite, block (rare) | 100.00 |
| Candleholder, 2-lite | 40.00 |
| Candleholder, 2-lite, "flame" center | 65.00 |
| Candleholder, 3-lite | 65.00 |
| Candle epergnette, 5" | 10.00 |
| Candle epergnette, 6", deep | 13.00 |
| Candle epergnette, 6½" | 10.00 |
| Cheese dish, 5½", ftd. | 20.00 |
| Cigarette holder | 50.00 |
| Comport, 6", low ftd. | 12.00 |
| Comport, 6½", jelly | 35.00 |
| Comport, 7", low ftd., oval | 40.00 |
| Creamer, ftd. | 20.00 |
| Creamer & sugar, individual, w/tray | 47.00 |
| Cruet, 3 oz., w/#122 stopper | 60.00 |
| Cup | 12.00 |
| Honey dish, 6½", ftd. | 22.00 |
| Mayonnaise, w/liner & ladle, 5½" | 50.00 |
| Plate, 7", salad | 6.00 |
| Plate, 8", luncheon | 8.00 |
| Plate, 10½", dinner | 45.00 |
| Plate, 11", sandwich | 18.00 |
| Plate, 13½", ftd., cake salver | 60.00 |
| Plate, 14", center handle, sandwich | 65.00 |
| Plate, 14", sandwich | 35.00 |
| Salt & pepper, pr. | 50.00 |
| Saucer | 3.00 |
| Stem, #5019, 1 oz., cordial | 50.00 |
| Stem, #5019, 3 oz., wine, blown | 15.00 |
| Stem, #5019, 3½ oz., cocktail | 10.00 |
| Stem, #5019, 5½ oz., sherbet/champagne | 7.00 |
| Stem, #5019, 10 oz., blown | 15.00 |
| Sugar, ftd. | 20.00 |
| Tray, 12", celery | 13.00 |
| Tumbler, #5019, 5 oz., ftd., juice, blown | 17.00 |
| Tumbler, #5019, 13 oz., ftd., tea, blown | 20.00 |
| Vase, 3½", violet | 45.00 |
| Vase, 7", ftd. | 25.00 |
| Vase, 7", ftd., fan shape | 40.00 |

# WILDFLOWER, Cambridge Glass Company, 1940's – 1950's

Colors: crystal, mainly; some pieces in color

You will find additional pieces of Wildflower on other Cambridge blanks. I have tried to show a major portion, but (as with other Cambridge patterns) there seems to be a never ending list. You can figure that, like Rose Point, almost any Cambridge blank may have been used to etch this pattern. I have given you the "ball park" to start. Price yellow or gold encrusted items up to 25% higher. Most collectors are searching for crystal! The hat shown on the bottom of page 223 will give many Cambridge/hat collectors palpitations!

| | Crystal |
|---|---|
| Basket, #3400/1182, 2 hdld., ftd., 6" | 25.00 |
| Bowl, #3400/1180, bonbon, 2 hdld., 5¼" | 18.00 |
| Bowl, bonbon, 2 hdld., ftd., 6" | 17.50 |
| Bowl, #3400/90, 2 pt., relish, 6" | 17.50 |
| Bowl, 3 pt., relish, 6½" | 17.50 |
| Bowl, #3900/123, relish, 7" | 18.00 |
| Bowl, #3900/130, bonbon, 2 hdld., 7" | 20.00 |
| Bowl, #3900/124, 2 pt., relish, 7" | 22.00 |
| Bowl, #3400/91, 3 pt., relish, 3 hdld., 8" | 25.00 |
| Bowl, #3900/125, 3 pt., celery & relish, 9" | 25.00 |
| Bowl, #477, pickle (corn), ftd., 9½" | 25.00 |
| Bowl, #3900/54, 4 ft., flared, 10" | 37.50 |
| Bowl, #3900/34, 2 hdld., 11" | 45.00 |
| Bowl, #3900/28, w/tab hand., ftd., 11½" | 45.00 |
| Bowl, #3900/126, 3 pt., celery & relish, 12" | 40.00 |
| Bowl, #3400/4, 4 ft., flared, 12" | 29.50 |
| Bowl, #3400/1240, 4 ft., oval, "ears" hand., 12" | 45.00 |
| Bowl, 5 pt., celery & relish, 12" | 35.00 |
| Butter dish, #3900/52, ¼ lb. | 175.00 |
| Butter dish, #3400/52, 5" | 115.00 |
| Candlestick, #3400/638, 3-lite, ea. | 35.00 |
| Candlestick, #3400/646, 5" | 25.00 |
| Candlestick, #3400/647, 2-lite, "fleur-de-lis," 6" | 30.00 |
| Candy box, w/cover, #3900/165 | 70.00 |
| Candy box, w/cover, #3900/165, rnd. | 65.00 |
| Cocktail icer, #968, 2 pc. | 65.00 |
| Cocktail shaker, #3400/175 | 85.00 |
| Comport, #3900/136, 5½" | 30.00 |
| Comport, #3121, blown, 5⅜" | 40.00 |
| Creamer, #3900/41 | 12.50 |
| Creamer, #3900/40, individual | 20.00 |
| Cup, #3900/17 or #3400/54 | 16.50 |
| Hat, #1704, 5" | 165.00 |
| Hat, #1703, 6" | 200.00 |
| Hurricane lamp, #1617, candlestick base, | 150.00 |
| Hurricane lamp, #1603, keyhole base & prisms | 195.00 |
| Ice bucket, w/chrome hand, #3900/671 | 65.00 |
| Oil, w/stopper, #3900/100, 6 oz. | 80.00 |
| Pitcher, ball, #3400/38, 80 oz. | 135.00 |
| Pitcher, #3900/115, 76 oz. | 165.00 |
| Pitcher, Doulton #3400/141 | 295.00 |

| | Crystal |
|---|---|
| Plate, #3900/20, bread/butter, 6½" | 7.50 |
| Plate, #3900/130, bonbon, 2 hdld., 7" | 17.50 |
| Plate, #3400/176, 7½" | 9.00 |
| Plate, #3900/161, 2 hdld., ftd., 8" | 22.50 |
| Plate, #3900/22, salad, 8" | 17.50 |
| Plate, #3400/62, 8½" | 15.00 |
| Plate, #3900/24, dinner, 10½" | 67.50 |
| Plate, #3900/26, service, 4 ftd., 12" | 35.00 |
| Plate, #3900/35, cake, 2 hdld., 13½" | 37.50 |
| Plate, #3900/167, torte, 14" | 37.50 |
| Plate, #3900/65, torte, 14" | 37.50 |
| Salt & pepper, #3400/77, pr. | 35.00 |
| Salt & pepper, #3900/1177 | 32.50 |
| Saucer, #3900/17 or #3400/54 | 3.50 |
| Set: 2 pc. Mayonnaise, #3900/19 (ftd. sherbet w/ladle) | 30.00 |
| Set: 3 pc. Mayonnaise, #3900/129 (bowl, liner, ladle) | 35.00 |
| Set: 4 pc. Mayonnaise #3900/111 (div. bowl, liner, 2 ladles) | 40.00 |
| Stem, #3121, cordial, 1 oz. | 55.00 |
| Stem, #3121, cocktail, 3 oz. | 22.50 |
| Stem, #3121, wine, 3½ oz. | 30.00 |
| Stem, #3121, claret, 4½ oz. | 40.00 |
| Stem, #3121, 4½ oz., low oyster cocktail | 18.00 |
| Stem, #3121, 5 oz., low parfait | 32.50 |
| Stem, #3121, 6 oz., low sherbet | 15.00 |
| Stem, #3121, 6 oz., tall sherbet | 17.50 |
| Stem, #3121, 10 oz., water | 25.00 |
| Sugar, 3900/41 | 12.50 |
| Sugar, indiv., 3900/40 | 20.00 |
| Tray, creamer & sugar, 3900/37 | 15.00 |
| Tumbler, #3121, 5 oz., juice | 17.50 |
| Tumbler, #3121, 10 oz., water | 20.00 |
| Tumbler, #3121, 12 oz., tea | 25.00 |
| Tumbler, #3900/115, 13 oz. | 28.00 |
| Vase, #3400/102, globe, 5" | 40.00 |
| Vase, #6004, flower, ftd., 6" | 35.00 |
| Vase, #6004, flower, ftd., 8" | 55.00 |
| Vase, #1237, keyhole ft., 9" | 60.00 |
| Vase, #1528, bud, 10" | 35.00 |
| Vase, #278, flower, ftd., 11" | 50.00 |
| Vase, #1299, ped. ft., 11" | 65.00 |
| Vase, #1238, keyhole ft., 12" | 95.00 |
| Vase, #279, ftd., flower, 13" | 110.00 |

Note: See Pages 228-229 for stem identification.

# YEOMAN, Blank #1184, A.H. Heisey & Co.

Colors: crystal, "Flamingo" pink, "Sahara" yellow, "Moongleam" green, "Hawthorne" orchid/pink, "Marigold" deep, amber/yellow; some cobalt

Etched patterns on Yeoman blank #1184 will bring 10% to 25% more than the prices listed below. Empress etch is the most commonly found pattern on Yeoman blanks and the most collectible. The main reason this pattern is so collectible is due to the colors in which it was made!

| | Crystal | Pink | Sahara | Green | Hawth. | Marigold |
|---|---|---|---|---|---|---|
| Ash tray, 4", hdld. (bow tie) .................. | 10.00 | 20.00 | 22.00 | 25.00 | 30.00 | 35.00 |
| Bowl, 2 hdld., cream soup ..................... | 12.00 | 20.00 | 25.00 | 30.00 | 35.00 | 40.00 |
| Bowl, finger .......................................... | 5.00 | 11.00 | 17.00 | 20.00 | 27.50 | 30.00 |
| Bowl, ftd., banana split ......................... | 7.00 | 23.00 | 30.00 | 35.00 | 40.00 | 45.00 |
| Bowl, ftd., 2 hdld., bouillon.................. | 10.00 | 20.00 | 25.00 | 30.00 | 35.00 | 40.00 |
| Bowl, 4½", nappy.................................. | 4.00 | 7.50 | 10.00 | 12.50 | 15.00 | 17.00 |
| Bowl, 5", low, ftd., jelly ....................... | 12.00 | 20.00 | 25.00 | 27.00 | 30.00 | 40.00 |
| Bowl, 5", oval, lemon ........................... | 7.00 | 10.00 | 15.00 | 18.00 | 19.00 | 25.00 |
| Bowl, 5", rnd., lemon............................ | 6.00 | 10.00 | 15.00 | 18.00 | 19.00 | 25.00 |
| Bowl, 5", rnd., lemon, w/cover ............. | 15.00 | 20.00 | 25.00 | 30.00 | 40.00 | 50.00 |
| Bowl, 6", oval, preserve........................ | 7.00 | 12.00 | 17.00 | 22.00 | 27.00 | 30.00 |
| Bowl, 6", vegetable .............................. | 5.00 | 10.00 | 14.00 | 16.00 | 20.00 | 24.00 |
| Bowl, 6½", hdld., bonbon...................... | 5.00 | 10.00 | 14.00 | 16.00 | 20.00 | 24.00 |
| Bowl, 8", rect., pickle/olive.................. | 12.00 | 15.00 | 20.00 | 25.00 | 30.00 | 35.00 |
| Bowl, 8½", berry, 2 hdld. ...................... | 14.00 | 22.00 | 25.00 | 30.00 | 35.00 | 50.00 |
| Bowl, 9", 2 hdld., veg., w/cover ............. | 35.00 | 55.00 | 60.00 | 70.00 | 95.00 | 175.00 |
| Bowl, 9", oval, fruit............................... | 20.00 | 25.00 | 35.00 | 45.00 | 55.00 | 55.00 |
| Bowl, 9", baker..................................... | 20.00 | 25.00 | 35.00 | 45.00 | 55.00 | 55.00 |
| Bowl, 12", low, floral............................ | 15.00 | 25.00 | 35.00 | 45.00 | 55.00 | 55.00 |
| Candle Vase, single, w/short prisms & inserts ........................................... | 90.00 | | | 150.00 | | |
| Cigarette box, (ashtray)........................ | 25.00 | 60.00 | 65.00 | 70.00 | 80.00 | 100.00 |
| Cologne bottle, w/stopper ..................... | 40.00 | 90.00 | 95.00 | 100.00 | 110.00 | 135.00 |
| Comport, 5", high ftd., shallow ............. | 15.00 | 25.00 | 37.00 | 45.00 | 55.00 | 70.00 |
| Comport, 6", low ftd., deep ................... | 20.00 | 30.00 | 34.00 | 40.00 | 42.00 | 48.00 |
| Creamer............................................... | 10.00 | 20.00 | 20.00 | 22.00 | 24.00 | 28.00 |
| Cruet, 2 oz., oil .................................... | 20.00 | 60.00 | 60.00 | 65.00 | 55.00 | 65.00 |
| Cruet, 4 oz., oil .................................... | 30.00 | 60.00 | 60.00 | 65.00 | | |
| Cup........................................................ | 5.00 | 15.00 | 20.00 | 25.00 | | |
| Cup, after dinner ................................. | 7.00 | 28.00 | 30.00 | 35.00 | 40.00 | 50.00 |
| Egg cup................................................. | 20.00 | 25.00 | 32.00 | 39.00 | 42.00 | 52.00 |
| Grapefruit, ftd. ..................................... | 10.00 | 17.00 | 24.00 | 31.00 | 38.00 | 45.00 |
| Gravy (or dressing) boat, w/underliner.... | 13.00 | 25.00 | 30.00 | 45.00 | 50.00 | 45.00 |
| Marmalade jar, w/cover......................... | 25.00 | 35.00 | 40.00 | 45.00 | 55.00 | 65.00 |
| Parfait, 5 oz. ........................................ | 10.00 | 15.00 | 20.00 | 25.00 | 30.00 | 35.00 |
| Pitcher, quart ....................................... | 35.00 | 55.00 | 65.00 | 75.00 | 125.00 | 160.00 |
| Plate, 2 hdld., cheese............................ | 5.00 | 10.00 | 13.00 | 15.00 | 17.00 | 25.00 |
| Plate, cream soup underliner................... | 5.00 | 7.00 | 9.00 | 12.00 | 14.00 | 16.00 |
| Plate, finger bowl underliner ................. | 3.00 | 5.00 | 7.00 | 9.00 | 11.00 | 13.00 |
| Plate, 4½", coaster................................ | 3.00 | 5.00 | 10.00 | 12.00 | | |
| Plate, 6".............................................. | 3.00 | 6.00 | 8.00 | 10.00 | 13.00 | 15.00 |
| Plate, 6", bouillon underliner................. | 3.00 | 6.00 | 8.00 | 10.00 | 13.00 | 15.00 |

| | Crystal | Pink | Sahara | Green | Hawth. | Marigold |
|---|---|---|---|---|---|---|
| Plate, 6½", grapefruit bowl | 7.00 | 12.00 | 15.00 | 19.00 | 27.00 | 32.00 |
| Plate, 7" | 5.00 | 8.00 | 10.00 | 14.00 | 17.00 | 22.00 |
| Plate, 8", oyster cocktail | 9.00 | | | | | |
| Plate, 8", soup | 9.00 | | | | | |
| Plate, 9", oyster cocktail | 10.00 | | | | | |
| Plate, 10½" | 20.00 | 50.00 | | 50.00 | 60.00 | |
| Plate, 10½", ctr. hand., oval, div. | 15.00 | 26.00 | | 32.00 | | |
| Plate, 11", 4 pt., relish | 20.00 | 27.00 | | 32.00 | | |
| Plate, 14" | 20.00 | | | | | |
| Platter, 12", oval | 10.00 | 17.00 | 19.00 | 26.00 | 33.00 | |
| Salt, ind. tub (cobalt: $30.00) | 10.00 | 20.00 | | 30.00 | | |
| Salver, 10", low ftd. | 15.00 | 30.00 | | 42.00 | | |
| Salver, 12", low ftd. | 10.00 | 25.00 | | 32.00 | | |
| Saucer | 3.00 | 5.00 | 7.00 | 7.00 | 10.00 | 10.00 |
| Saucer, after dinner | 3.00 | 5.00 | 7.00 | 8.00 | 10.00 | 10.00 |
| Stem, 2¾ oz., ftd., oyster cocktail | 4.00 | 8.00 | 10.00 | 12.00 | 14.00 | |
| Stem, 3 oz., cocktail | 10.00 | 12.00 | 17.00 | 20.00 | | |
| Stem, 3½ oz., sherbet | 5.00 | 8.00 | 11.00 | 12.00 | | |
| Stem, 4 oz., fruit cocktail | 3.00 | 5.00 | 7.00 | 9.00 | | |
| Stem, 4½ oz., sherbet | 3.00 | 5.00 | 7.00 | 9.00 | | |
| Stem, 5 oz., soda | 9.00 | 8.00 | 12.00 | 12.00 | | |
| Stem, 5 oz., sherbet | 5.00 | 5.00 | 7.00 | 9.00 | | |
| Stem, 6 oz., champagne | 6.00 | 16.00 | 18.00 | 22.00 | | |
| Stem, 8 oz. | 5.00 | 12.00 | 18.00 | 20.00 | | |
| Stem, 10 oz., goblet | 10.00 | 15.00 | 20.00 | 25.00 | | |
| Sugar, w/cover | 15.00 | 40.00 | 35.00 | 40.00 | 40.00 | 40.00 |
| Sugar shaker, ftd. | 50.00 | 95.00 | | 110.00 | | |
| Syrup, 7 oz., saucer ftd. | 30.00 | 75.00 | | | | |
| Tray, 7" x 10", rect. | 26.00 | 30.00 | 40.00 | 35.00 | | |
| Tray, 9", celery | 10.00 | 14.00 | 16.00 | 15.00 | | |
| Tray, 11", ctr. hand., 3 pt. | 15.00 | 20.00 | 24.00 | | | |
| Tray, 12", oblong | 16.00 | 19.00 | 24.00 | | | |
| Tray, 13", 3 pt., relish | 20.00 | 27.00 | 32.00 | | | |
| Tray, 13", celery | 20.00 | 27.00 | 32.00 | | | |
| Tray, 13", hors d'oeuvre, w/cov. ctr. | 32.00 | 42.00 | 52.00 | 75.00 | | |
| Tray insert, 3½" x 4½" | 4.00 | 6.00 | 7.00 | 8.00 | | |
| Tumbler, 2½ oz., whiskey | 3.00 | 8.00 | 10.00 | 12.00 | | |
| Tumbler, 4½ oz., soda | 4.00 | 6.00 | 10.00 | 15.00 | | |
| Tumbler, 8 oz. | 4.00 | 12.00 | 17.00 | 20.00 | | |
| Tumbler, 10 oz., cupped rim | 4.00 | 15.00 | 20.00 | 22.50 | | |
| Tumbler, 10 oz., straight side | 5.00 | 15.00 | 20.00 | 22.50 | | |
| Tumbler, 12 oz., tea | 5.00 | 20.00 | 25.00 | 30.00 | | |
| Tumbler cover (unusual) | 35.00 | | | | | |

# CAMBRIDGE STEMS

1066
11 oz. Goblet

1402
Brandy Inhaler (Tall)

3025
10 oz. Goblet

3035
3 oz. Cocktail

3077
6 oz. Tall Sherbet

3104
1 oz. Cordial

3106
9 oz. Goblet Tall Bowl

3115
3½ oz. Cocktail

3120
6 oz. Tall Sherbet

3121
10 oz. Goblet

# CAMBRIDGE STEMS

3122
9 oz. Goblet

3124
3 oz. Wine

3126
7 oz. Tall Sherbet

3130
6 oz. Tall Sherbet

3135
6 oz. Tall Sherbet

3400
9 oz. Lunch Goblet

3500
10 oz. Goblet

3600
2½ oz. Wine

3775
4½ oz. Claret

3625
4½ oz. Claret

3779
1 oz. Cordial

# HEISEY'S "ALEXANDRITE" COLOR (rare)

**Row 1:**
Candlesticks, Trident, pr. (134)...................... 750.00
Cathedral vase (1413).................................... 800.00

**Row 2:**
Tumbler, 12 oz., ftd., soda,
  Creole (3381) .............................................. 120.00
Tumbler 5 oz., ftd., soda, Creole (3381).......... 100.00
Tumbler, 8½ oz., ftd., soda, Creole (3381) ...... 110.00
Tumbler, 2½ oz., bar, Glenford (3481) ............ 200.00

**Row 3:**
Ball vase, 9" (4045)......................................... 800.00
Ball vase, 4" (4045)......................................... 360.00
Ball vase, 6" (4045)......................................... 420.00

**Row 4:**
Plate, Colonial Star (1150) ............................. 325.00
Plate, Yeoman .............................................. 40.00
Stem, 2½ oz., wine, Creole (3381) ................. 160.00
Stem, 11 oz., water goblet, Creole (3381) ....... 220.00

**Row 1:**

Stem, water, Plymouth (3409 ................................. 600.00
Tumbler, 2½ oz. wine Gascony (3397) ................... 145.00
Tumbler, 11 oz. low footed goblet Gascony (3397) 340.00
Decanter, Gascony (3397) ...................................... 700.00
Tumbler, 14 oz. footed soda, New Era (4044) ......... 165.00
Stem, 10 oz. goblet, New Era (4044) ...................... 150.00

**Row 2:**

Plate, Cactus (1432) ............................................... 250.00
Beer mug, Old Sandwich (1404) .............................. 220.00
Cream pitcher, Old Sandwich (1404)..................... 320.00
Candleholder, single, Old Sandwich (1404).......... 190.00

**Row 3:**

Candleholder, single, Empress (135)...................... 220.00
Floral bowl, Empress (1401).................................... 365.00

Ash tray, Empress (1401)........................................ 220.00
Candy w/cover, Empress (1401)............................. 375.00

**Row 4:**

Vase, favor, Diamond Optic (4230) ........................ 150.00
Tub salt, Revere (1183) .......................................... 75.00
Vase, favor, Diamond Optic (4229) ........................ 195.00
Vase, favor, (4228)................................................. 180.00
Vase, 2", ball (4045) .............................................. 460.00
Vase, ivy ball (4224)............................................... 250.00
Ash tray, individual, Empress (1401) ..................... 45.00
Tumbler, Arch (1417).............................................. 60.00

**Row 5:**

Vase, 6", ball (4045) .............................................. 360.00
Vase, 12", ball (4045) ............................................ 2500.00
Vase, 9", ball (4045) .............................................. 700.00

# HEISEY'S "COBALT" COLOR (rare)

**Row 1:**

| | |
|---|---|
| Stem, 10 oz., water, Spanish (3404) | 125.00 |
| Candleholder, Ipswich (1405) | 260.00 |
| Plate, 8", square, Empress (1401) | 60.00 |

**Row 2:**

| | |
|---|---|
| Stem, 5½ oz., saucer champagne, Spanish (3404) | 75.00 |
| Tumbler, 12 oz., ftd., soda, Spanish (3404) | 60.00 |
| Stem, 3½ oz., cocktail, Spanish (3404) | 85.00 |
| Stem, 1 oz., cordial, Spanish (3404) | 200.00 |
| Stem, 5½ oz., sherbet, Spanish (3404) | 80.00 |

**Row 3:**

| | |
|---|---|
| Candlestick, 6" (135) | 220.00 |
| Salt and pepper pr., (25) | 255.00 |
| Ash tray, Empress (1401) | 220.00 |
| Candy w/cover, Empress (1401) | 375.00 |

**Row 4:**

| | |
|---|---|
| Plate, 8", round, Empress (1401 | 60.00 |
| Vase, Cathedral (1413) | 325.00 |
| Candy w/cover, short, Aristocrat (1430) | 800.00 |

**Row 1:**
Vase, 9", Warwick (1428)................................. 240.00
Bowl, 11", floral, Warwick (1428)................... 265.00
Vase, 7", Warwick (1428)................................ 230.00
**Row 2:**
Tumbler, 1 oz., cordial, Carcassonne (3390) ... 225.00
Tumbler, 2½ oz., wine, ftd., Carcassonne
   (3390) ........................................................... 110.00
Stem, 6 oz., saucer champagne, Carcassonne
   (3390) ........................................................... 55.00
Tumbler, 12 oz., soda, ftd., Carcassonne
   (3390) ........................................................... 70.00
Stem, 11 oz., tall stem, Carcassonne (3390) ... 95.00

Tumbler, 8 oz., soda, Carcassonne (3390) ........ 65.00
**Row 3:**
Candleholder, 2-lite, Thumbprint
   and Panel (1433)........................................... 135.00
Bowl, 12", floral, Thumbprint and Panel
   (1433) ........................................................... 200.00
Cigarette holder, Carcassonne (3390) ............. 110.00
**Row 4:**
Vase, 9", Tulip (1420) .................................... 350.00
Cocktail shaker, Cobel (4225) ....................... 450.00
Candy w/cover, tall, Aristocrat (1430)............1000.00
Candleholder, 2-lite, Crocus (140).................. 400.00

# HEISEY'S "DAWN" COLOR (rare)

Ash tray, 6", square, Prism Square ................. 95.00
Bowl, 6¾", jelly Leaf (1565) ........................... 40.00
Butter dish, ¼ pound, Cabochon (1951)......... 175.00
Creamer, Cabochon (1951) ............................ 50.00
Sherbet, 20th Century (1415)........................ 35.00

Sugar, Cabochon (1951) .................................. 50.00
Tray, 12", 4 pt. variety, Octagon (500)............ 350.00
Tumbler, 4", 10 oz., water, Coleport (1487) .... 30.00
Tumbler, 5¼", 13 oz., iced tea, Coleport
  (1487) ......................................................... 40.00

Tumbler, 5 oz., ftd. soda Kohinoor (4085) ................. $550.00+ ea.

Notice the top soda has a blue top and foot with a crystal stem while the bottom left one has a blue top and crystal stem and foot. The bottom right soda is all blue.

# HEISEY'S TANGERINE COLOR (rare)

Creamer, Empress blank (1401) .................................................. 650.00
Cup, Empress blank (1401) ........................................................ 800.00
Saucer, Empress blank (1401) .................................................... 200.00
Sugar, Empress blank (1401) ...................................................... 650.00

# HEISEY'S ZIRCON (LIMELIGHT) COLOR (rare)

Bowl, 6", hdld., mayonnaise, Fern (1495) ...................................................................... 65.00
Bowl, 14", floral, Kohinoor (1488) ................................................................................ 1,000.00
Candelabra, Kohinoor (1488) ...................................................................................... 700.00
Plate, 5", Beehive (1238)............................................................................................... 65.00
Plate, 8", Beehive (1238)............................................................................................... 85.00
Relish, ftd., hdld., 3 pt., Fern (1495)........................................................................... 350.00
Stem, 9 oz., water, Kohinoor (4085)............................................................................. 120.00
Stem, 5½ oz. saucer champagne, Kohinoor (4085)...................................................... 80.00
Stem, 9 oz., short water, Stanhope (4083) ................................................................... 95.00
Stem, 6 oz., sherbet, Coventry (4090) .......................................................................... 40.00

## Books By Gene Florence

Collector's Encyclopedia of Depression Glass ......................................$19.95

Collectible Glassware from the 40's 50's 60's ................................$19.95

Pocket Guide to Depression Glass.........................................$9.95

Collector's Encyclopedia of Occupied Japan I ...........................$14.95

Collector's Encyclopedia of Occupied Japan II...........................$14.95

Collector's Encyclopedia of Occupied Japan III..........................$19.95

Collector's Encyclopedia of Occupied Japan IV .........................$14.95

Collector's Encyclopedia of Occupied Japan V .........................$14.95

Elegant Glassware of the Depression Era ................................$19.95

Very Rare Glassware of the Depression Years.............................$24.95

Very Rare Glassware of the Depression Years Second Series....................$24.95

Very Rare Glassware of the Depression Years Third Series .....................$24.95

The Standard Baseball Card Price Guide .................................$9.95

Copies of these books may be ordered from:

**Gene Florence**
(May 15 – Nov. 30)     (Dec. 1 – May 14)
P.O. Box 22186         P.O. Box 64
Lexington, KY 40522  Astatula, Florida 34705
or
**Collector Books**
P.O. Box 3009
Paducah, KY 42002-3009

Add $2.00 postage for the first book, 30¢ for each additional book.

## A Publication I Recommend

### DEPRESSION GLASS **DAZE**

P.O. Box 576F, Otisville, MI 48463

*A monthly newspaper devoted to the collecting of colored glass (depression glass & china) – features ads, articles, prices, news pertaining to this hobby. (12 issues)*

Name _____

Address _____

City _____ State ____ Zip _____

☑ *Please check one:*

❑ New
❑ 1 Yr. $21.00          ❑ Free Sample Copy
❑ 2 Yrs. $40.00        ❑ Canada $22.00

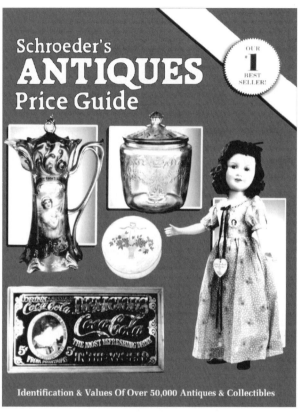